Overview of the Universe

P9-CBW-978

Informative Tables

Physical Constants, Astronomical Symbols,
Galaxy & Solar System, Constellations, Stars and a Celestial Atlas

Monthly Star Charts

Telescopes & Binoculars

Observing the Moon & its Phases

Observing the Planets

Observing Tips ✦ Monthly Sunrise & Sunset Positions,
Oppositions, Elongations & Conjunctions

Observing Meteors, Comets, our Sun & Eclipses

Observing Deep Sky Objects

Star Clusters, Nebulae & Galaxies
plus Double & Variable Stars

Sunrises & Sunsets

Time Zones, Universal Time and
Sunrise & Sunset for more than 200 North American Cities

Glossary, Mythology, History & Index

A Ken Press Book
"Bringing Astronomy to Everyone"

Published by Ken Press, Tucson, Arizona USA
(520) 743-3200 or ken@kenpress.com

Other Ken Press books by Ken Graun

The Next Step: Finding and Viewing Messier's Objects
Touring the Universe: A Practical Guide to Exploring the Cosmos thru 2017
Our Earth and the Solar System
Our Galaxy and the Universe
Our Constellations and their Stars
David H. Levy's Guide to the Stars (planispheres, co-author)

Visit
www.whatsouttonight.com

———

Publisher's Cataloging-in-Publication Information

Graun, Ken.

 What's out tonight? : celestial almanac & astronomy field guide, 2000 to 2050 /
Ken Graun. – 3rd ed. – Tucson, Ariz. : Ken Press, 2007.

  p. ; cm.

  ISBN-13: 978-1-928771-50-0
  ISBN-10: 1-928771-50-5
  First ed. published in 1999 as: What's out tonight? : 50 year
astronomy field guide, 2000 to 2050.
  Provides tables for selected celestial events, monthly star charts,
charts of the moon, and information about the universe and the
history of astronomy.
  Includes index.

   1. Astronomy–Observers' manuals. 2. Astronomy–Amateurs' manuals. I. Title.

QB64.G73 2007   2005937967
520–dc22   0107

Printed in Canada

Foreword

Astronomy has the entire Universe as its theater. Every night, we can go out, look onto the stage and see what's playing. It's the grandest show. There is none larger, more spectacular or more dynamic.

The show has been playing since the beginning of time. Our earliest ancestors watched it but understood little of what they saw. That changed in 1609 when Galileo and other scientists pointed the first telescopes upward. Now, 400 years later, we have a basic understanding of the Universe. We know that the cosmos is a magnificent symphony, but with many parts that we still must learn.

Astronomy is not a simple science. It draws upon every discipline, from biology to nuclear physics, and engages the most complex mathematics in order to make sense out of the Universe. Fortunately, no knowledge or understanding of these specialized fields is required to go out, look up and enjoy the heavens for all it has to offer.

This book is your 50 year playbill for heaven's cast of characters.

May you enjoy the performances and make friends with the stars.

Ken Graun
Spring 2006

Top. One of Galileo's earliest Moon drawings made using a telescope.
Bottom. A reproduction of Galileo's telescope.

The Universe is Full of Galaxies

1 If you held the Universe in your hands, and looked close, you would see fuzzy specks everywhere. Each of these fuzzy spots would be a galaxy. There is estimated be about 125 billion galaxies in the Universe. A galaxy is a grouping of stars — anywhere from a billion to a trillion that are held together by their collective gravity. This *Hubble Space Telescope* photo is a snapshot of deep space. All of these specks are galaxies billions of light years away. EACH of these dots or blobs represent the collection of billions of stars. Galaxies are all that astronomers see when they look deep into space.

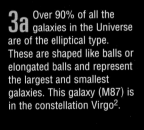

2 Galaxies cluster together. Our Milky Way Galaxy is a member of what astronomers call the Local Group which totals about three dozen galaxies, including the famous Andromeda Galaxy (M31)[1].

Clusters of galaxies are further organized into superclusters, configured somewhat like strands that stretch across huge expanses of the Universe.

There are 3 Basic Galaxy Shapes

3a Over 90% of all the galaxies in the Universe are of the elliptical type. These are shaped like balls or elongated balls and represent the largest and smallest galaxies. This galaxy (M87) is in the constellation Virgo[2].

3b Spiral galaxies, like this one in Pisces[2] (M74) represent at most 5% of the galaxies. They are fairly large and strikingly visible. Shaped like dishes, they have a bulged center out of which curved arms radiate. Spirals have active star formation occurring in their arms. Our Sun is in a spiral galaxy.

3c Finally, there are irregular galaxies that have irregular shapes or scrambled insides. Some are the result of galaxies colliding and merging. Others get deformed by the gravity of larger galaxies pulling on them. Here is a closeup of an irregular galaxy (M82) with mixed-up insides, located in Ursa Major[2].

Continues on page 6

[1] This and the other "M" numbers used here are catalogue designations. See more about this on page 244.
[2] Galaxies are much farther outside our galaxy and are not actually in these constellations, but lie in their direction.

Universe Overview

The Universe contains everything that we know to exist. For a long time, it was thought that the Earth was at its center. However, today we know that Earth is just one small planet revolving around an average-size star that we call the Sun, residing with billions of other stars collectively referred to as a galaxy. And, there are billions of galaxies scattered throughout the Universe.

If you are not familiar with the kinds of objects that are in the Universe, I encourage you to read and reflect on the summary presented on pages 4, 6 and 7.

An accurate illustration of our Milky Way Galaxy. The yellow dot marks our Sun.

A Sense of Scale and Space

The size of the Universe as well as the distance between galaxies and even stars is unfathomable compared to the distances that we deal with on an everyday basis.

It is currently estimated that the Universe came into existence about 14 billion years ago and has since been expanding at the rate of the speed of light. Based on this, our Universe has a diameter of about 165,000,000,000,000,000,000,000 miles and growing every second.

When you look up into the night sky, almost everything that you see is part of our own Milky Way Galaxy.

The Universe is riddled with about 125 billion galaxies and for their size, the distance between them is not that great. For example, the diameter of our Milky Way Galaxy is about 80,000 light years and that of the nearby Andromeda Galaxy twice that, however, they are a "mere" 31 diameters of our Milky Way Galaxy from each other.

Proportionally, the distances between stars is incredible, hence the sometimes made statement that two galaxies could pass through one another without any of their stars colliding. The nearest star to our Sun, Proxima Centauri, is 4⅓ light years away. This is 29 million (29,000,000) diameters of our Sun, a truly big number compared to the *relative* distances and sizes of galaxies.

When I give talks about our Solar System, I model the size of our Solar System based on the Earth being the size of a penny. At this scale, the Sun would be 6¾ feet in diameter with the Earth 725 feet away, Pluto out at 5½ miles and Proxima Centauri, the closest star — 37,000 miles away.

Stars are Born within Gas Clouds called Nebulae that Reside in Galaxies

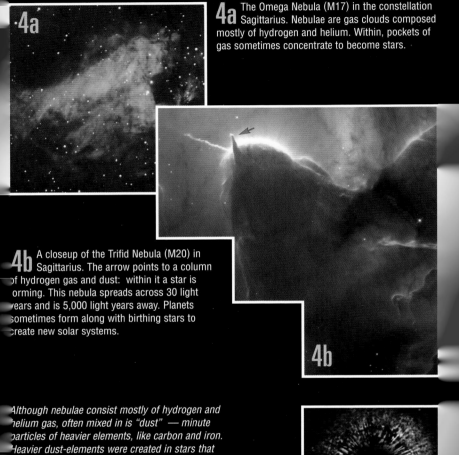

4a The Omega Nebula (M17) in the constellation Sagittarius. Nebulae are gas clouds composed mostly of hydrogen and helium. Within, pockets of gas sometimes concentrate to become stars.

4b A closeup of the Trifid Nebula (M20) in Sagittarius. The arrow points to a column of hydrogen gas and dust: within it a star is forming. This nebula spreads across 30 light years and is 5,000 light years away. Planets sometimes form along with birthing stars to create new solar systems.

Although nebulae consist mostly of hydrogen and helium gas, often mixed in is "dust" — minute particles of heavier elements, like carbon and iron. Heavier dust-elements were created in stars that have since died and spewed out some of their material into space. Worlds like Earth are formed when these heavier dust particles clump together.

4c Two protoplanetary disks out of which planets may form. The donut-shaped object is of a dust-laden debris field surrounding a new star that is about the same size as our Sun. The blue-spiked photograph shows a debris field edge-on. Both photographs had the light from their suns blocked in order to image this surrounding material.

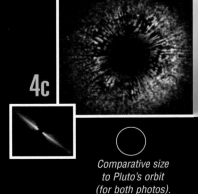

Comparative size to Pluto's orbit (for both photos).

Stars are Born Together in Clusters

5a Anywhere from a dozen to a hundred or more stars can be born from a nebula. Here is a beautiful cluster, designated M6, located in the constellation Scorpius. The Pleiades (M45), visible in winter, is the best known example of a naked-eye cluster.

5b Special clusters, called globular clusters, contain thousands to hundreds of thousands of stars. Older stars comprise these objects which resemble cotton balls. They often surround galaxies. Our Milky Way Galaxy has about 200 of them that surround it in a spherical halo.

Stars Eventually Die, often leaving a beautiful Remnant

All stars die. In their death throes, they form either planetary nebulae or supernova remnants.

6a Planetary nebulae have nothing to do with planets. That's just an old name that stuck. They are the shedded atmospheres of average-sized stars like our Sun before these shrink down to become white dwarfs.

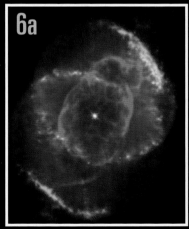

6b Stars with masses much greater than our Sun die with violent supernova explosions. Although they leave behind remnants, the stars shrinks down to become neutron stars or black holes. As the remnants expand into space, some of it eventually gets recycled back into new stars and planets. Pictured is the Crab Nebula (M1) in Taurus.

Physical Constants & Measurements

Length

1 inch (in) = 25.4 millimeters exactly; 2.54 centimeters
1 centimeter (cm) = 0.394 inch; 10 millimeters
1 yard (yd) = 0.9144 meters; 36 inches
1 meter (m) = 1.094 yards; 39.37 inches; 100 centimeters; 1,000 millimeters
1 mile (mi) = 1.609344 kilometers; 5,280 feet; 1,760 yards
1 kilometer (km) = 0.621371 miles; 3,281 feet; 1,000 meters
1 astronomical unit (AU) = 92,955,778 miles; 149,597,871 kilometers;
    8.3 light-minutes; this is the average distance from the Earth to the Sun
1 light year (ly) = 63,240 astronomical units; 5,879,000,000,000 miles which
    is nearly 6 trillion miles; 9,461,000,000,000 kilometers
1 parsec (pc) = 3.26 light years; 206,265 astronomical units

Weight/Mass

1 ounce (oz) = 28.35 grams
1 gram (g *or* **gm)** = 0.0353 ounces
1 pound (lb) = 0.454 kilograms; 16 ounces
1 kilogram (kg) = 2.205 pounds; 1,000 grams
1 ton = 2,000 pounds; 907 kilograms
1 metric ton (t) = 1,000 kilograms; 2,205 pounds

Temperature

0° Fahrenheit (F) = −17.8° C; lowest temperature for mixture of water/ice/salt
0° Celsius (C) = 32° F; 273.16K (Kelvin); pure water freezes
212° Fahrenheit = 100° C; 373.16K (Kelvin); pure water boils
Absolute Zero = 0K (Kelvin); − 459.7° F; −273.16° C

Volume

1 cubic inch = 16.39 cubic centimeters
1 cubic centimeter (cc, ml *or* **cm³)** = 0.061 cubic inches
1 cubic yard = 0.765 cubic meters
1 cubic meter (m³) = 1.308 cubic yards

Speed of Light

Speed of Light = 186,282 miles/second; 299,792 kilometers/second

Facing page. *The WIYN telescope atop Kitt Peak, near Tucson, Arizona boasts a 3½ meter diameter telescope mirror. Telescopes like this help gather astronomical data. WIYN is an acronym for a consortium of four organizations that built this telescope.*

Abbreviations & Visible Light

Unit Abbreviations

Length
nm	Nanometer
mm	Millimeter
cm	Centimeter
in *or* "	Inch
ft *or* '	Feet
m	Meter
km	Kilometer
mi	Mile
AU	Astronomical Unit
ly	Light-Year
pc	Parsec

Weight/Mass
oz	Ounce
g *or* gm	Gram
lb	Pound
kg	Kilogram
t	Metric Ton

Angular Measurements
°	Degree
'	Minute
"	Second

Volume
ml	Milliliter

Temperature
F	Fahrenheit
C	Celsius
K	Kelvin

Time
s *or* sec	Second
m *or* min	Minute
h	Hour
d	Day
yr *or* a	Year

Power
W	Watt

Celestial Coordinates
RA or α   Right Ascension[1] (Expressed using h, m and s. Example: 8h 27m 05s)
Dec or δ   Declination[1] (Expressed using the ° ' " symbols. Example: 2° 04' 59")

[1]Right Ascension and Declination are used to define the position of all celestial objects. Right Ascension is analogous to longitude, except that it is based on 24 intervals, corresponding to the 24 hours of a day, or more precisely, the time it takes the celestial sphere to "rotate" one complete turn, which is about 4 minutes less than clock time (This is known as Sidereal time.). Declination is analogous to latitude and uses similar nomenclature.

Wavelengths of Visible Light & Eye Sensitivity

Wavelength of Visible Light[1]		Approximate Visible Light Sensitivity of Eyes	
VIOLET	420 nm	Daytime ✦ RANGE Visible to Eyes	400 to 750 nm
BLUE	470 nm	Nighttime ✦ RANGE Visible to Eyes[2]	400 to 620 nm
GREEN	530 nm	Daytime PEAK Sensitivity of Eyes	555 nm
YELLOW	580 nm	Nighttime PEAK Sensitivity of Eyes[2]	510 nm
ORANGE	610 nm		
RED	660 nm		

[1]The wavelength of visible light is expressed in nanometers. A nanometer is 1 billionth (10^{-9}) of a meter. 500 nanometers is about 1/50,000 of an inch. [2]Nighttime dark-adapted eyes. It takes 15 or more minutes for the eyes to reach full dark adaptation.

Greek Alphabet[1]

	Case[2]				Case[2]				Case[2]	
	Lower	Upper			Lower	Upper			Lower	Upper
ALPHA	α	A		IOTA	ι	I		RHO	ρ	P
BETA	β	B		KAPPA	κ	K		SIGMA	σ	Σ
GAMMA	γ	Γ		LAMBDA	λ	Λ		TAU	τ	T
DELTA	δ	Δ		MU	μ	M		UPSILON	υ	Y
EPSILON	ε	E		NU	ν	N		PHI	ϕ	Φ
ZETA	ζ	Z		XI	ξ	Ξ		CHI	χ	X
ETA	η	H		OMICRON	o	O		PSI	ψ	Ψ
THETA	ϑ or θ	Θ		PI	π	Π		OMEGA	ω	Ω

[1]The lowercase letters of the Greek alphabet are used to designate the brightest stars within each constellation. For example, Polaris, the North Star is designated α Ursae Minoris. Ursae Minoris is the genitive form of Ursa Minor. This system of using the Greek letters is also known as Bayer letters. [2]Only the lowercase is used to designate stars.

Solar System Members

SUN	$\odot$	JUPITER	$\jupiter$	MOON in General	
MERCURY	$\mercury$	SATURN	$\saturn$	NEW MOON	●
VENUS	$\venus$	URANUS		FIRST QUARTER	
EARTH	$\oplus$	NEPTUNE		FULL MOON	○
MARS	$\mars$	PLUTO		LAST QUARTER[1]	

[1]Also referred to as the Third Quarter.

Signs of the Zodiac[1]

1[2] PISCES		5 CANCER		9 SCORPIUS	
2 ARIES		6 LEO		10 SAGITTARIUS	
3 TAURUS		7 VIRGO		11 CAPRICORNUS	
4 GEMINI		8 LIBRA		12 AQUARIUS	

[1]The zodiacal constellations lie on the ecliptic, the apparent path the Sun traces through the sky during a year. Although I have listed the traditional 12 constellations of the zodiac, there are actually 13 constellations that cross the ecliptic. The southern portion of Ophiuchus, the Snake Bearer, crosses the ecliptic between Scorpius and Sagittarius. [2]The numbers 1 through 12 represent the order the Sun passes through these constellations during the year. This list starts with Pisces, the constellation where the Sun resides at the start of Spring (Vernal Equinox).

Notations & Temperature

Powers of 10

Throughout science, very large numbers are expressed as powers of 10 (using what is known as Scientific Notation) because it is impractical to print or write long numbers. For those who are unfamiliar with Scientific Notation, the following examples are provided to give you a feel for this notation.

$10^1 = 10$ (also, $1 \times 10^1 = 10$ *and* $1.0 \times 10^1 = 10$)
$10^2 = 100$ (also, $1 \times 10^2 = 100$ *and* $1.0 \times 10^2 = 100$)
$10^3 = 1,000$
$10^5 = 100,000$ *(one hundred thousand)*
$10^6 = 1,000,000$ *(1 million)*
$10^9 = 1,000,000,000$ *(1 billion)*
$10^{12} = 1,000,000,000,000$ *(1 trillion)*
$3.44 \times 10^3 = 3,440$ *(move decimal point 3 places to the right)*
$9.296 \times 10^7 = 92,960,000$ *(move decimal point 7 places to the right)*

$10^{-1} = 0.1 = \frac{1}{10}$ (also, 1×10^{-1} *or* $1.0 \times 10^{-1} = 0.1$)
$10^{-2} = 0.01 = \frac{1}{100}$
$10^{-5} = 0.00001 = \frac{1}{100,000}$

Fahrenheit & Celsius Temperature Conversions

Below are the formulae and examples to change between the Fahrenheit and Celsius temperature scales.

The formula to change from Fahrenheit to Celsius is $°C = (°F - 32) \times 0.556$	The formula to change from Celsius to Fahrenheit is $°F = (°C \times 1.8) + 32$
EXAMPLES	EXAMPLES
A. Change 229° F to Celsius	C. Change 100° C to Fahrenheit
1. $°C = (229 - 32) \times 0.556$	1. $°F = (100 \times 1.8) + 32$
2. $°C = (197) \times 0.556$	2. $°F = (180) + 32$
3. $°C = 197 \times 0.556$	3. $°F = 180 + 32$
4. $°C = 109.5$	4. $°F = 212$
B. Change $-45°$ F to Celsius	D. Change $-13°$ C to Fahrenheit
1. $°C = (-45 - 32) \times 0.556$	1. $°F = (-13 \times 1.8) + 32$
2. $°C = (-77) \times 0.556$	2. $°F = (-23.4) + 32$
3. $°C = -77 \times 0.556$	3. $°F = -23.4 + 32$
4. $°C = -42.8$	4. $°F = 8.6$

Star Magnitude ★ Scale of Brightness

Long ago, when the ancients looked up and studied the stars, they classified them by their brightness. We still use this same system of **magnitudes** today, however, we now have instruments to accurately measure a star's brightness. This scale ranges, at its brightest, from –27 (spoken as "minus twenty-seven" or "negative twenty-seven") for the Sun to over +30 (spoken as "thirty") for the faintest galaxies.

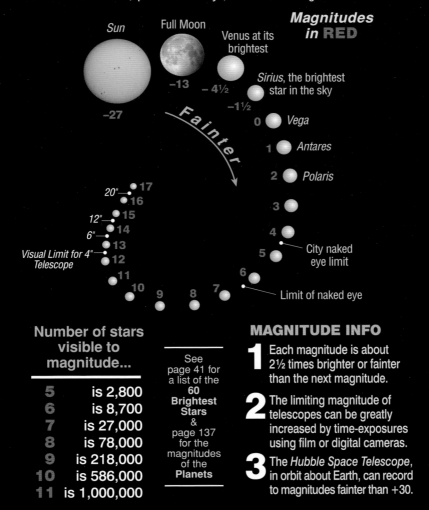

Number of stars visible to magnitude...		MAGNITUDE INFO

Number of stars visible to magnitude...

5	is 2,800
6	is 8,700
7	is 27,000
8	is 78,000
9	is 218,000
10	is 586,000
11	is 1,000,000

See page 41 for a list of the **60 Brightest Stars** & page 137 for the magnitudes of the **Planets**

MAGNITUDE INFO

1 Each magnitude is about 2½ times brighter or fainter than the next magnitude.

2 The limiting magnitude of telescopes can be greatly increased by time-exposures using film or digital cameras.

3 The *Hubble Space Telescope*, in orbit about Earth, can record to magnitudes fainter than +30.

Apparent Magnitude vs. Absolute Magnitude. Apparent magnitude refers to the brightness of the stars as we see them in the night sky and does not provide any information about their true brightness in relation to one another. For example, a star in the sky can appear bright simply because it is closer to us than other stars. However, Absolute Magnitude provides true comparative information on the brightness of stars. It is a scale of magnitude based on all stars placed at the "standard" distance of 10 parsecs (32.6 light years). At this distance (from us), our Sun diminished to the faint magnitude of +4.8.

13

The Universe & Our Galaxy

The Universe

Age: 13.7 to 14 billion years (13,700,000,000 to 14,000,000,000)

Galaxy Count: around 125 billion (125,000,000,000)

Chemical Composition: 75% Hydrogen, 25% Helium. There are just trace amounts of all the other elements.

Origin: created in an explosion called the "Big Bang"

Type: Current evidence suggests a Universe that will expand forever, however, our understanding of how the Universe works is far from complete so no definitive answer is possible at this time.

Our Milky Way Galaxy

Type of Galaxy: moderately barred spiral

Diameter: about 80,000 light years but it is often expressed as an even 100,000 light years

Central Bulge: about 10,000 light years across (within the plane of the Milky Way disk) and 6,500 light years thick

Mass: around 1 trillion (1,000,000,000,000) times the mass of the Sun

Number of Stars: estimated at 100 billion

Distance of our Sun from Center: about 30,000 light years

Location of our Sun: See the illustration on page 5. Our Sun is located on the inner edge of a spiral arm named Orion-Cygnus. The arm farther out is called Perseus and the one closer in is Sagittarius.

Coordinates to Center: Right Ascension: 17h 45.7m, Declination: −29° 00' which resides in the direction of the constellation Sagittarius

Revolution Velocity at Sun: 155 miles/sec (558,000 miles/hr); 250 km/sec

Revolution Period at Sun: about 220 million years

Companion Galaxies: The Large and Small Magellanic Clouds (LMC & SMC) are dwarf galaxies that can be seen with the naked eye from the southern hemisphere. The LMC, in the constellation Dorado, is 160,000 light years away (2 Milky Way diameters). The SMC, in the constellation Tucana is 195,000 light years away.

Local Group Member: Our Milky Way Galaxy is one of about three dozen galaxies gravitationally bound to one another and collectively referred to as the Local Group. The Andromeda Galaxy, followed by our Milky Way Galaxy are the two largest galaxies in the Local Group.

Distance to Andromeda Galaxy (M31): about 2.5 million light years or 31 times the diameter of our Milky Way Galaxy. The Andromeda Galaxy is visible to the naked eye.

Facing page. This galaxy, located in the direction of the constellation Eridanus (designated NGC 1232), is similar in size and appearance to our Milky Way Galaxy. Why don't we have a picture of our Milky Way Galaxy? Simply because our spacecrafts cannot travel far enough away to take such a picture. The farthest a spacecraft has traveled is a little beyond Pluto.

Our Sun

Equatorial Diameter: 865,278 miles; 1,392,530 km

Mass: 332,946.0 Earth masses or 4.3860 x 10^{30} pounds; 1.9891 x 10^{30} kg

Average Density: 1.41 gm/cm^3 (water is 1.00 gm/cm^3)

Rotation: 25.38 days at the equator and 35 days near the poles. Below a depth of 124,000 miles (200,000 km) the Sun appears to rotate at a stable 27 days, from equator to poles.

Inclination of Axis to Earth's Orbit: 7.25°

Visual Magnitude: −26.75

Absolute Magnitude: +4.82 (This would be the magnitude of the Sun if it were placed at a distance of 10 parsecs from Earth. This distance is used to compare the actual magnitude of *all* stars.)

Temperatures: Surface temperature averages 10,000° F (5,500° C; 5,800K). Sunspots are cooler areas on the surface and average 6,300° F (3,500° C). The Sun's core is estimated to reach 27,000,000° F (15,000,000° C)

Star Classification: G2 V   (The **G** refers to the spectral classification scale O•B•A•F•G•K•M•R•N•S where O are the hottest and S the coolest stars. The **2** refers to a finer 0–9 subtype of the spectral scale and the Roman numeral **V** indicates that the Sun is a typical star in its class.)

Energy Output: 3.85 x 10^{26} watts. Energy just outside Earth's atmosphere is 1.37 kilowatts per square meter.

Solar Wind Speed near Earth: about 280 miles/sec; 450 km/sec. Travel time from the Sun to the Earth is about 4 days.

Composition: 92.1% Hydrogen, 7.8% Helium, with traces of Oxygen (0.061%), Carbon (0.030%), Nitrogen (0.0084%), Neon (0.0076%), Iron (0.0037%), Silicon (0.0031%), Magnesium (0.0024%), Sulfur (0.0015%), and other elements (0.0015%)

Gravity: 27.9 times the gravity of Earth at its photosphere "surface"

Escape Velocity: 384 miles/sec (1.4 million miles/hour); 617.5 km/sec

Sunspot Cycle: about 11.1 years, but varying from 8 to 16 years

Location in Galaxy: See Our Milky Way Galaxy on page 15.

Nearest Neighbor: Proxima Centauri, a star in the constellation Centaurus, is 4.2 light years away. Proxima is an 11th magnitude star and is not visible to the naked eye.

Age: about 4.6 billion years

Facing page. This image of the Sun's surface shows coronal loops which are composed of plasma (particles of electrons and positive ions) and shaped by intense magnetic fields. The large loop spans 30 Earth diameters.

Our Planet Earth

Equatorial Diameter: 7,926.4 miles; 12,756.3 km
Polar Diameter: 7,899.8 miles; 12,713.5 km
Mass: 1.317×10^{25} pounds; 5.974×10^{24} kg
Average Density: 5.52 gm/cm^3 (water is 1.00 gm/cm^3)
Inclination of Axis to Orbit: 23.4393° with North Pole pointing roughly
   to the star Polaris in the constellation Ursa Minor (Little Dipper)
Precession of Axis: 50.29" a year around a 47° diameter circular arc.
   Total precession period is about 25,800 years.
Day: Synodic day (time used for clocks) is 86,400 seconds or 24 hours.
   Sidereal day (one complete rotation on its axis) is 86,164.1 seconds
   or 23 hours, 56 minutes, 4.1 seconds.
Year: 365.2564 days; 365 days, 6 hours, 9 minutes, 10 seconds
Distances from the Sun: *Average:* 92,955,800 miles; 149,597,870 km;
   8.3 light-minutes. This distance is also known as an astronomical unit.
   Closest: 91,403,000 miles; 147,099,000 km occuring on (or near)
   January 4th. *Farthest:* 94,508,000 miles; 152,096,000 km occuring
   on (or near) July 4th.
Average Orbital Speed: 18.5 miles/sec (66,600 miles/hour); 29.8 km/sec
Eccentricity of Orbit: 0.017 (from the mathematical definition of eccentricity)
   or 0.015% as defined in the Orbital table on page 24
Acceleration of Gravity at Sea Level: 32.2 feet/sec^2; 9.81 meters/sec^2
Escape Velocity at Equator: 6.96 miles/sec (25,000 miles/hour); 11.2 km/sec
Albedo: reflects 37% of sunlight or greater depending on cloud cover
Temperature Range: averages 59° F (15° C); highest recorded,
   136° F (58° C); lowest recorded, −129° F (−89° C)
Pressure at Sea Level: 1 atmosphere (1 bar); 14.7 pounds/inch^2;
   760.0 mm-Hg (mercury); 101.3 kPascals
Speed of Sound at Sea Level: 1,087 feet/sec (741.5 miles/hour); 331.5 meters/sec
Elevations: Mount Everest: 29,028 feet (5.5 miles); 8,848 meters.
   Marianas Trench: 36,198 feet (6.9 miles); 11,033 meters
Coordinates of Magnetic Poles: North Magnetic Pole: 76° N, 101° W;
   South Magnetic Pole: 66° S, 140° E
Composition of Atmosphere: 77% Nitrogen, 21% Oxygen, 1% Water,
   0.9% Argon with traces of many other gases
Thickness of Atmosphere: 75% of the atmosphere lies within 7 miles (11km)
   of sea level and "ends" at a height of 62 miles (100 km)
Land & Sea: 29% of the surface is land and 71% ocean
Core: The Earth has an outer liquid core with a diameter of about 4,350 miles
   (7,000 kilometers) containing an inner solid core having a diameter of about
   1,500 miles. Both cores are premodominately Iron, but contain some Nickel
   and other lighter elements with temperatures reaching as high as 9,000° F.
Age: about 4.6 billion years

Facing page. Earth during the Apollo 17 Moon mission in 1972.   19

Our Moon

Diameter: 2,160 miles; 3,476 km which is 27.3% of Earth's diameter
Volume: 2.03% of Earth's volume
Mass: 1.62 x 10^{23} pounds; 7.35 x 10^{22} kg (1.23% of Earth's mass)
Surface Area: 7.4% of Earth's surface area
Average Density: 3.34 gm/cm^3 (water is 1.00 gm/cm^3)
Gravity: 0.165 times the gravity of Earth
Escape Velocity: 1.5 miles/sec (5,369 miles/hour); 2.4 km/sec
Average Distance from Earth (measured from the centers of both bodies):
    238,856 miles; 384,401 km; 1.3 light-seconds
Closest Distance to Earth: 221,457 miles; 356,400 km
Farthest Distance from Earth: 252,711 miles; 406,700 km
Eccentricty of Orbit: 0.055 or 0.16% as defined on page 24.
Sidereal Revolution Period (One Complete Orbit): 27.322 days
Synodic Revolution (New Moon to New Moon Period):
    29 days, 12 hours, 44 minutes, 3 seconds
Average Orbital Velocity: 2,287 miles/hr; 3,681 km/hr
Arc Degrees of Movement in Sky: 0.51° per hour; 12.2° per day
Inclination of Orbit to Earth's Orbit: 5.1°
Rotation Period of Nodes: 18.61 years. The nodes represent the "line"
    created by the "intersection" of the Moon's orbit to Earth's. Its rotation
    plays a major role in the frequency of eclipses.
Rotation Period on Axis: The rotational period is the same as the Synodic
    Revolution, thus the same side of the Moon always faces Earth.
Inclination of Axis: 6.7° to its orbital plane
Albedo: reflects 11% of sunlight
Magnitude at Full Moon: −12.6
Temperature Range: −300° F (−184° C) to 266° F (130° C);
    Poles remain at a constant −140° F (−96° C);
    One meter under the surface remains at a constant −31° F (−35° C)
Surface Elevation Range: 11 miles; 17.7 km (lowest to highest points).
    Both points are located on the far side. The coordinates for the lowest
    and highest points are not known precisely but one set is as follows:
    lowest [70° S, 171° E], highest [3.4° N, 160° E] .
Surface Soil (Regolith) Composition: Oxygen 42%, Silicon 21%,
    Iron 13%, Calcium 8%, Aluminum 7%, Magnesium 6% and Other 3%.
    The Moon's surface has slightly more Iron, Calcium and Magnesium
    than on Earth's surface.
Age: a little less than 4.6 billion years

Facing page. An image of the Moon from the Galileo
spacecraft on its journey to Jupiter in 1992.

Solar System Physical Data

Physical Properties of Solar System Members

	Equatorial Diameter		Mass[1] Earth=1	Density[2] H_2O=1	Gravity[3] Earth=1	Albedo[4]
SUN	865,278 miles	1,392,530 km	332,946	1.41	27.9	n/a
MERCURY	3,032 miles	4,879 km	0.055	5.43	0.38	11%
VENUS	7,521 miles	12,104 km	0.815	5.25	0.90	65%
EARTH	7,926 miles	12,756 km	1	5.52	1.00	37%
MARS	4,228 miles	6,805 km	0.107	3.95	0.38	15%
JUPITER	88,844 miles	142,980 km	317.8	1.33	2.53	52%
SATURN	74,900 miles[5]	120,540 km[5]	95.2	0.69	1.06	47%
URANUS	31,764 miles	51,120 km	14.5	1.29	0.90	51%
NEPTUNE	30,777 miles	49,530 km	17.2	1.64	1.14	41%
PLUTO	1,433 miles	2,306 km	0.0025	2.03	0.08	30%

[1]Earth's mass is 1.32 x 10^{25} pounds (5.97 x 10^{24} kg). [2]Density per unit volume as compared to water. For comparsion, the density of alumium is 2.7 and iron is 7.7. [3]Gravity at equator. [4]Albedo is the amount of sunlight reflected by the Planet. [5]Saturn without rings. Visible rings are approximately 170,000 miles (273,600 km) in diameter.

	Rotational Period (Planet's Day)	Escape Velocity[1]		Oblateness[2]	Inclination to Orbit[3]
SUN	25 to 35 days[4]	384 miles/s	617.5 km/s	0	7.2°[5]
MERCURY	58.7 days	2.6 miles/s	4.2 km/s	0	0.0°
VENUS	243.0 days	6.5 miles/s	10.4 km/s	0	177.4°
EARTH	1 day	6.96 miles/s	11.2 km/s	0.34%	23.4°
MARS	24.62 hours	3.1 miles/s	5.0 km/s	0.74%	25.2°
JUPITER	9.84 hours	37 miles/s	59.5 km/s	6.5%	3.1°
SATURN	10.23 hours	22.1 miles/s	35.5 km/s	9.8%	25.3°
URANUS	17.9 hours	13.2 miles/s	21.3 km/s	2.3%	97.9°
NEPTUNE	19.2 hours	14.6 miles/s	23.5 km/s	1.7%	28.3°
PLUTO	6.4 days	0.8 miles/s	1.3 km/s	unknown	123°

[1]At equator. [2]Bulging at the equator caused by rotation of Planet on axis. Percentage indicates the amount of extra equatorial diameter as compared to the polar diameter. [3]Inclination of Planet's rotational axis to Planet's orbit around Sun. [4]Sun rotates about 10 days faster at its equator than at its poles. [5]Inclination of Sun's rotational axis to Earth's orbit.

Facing page. A closeup of the Great Red Spot and surrounding clouds on Jupiter. The Great Red Spot is at the top of this picture and is physically larger than Earth. This hurricane-type vortex spans 25,000 miles (40,000 kilometers).

Solar System Orbital Data

Orbital Properties of Solar System Members

| | Average Distance from Sun[1] | | | Eccentricity[3] |
	Astronomical Units (AU)[2]	Miles	Kilometers	
MERCURY	0.387	35,980,000	57,910,000	2.2%
VENUS	0.723	67,230,000	108,200,000	0.003%
EARTH	1.000	92,955,800	149,597,870	0.015%
MARS	1.524	141,640,000	227,940,000	0.44%
JUPITER	5.203	483,630,000	778,330,000	0.16%
SATURN	9.539	886,680,000	1,426,980,000	0.16%
URANUS	19.191	1,783,950,000	2,870,990,000	0.12%
NEPTUNE	30.061	2,794,350,000	4,497,070,000	0.004%
PLUTO	39.529	3,674,490,000	5,913,520,000	3.3%

[1]The Planets' orbits around the Sun are ellipses, not circles. Thus, they have a closest and farthest distance to the Sun. [2]One astronomical unit is the average distance of the Earth to the Sun, 92,955,800 miles. [3]Eccentricity is normally expressed as a decimal and represents the elongation of a Planet's elliptical orbit. Ellipses have both a major (longer) and minor (shorter) axis. For clarity, I have expressed eccentricity as a percentage indicating how much longer the major axis is as compared to the minor axis. Although the Planets' orbits are ellipses, all nine have orbits that are very close to circles. Seven of the Planets have eccentricities less than 1%.

	Revolution Around Sun (Planet's Year)	Average Orbital Velocity		Inclination of Orbit to Earth's Orbit
MERCURY	87.97 days	29.76 miles/s	47.89 km/s	7.00°
VENUS	224.70 days	21.77 miles/s	35.03 km/s	3.39°
EARTH	365.26 days	18.51 miles/s	29.79 km/s	0.00°
MARS	686.98 days	14.99 miles/s	24.13 km/s	1.85°
JUPITER	11.86 years	8.12 miles/s	13.06 km/s	1.31°
SATURN	29.42 years	5.99 miles/s	9.64 km/s	2.49°
URANUS	83.75 years	4.23 miles/s	6.81 km/s	0.77°
NEPTUNE	163.73 years	3.37 miles/s	5.43 km/s	1.77°
PLUTO	248.03 years	2.95 miles/s	4.74 km/s	17.15°

Solar System Atmospheres

Atmospheres of Solar System Members

	Description of Atmosphere	Temperature
MERCURY	No atmosphere[1]	800° F Day (427° C) −300° F Night (−184° C)
VENUS	96% Carbon Dioxide, 3.5% Nitrogen *Atmospheric Pressure: 90 bars*	Averages 900° F (482° C)
EARTH	77% Nitrogen, 21% Oxygen, 1% Water, 1% Argon *Atmospheric Pressure: 1 bar*	Averages 59° F (15° C) Highest 136° F (58° C) Lowest −129° F (−89° C)
MARS[2]	95% Carbon Dioxide, 2.7% Nitrogen, 1.6% Argon, 0.2% Oxygen *Atmospheric Pressure: 0.007 bar*	Averages −67° F (−55° C) High 80° F (27° C) Low −207° F (−133° C)
JUPITER[3]	90% Hydrogen Gas, 10% Helium Gas	−243° F (−153° C) just below cloudtops
SATURN[3]	97% Hydrogen Gas, 3% Helium Gas	−301° F (−185° C) just below cloudtops
URANUS[3]	83% Hydrogen Gas, 15% Helium Gas 2% Methane Gas	−323° F (−197° C) just below cloudtops
NEPTUNE[3]	74% Hydrogen Gas, 25% Helium Gas 1% Methane Gas	−373° F (−225° C) just below cloudtops
PLUTO	100% Methane Gas? Some Nitrogen? *Extremely low atmospheric pressure*	−419° F (−233° C)

[1]Mercury has no atmosphere in the conventional sense, however, there are trace quantities of Helium, Sodium and Oxygen and an atmospheric pressure of 10^{-15} bars. [2]Since the atmospheric pressure on Mars is low, temperature can decrease by as much as 18 F° (10 C°) from the surface to a height of just 3 feet (1 meter). [3]Jupiter, Saturn, Uranus and Neptune are Gas Giants and thus do not have, in the conventional sense, a surface below the clouds. Therefore, they do not have a reference point from which to measure a standard atmospheric pressure.

Solar System Moons

Major Moons of the Planets[1]

	Moon Name	Average Distance from Planet[2]	Revolution Period[3]	Diameter	Visual Magnitude[4]
MERCURY	*Mercury has no moons*				
VENUS	*Venus has no moons*				
EARTH	*Earth has 1 moon*				
	Moon	238,920 miles 384,500 km	27.3 days	2,160 miles 3,476 km	−12.7
MARS	*Mars has 2 moons*				
	Phobos	5,830 miles 9,380 km	7.7 hours	17x13 miles 27 x 21 km	11.6
	Deimos	14,580 miles 23,460 km	1.3 days	10 x 8 miles 16 x 13 km	12.7
JUPITER	*Jupiter has 63 known moons[5] (This count will most likely rise)*				
	Io	262,000 miles 421,600 km	1.77 days	2,255 miles 3,629 km	5.0
	Europa	416,900 miles 670,900 km	3.55 days	1,950 miles 3,138 km	5.3
	Ganymede	664,900 miles 1,070,000 km	7.16 days	3,270 miles 5,261 km	4.6
	Callisto	1,171,000 miles 1,885,000 km	16.69 days	2,980 miles 4,800 km	5.6
SATURN	*Saturn has 56 known moons[6] (This count will most likely rise)*				
	Mimas	116,200 miles 187,000 km	0.9 days	242 miles 390 km	12.5
	Enceladus	147,900 miles 238,000 km	1.4 days	311 miles 500 km	11.8
	Tethys	183,300 miles 295,000 km	1.9 days	659 miles 1,060 km	10.3
	Dione	234,900 miles 378,000 km	2.7 days	699 miles 1,120 km	10.4
	Rhea	326,800 miles 526,000 km	4.5 days	951 miles 1,530 km	9.7
	Titan	758,100 miles 1,221,000 km	15.9 days	3,200 miles 5,150 km	8.4
	Iapetus	2,212,700 miles 3,561,000 km	79.3 days	907 miles 1,460 km	11.0

Facing page. *Titan, Saturn's largest moon has a nitrogen/methane atmosphere. The inset shows Titan's surface as imaged by the Huygen's probe in 2005.*

Solar System Moons

Major Moons of the Planets[1]

	Moon Name	Average Distance from Planet[2]	Revolution Period[3]	Diameter	Visual Magnitude[4]
URANUS	*Uranus has 27 known moons*[7]	*(This count will most likely rise)*			
	Ariel	118,600 miles 190,900 km	2.5 days	721 miles 1,160 km	14.0
	Umbriel	165,300 miles 266,000 km	4.1 days	739 miles 1,190 km	14.9
	Titania	271,100 miles 436,300 km	8.7 days	1,000 miles 1,610 km	13.9
	Oberon	362,500 miles 583,400 km	13.5 days	963 miles 1,550 km	14.1
NEPTUNE	*Neptune has 13 known moons*[8]	*(This count will most likely rise)*			
	Triton	220,000 miles 354,000 km	5.9 days	1,678 miles 2,700 km	13.6
	Nereid[1]	3,423,800 miles 5,510,000 km	365.2 days	211 miles 340 km	19.7
PLUTO[10]	*Pluto has 3 known moons*[9]	*(This count could rise)*			
	Charon	11,900 miles 19,100 km	6.4 days	746 miles 1,200 km	17

NOTE: All moon data and counts are current as of June, 2006.
[1]Data for only the major moons are provided because the lesser moons are small and require large telescopes and photographic means to identify. A typical example of these lesser moons is Nereid, Neptune's second largest moon, which is listed in this table. [2]Distance measured from center of Planet. [3]Orbit around Planet. [4]Visual magnitude from Earth at Planet's closest approach. [5]The named moons of **JUPITER** are (from innermost to outermost): Metis, Adrastea, Amalthea, Thebe, Io, Europa, Ganymede, Callisto, Themisto, Leda, Himalia, Lysithea, Elara, Carpo, Euporie, Thelxinoe, Euanthe, Helike, Orthosie, Iocaste, Ananke, Praxidike, Harpalyke, Hermippe, Orthosie, Thyone, Mneme, Aitne, Kale, Taygete, Chaldene, Erinome, Aoede, Kallichore, Kalyke, Eurydome, Pasithee, Cyllene, Eukelade, Hegemone, Arche, Isonoe, Pasipaë, Sinope, Sponde, Autonoe, Callirrhoe and Megaclite. [6]The named moons of **SATURN** are (from innermost to outermost): Pan, Daphnis, Atlas, Prometheus, Pandora, Epimetheus & Janus, Mimas, Methone, Pallene, Enceladus, Tethys & Telesto & Calypso, Dione & Polydeuces & Helene, Rhea, Titan, Hyperion, Iapetus, Kiviuq, Ijiraq, Phoebe, Paaliaq, Skathi, Albiorix, Erriapo, Siarnaq, Tarvos, Mundilfari, Narvi, Suttungr, Thrymr and Ymir. [7]The named moons of **URANUS** are (from innermost to outermost): Cordelia, Ophelia, Bianca, Cressida, Desdemona, Juliet, Portia, Rosalind, Cupid, Belinda, Perdita, Puck, Mab, Miranda, Ariel, Umbriel, Titania, Oberon, Francisco, Caliban, Stephano, Trinculo, Sycorax, Margaret, Prospero, Setebos and Ferdinand. [8]The named moons of **NEPTUNE** are (from innermost to outermost): Naiad, Thalassa, Despina, Galatea, Larissa, Proteus, Triton, Nereid and Psamathe. [9]The named moons of **PLUTO** are (from innermost to outermost): Charon, Nix and Hydra.
[10]See page 155 for a discussion about Pluto's planetary status.

Solar System Comparison

QUICK COMPARISON of Solar System Members

	Distance from Sun[1]		Diameter[3]	Mass[4]	Volume[5]
	Earth=1	*Light Time[2]*	*Earth=1*	*Earth=1*	*Earth=1*
SUN	n/a	n/a	109	333,000	1,300,000
MERCURY	0.4	3.2 minutes	0.4	0.06	0.06
VENUS	0.7	6 minutes	0.95	0.8	0.9
EARTH	1	8.3 minutes	1	1	1
MARS	1.5	12.7 minutes	0.5	0.1	0.15
JUPITER	5.2	43.3 minutes	11.2	318	1,326
SATURN	9.5	1h 19min	9.5	95	771
URANUS	19	2h 40min	4	15	63
NEPTUNE	30	4h 10min	3.8	17	58
PLUTO	39.5	5h 29min	0.2	0.003	0.006

[1]The average distance from the Earth to the Sun is 92,955,800 miles (149,597,870 km) and is also known as 1 astronomical unit (AU). [2]The time it takes for light to travel from the Sun to the respective Planet. Light travels at 186,282 miles/sec (299,792 km/sec). [3]Earth's equatorial diameter is 7,926 miles (12,756 km). [4]Earth's mass is 1.32×10^{25} pounds (5.97×10^{24} kg). [5]Earth's volume is 2.6×10^{11} cubic miles (1.1×10^{12} km³).

Eight of the nine Planets as imaged by spacecraft. The top four, known as the Terrestrial Planets, are Mercury, Venus, Earth (our Moon is to the right of Earth) and Mars. The bottom four are the Gas Giants — Jupiter Saturn, Uranus and Neptune. Pluto is not pictured because it has not yet been visited and imaged by an exploratory spacecraft. Planet sizes are not to scale.

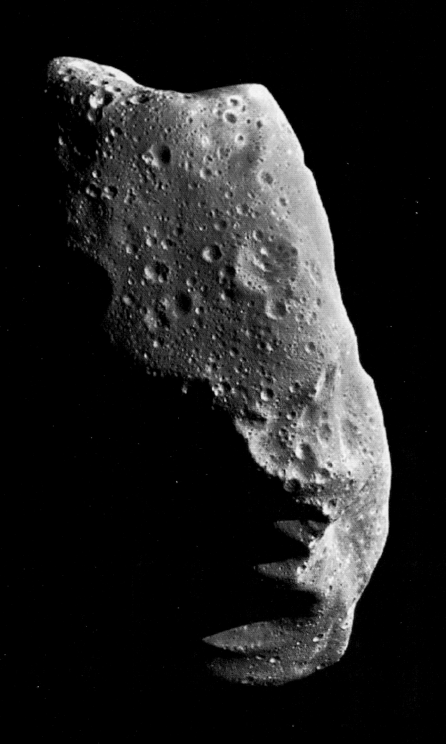

Minor Planets or Asteroids

Major Asteroids[1]

Name	Longest Length[2]		Average Distance from Sun[3]	Orbital Period	Orbital Inclination[4]
CERES	594 miles	957 km	2.77 AU	4.60 years	10.6°
PALLAS	325 miles	524 km	2.77 AU	4.62 years	34.8°
VESTA	318 miles	512 km	2.36 AU	3.63 years	7.1°
HYGIEA	276 miles	444 km	3.14 AU	5.56 years	3.8°
INTERAMNIA	204 miles	329 km	3.06 AU	5.36 years	17.3°
DAVIDA	203 miles	326 km	3.17 AU	5.63 years	15.9°
EUNOMIA	199 miles	320 km	2.64 AU	4.30 years	11.7°
EUROPA	188 miles	302 km	3.10 AU	5.46 years	7.5°
JUNO	170 miles	274 km	2.67 AU	4.36 years	13.0°
SYLVIA	162 miles	261 km	3.49 AU	6.52 years	10.9°
EUPHROSYNE	159 miles	256 km	3.15 AU	5.59 years	26.3°
PSYCHE	149 miles	239 km	2.92 AU	5.00 years	3.1°
THISBE	144 miles	232 km	2.77 AU	4.60 years	5.2°
CYBELE	143 miles	230 km	3.43 AU	6.36 years	3.5°
BAMBERGA	142 miles	228 km	2.68 AU	4.39 years	11.1°
PATIENTIA	140 miles	225 km	3.06 AU	5.35 years	15.2°

[1]Presented here are the 16 largest asteroids in the asteroid belt between Mars and Jupiter. It is estimated that there are billions of asteroids having a total mass about 1/1,000 of Earth's mass and a total volume equal to half the diameter of our Moon. [2]Ceres is the only asteroid that is spherical in shape. These lengths may change with new research. [3]For comparison, Mars is 1.5 AU from the Sun and Jupiter is 5.2 AU from the Sun. [4]Inclination to Earth's orbit.

Near-Earth Asteroids. There are three types of asteroids that approach Earth and are categorized as Aten, Apollo and Amor. **Aten** asteroids, which total about 300 asteroids, orbit inside of Earth's orbit. **Apollo** asteroids have orbits that are slightly larger than Earth's, and **Amor** asteroids orbit inside of Mars' orbit. About 3,200 known Amor-Apollo asteroids could potentially cross Earth's orbit.

Facing page. The asteroid Ida, the second asteroid ever to be imaged. This view of Ida was returned by the Galileo spacecraft in August 1992 on its journey to Jupiter. Ida is about 32 miles in length (52 km) and has a small moon, named Dactyl, revolving around it. Dactyl is about one mile in diameter (1.7 km).

Page 32. Orion is one of the most easily and widely recognized constellations. Many of the constellations that we recognize today were also used in ancient times. The Egyptians not only recognized the stars that make up Orion, they used the three belt stars as a pattern for the alignment and size of the three pyramids at Giza.

Constellations

The 88 Constellations

Constellation Name	3 & 4 Letter Abbreviation	Meaning *Latin Genitive*[1]	Page Number Reference to Celestial Atlas[2]
ANDROMEDA	And / Andr	Daughter of Cassiopeia / *Andromedae*	**44**, 43, 45
ANTLIA	Ant / Antl	Air Pump / *Antliae*	**46**, 47
APUS	Aps / Apus	Bird of Paradise / *Apodis*	**50**
AQUARIUS	Aqr / Aqar	Water Bearer / *Aquarii*	**44**, 49
AQUILA	Aql / Aqil	Eagle / *Aquilae*	**49**
ARA	Ara / Arae	Altar / *Arae*	**50**, 48, 49
ARIES	Ari / Arie	Ram / *Arietis*	**44**, 45
AURIGA	Aur / Auri	Charioteer / *Aurigae*	**45**, 43, 46
BOOTES	Boo / Boot	Herdsman / *Bootis*	47, **48**, 43
CAELUM	Cae / Cael	Engraving Tool / *Caeli*	**45**, 46, 50
CAMELOPARDALIS	Cam / Caml	Giraffe / *Camelopardalis*	**43**
CANCER	Cnc / Canc	Crab / *Cancri*	**46**
CANES VENATICI	CVn / CVen	Hunting Dog / *Canum Venaticorum*	43, **47**, 48
CANIS MAJOR	CMa / CMaj	Big Dog / *Canis Majoris*	**46**, 45
CANIS MINOR	CMi / CMin	Little Dog / *Canis Minoris*	**46**
CAPRICORNUS	Cap / Capr	Sea Goat / Capricorni	**49**, 44
CARINA	Car / Cari	Ship's Keel / *Carinae*	**50**
CASSIOPEIA	Cas / Cass	Queen / *Cassiopeiae*	**43**

Greek Alphabet

α alpha, β beta, γ gamma, δ delta, ε epsilon, ζ zeta, η eta, θ theta, ι iota, κ kappa, λ lambda, μ mu, ν nu, ξ xi, ο omicron, π pi, ρ rho, σ sigma, τ tau, υ upsilon, φ phi, χ chi, ψ psi, ω omega

[1]The Latin Genitive form is used in conjunction with the Greek letter designation of individual stars in the constellations. For example, the star Rigil Kent in Centaurus is designated α so it would be referred to as α Centauri (Alpha Centauri). [2]Bolded page numbers indicate the chart(s) which best shows the constellation.

Constellations

The 88 Constellations

Constellation Name	3 & 4 Letter Abbreviation	Meaning *Latin Genitive*[1]	Page Number Reference to Celestial Atlas[2]
CENTAURUS	Cen	Centaur	**50**, 47, 48
	Cent	*Centauri*	
CEPHEUS	Cep	King	**43**
	Ceph	*Cephei*	
CETUS	Cet	Whale	**44, 45**
	Ceti	*Ceti*	
CHAMAELEON	Cha	Chameleon	**50**
	Cham	*Chamaeleontis*	
CIRCINUS	Cir	Drawing Compass	**50**
	Circ	*Circini*	
COLUMBA	Col	Dove	**45, 46**, 50
	Colm	*Columbae*	
COMA BERENICES	Com	Berenice's Hair	**47, 48**
	Coma	*Comae Berenices*	
CORONA AUSTRALIS	CrA	Southern Crown	**48, 49**, 50
	CorA	*Coronae Australis*	
CORONA BOREALIS	CrB	Northern Crown	**48**
	CorB	*Coronae Borealis*	
CORVUS	Crv	Crow	**47**
	Corv	*Corvi*	
CRATER	Crt	Cup	**47**
	Crat	*Crateris*	
CRUX	Cru	Southern Cross	**50**
	Crux	*Crucis*	
CYGNUS	Cyg	Swan	**49**, 43
	Cygn	*Cygni*	
DELPHINUS	Del	Dolphin	**49**
	Dlph	*Delphini*	
DORADO	Dor	Goldfish	**50**
	Dora	*Doradus*	
DRACO	Dra	Dragon	**43**
	Drac	*Draconis*	
EQUULEUS	Equ	Little Horse	**44, 49**
	Equl	*Equulei*	
ERIDANUS	Eri	River Eridanus	**45**, 44, 50
	Erid	*Eridani*	

[1]The Latin Genitive form is used in conjunction with the Greek letter designation of individual stars in the constellations. For example, the star Antares in Scorpius is designated α so it would be referred to as α Scorpii (Alpha Scorpii). [2]Bolded page numbers indicate the chart(s) which best shows the constellation.

The 88 Constellations

Constellation Name	3 & 4 Letter Abbreviation	Meaning *Latin Genitive*[1]	Page Number Reference to Celestial Atlas[2]
FORNAX	For	Furnace	**45**, 44
	Forn	*Fornacis*	
GEMINI	Gem	Twins	**46**, 45
	Gemi	*Geminorum*	
GRUS	Gru	Crane	**44**, 49, 50
	Grus	*Gruis*	
HERCULES	Her	The Son of Zeus	**48**, 49
	Herc	*Herculis*	
HOROLOGIUM	Hor	Clock	**50**, 45
	Horo	*Horologii*	
HYDRA	Hya	Sea Serpent	**46**, **47**, 48
	Hyda	*Hydrae*	
HYDRUS	Hyi	Water Snake	**50**
	Hydi	*Hydri*	
INDUS	Ind	Indian	**50**, 49
	Indi	*Indi*	
LACERTA	Lac	Lizard	**43**, **44**, **49**
	Lacr	*Lacertae*	
LEO	Leo	Lion	**47**, 46
	Leon	*Leonis*	
LEO MINOR	LMi	Little Lion	**46**, **47**
	LMin	*Leonis Minoris*	
LEPUS	Lep	Hare	**45**, **46**
	Leps	*Leporis*	
LIBRA	Lib	Scales	**48**, 47
	Libr	*Librae*	
LUPUS	Lup	Wolf	**48**, 47, 50
	Lupi	*Lupi*	
LYNX	Lyn	Lynx	**43**, 46, 47
	Lync	*Lyncis*	
LYRA	Lyr	Lyre	**49**, 48
	Lyra	*Lyrae*	
MENSA	Men	Table Mountain	**50**
	Mens	*Mensae*	
MICROSCOPIUM	Mic	Microscope	**49**, 44, 50
	Micr	*Microscopii*	

Greek Alphabet

α alpha
β beta
γ gamma
δ delta
ε epsilon
ζ zeta
η eta
θ theta
ι iota
κ kappa
λ lambda
μ mu
ν nu
ξ xi
ο omicron
π pi
ρ rho
σ sigma
τ tau
υ upsilon
φ phi
χ chi
ψ psi
ω omega

[1]The Latin Genitive form is used in conjunction with the Greek letter designation of individual stars in the constellations. For example, the star Enif in Pegasus is designated ε so it would be referred to as ε Pegasi (Epsilon Pegasi). [2]Bolded page numbers indicate the chart(s) which best shows the constellation.

Constellations

The 88 Constellations

Constellation Name	3 & 4 Letter Abbreviation	Meaning *Latin Genitive*[1]	Page Number Reference to Celestial Atlas[2]
MONOCEROS	Mon Mono	Unicorn *Monocerotis*	**46**, 45
MUSCA	Mus Musc	Fly *Muscae*	**50**
NORMA	Nor Norm	Level *Normae*	**48, 50**
OCTANS	Oct Octn	Octant *Octantis*	**50**
OPHIUCHUS	Oph Ophi	Snake Holder *Ophiuchi*	**48**, 49
ORION	Ori Orio	The Hunter *Orionis*	**45**, 46
PAVO	Pav Pavo	Peacock *Pavonis*	**50**
PEGASUS	Peg Pegs	The Winged Horse *Pegasi*	**44**, 49
PERSEUS	Per Pers	Rescuer of Andromeda *Persei*	**43**, 45
PHOENIX	Phe Phoe	Phoenix *Phoenicis*	**50**, 44, 45
PICTOR	Pic Pict	Easel *Pictoris*	**50**
PISCES	Psc Pisc	Fishes *Piscium*	**44**, 45
PISCIS AUSTRINUS	PsA PscA	Southern Fish *Piscis Austrini*	**44, 49**
PUPPIS	Pup Pupp	Ship's Stern *Puppis*	**46**, 45, 50
PYXIS	Pyx Pyxi	Ship's Compass *Pyxidis*	**46**
RETICULUM	Ret Reti	Eyepiece Reticle *Reticuli*	**50**
SAGITTA	Sge Sgte	Arrow *Sagittae*	**49**
SAGITTARIUS	Sgr Sgtr	Archer *Sagittarii*	**48, 49**

[1]The Latin Genitive form is used in conjunction with the Greek letter designation of individual stars in the constellations. For example, the star Pollux is designated β in the constellation Gemini and would be referred to as β Geminorum (Beta Geminorum). [2]Bolded page numbers indicate the chart(s) which best shows the constellation.

Constellations

The 88 Constellations

Constellation Name	3 & 4 Letter Abbreviation	Meaning *Latin Genitive*[1]	Page Number Reference to Celestial Atlas[2]
SCORPIUS	Sco Scor	Scorpion *Scorpii*	**48**, 49, 50
SCULPTOR	Scl Scul	Sculptor's Apparatus *Sculptoris*	**44**
SCUTUM	Sct Scut	Shield *Scuti*	**48**, 49
SERPENS[3]	Ser Serp	Snake *Serpentis*	**48**, 49
SEXTANS	Sex Sext	Sextant *Sextantis*	**46**, 47
TAURUS	Tau Taur	Bull *Tauri*	**45**, 46
TELESCOPIUM	Tel Tele	Telescope *Telescopii*	**48**, 49, 50
TRIANGULUM	Tri Tria	Triangle *Trianguli*	**44**, 45
TRIANGULUM AUSTRALE	TrA TrAu	Southern Triangle *Trianguli Australis*	**50**
TUCANA	Tuc Tucn	Toucan *Tucanae*	**50**
URSA MAJOR	UMa UMaj	Big Bear *Ursae Majoris*	**43**, 46, 47, 48
URSA MINOR	UMi UMin	Little Bear *Ursae Minoris*	**43**
VELA	Vel Velr	Sail *Velorum*	**46**, **50**, 47
VIRGO	Vir Virg	Virgin *Virginis*	**47**, 48
VOLANS	Vol Voln	Flying Fish *Volantis*	**50**
VULPECULA	Vul Vulp	Little Fox *Vulpeculae*	**49**

Greek Alphabet

α alpha
β beta
γ gamma
δ delta
ε epsilon
ζ zeta
η eta
θ theta
ι iota
κ kappa
λ lambda
μ mu
ν nu
ξ xi
ο omicron
π pi
ρ rho
σ sigma
τ tau
υ upsilon
φ phi
χ chi
ψ psi
ω omega

[1]The Latin Genitive form is used in conjunction with the Greek letter designation of individual stars in the constellations. For example, the star Capella in Auriga is designated α so it would be referred to as α Aurigae (Alpha Aurigae). [2]Bolded page numbers indicate the chart(s) which best shows the constellation. [3]The constellation Serpens is the only constellation that has two discontinous boundaries. They lie on opposite sides of Ophiuchus. The northwest portion is referred to as Serpens Caput (head) and the southeast portion as Serpens Cauda (tail).

Names of Stars

Commonly Used Names of Stars

Name of Star (Magnitude)	Constellation	Greek Letter Desig[1]	Name of Star (Magnitude)	Constellation	Greek Letter Desig[1]
ACAMAR (3.3)	Eridanus	θ	**ALPHEKKA** (2.2)	Corona Borealis	α
ACHERNAR (0.5)	Eridanus	α	**ALPHERATZ** (2.1)	Andromeda	α
ACRUX (0.8)	Crux	α	**ALRAKIS** (5.1)	Draco	μ
ACUBENS (4.3)	Cancer	α	**ALRESCHA** (3.9)	Pisces	α
ADHAFERA (3.4)	Leo	ζ	**ALSHAIN** (3.9)	Aquila	β
ADHARA (1.5)	Canis Major	ε	**ALSUHAIL** (2.2)	Vela	λ
ALBALI (3.8)	Aquarius	ε	**ALTAIR** (0.8)	Aquila	α
ALBIREO (3.4)	Cygnus	β	**ALTAIS** (3.1)	Draco	δ
ALCHIBA (4.2)	Corvus	α	**ALTERF** (4.5)	Leo	λ
ALCOR (4.0)	Ursa Major	80[1]	**ALUDRA** (2.4)	Canis Major	η
ALDEBARAN (0.9)	Taurus	α	**ALULA AUSTRALIS** (3.9)	UMaj	ξ
ALDERAMIN (2.5)	Cepheus	α	**ALULA BOREALIS** (3.5)	UMaj	ν
ALFIRK (3.2)	Cepheus	β	**ALYA** (4.5)	Serpens	θ
ALGEDI (3.6)	Capricorn	α	**ANCHA** (4.3)	Aquarius	θ
ALGENIB (2.8)	Pegasus	γ	**ANKAA** (2.4)	Phoenix	α
ALGIEBA (2.6)	Leo	γ	**ANTARES** (1.1)	Scorpius	α
ALGOL (2.1)	Perseus	β	**ARCTURUS** (−0.1)	Bootes	α
ALGORAB (2.9)	Corvus	δ	**ARKAB** (4.5)	Sagittarius	β
ALHENA (1.9)	Gemini	γ	**ARNEB** (2.6)	Lepus	α
ALIOTH (1.8)	Ursa Major	ε	**ASCELLA** (2.6)	Sagittarius	ζ
ALKAID (1.9)	Ursa Major	η	**ASELLUS AUSTRALIS** (4.2)	Canc	δ
ALKALUROPS (4.5)	Bootes	μ	**ASELLUS BOREALIS** (4.7)	Canc	γ
ALKES (4.2)	Crater	α	**ASPIDISKE** (2.2)	Carina	ι
ALMAAK (2.1)	Andromeda	γ	**ATIK** (2.8)	Perseus	ζ
ALNAIR (1.7)	Grus	α	**ATRIA** (1.9)	Triangulum Australe	α
ALNASL (3.1)	Sagittarius	γ	**AVIOR** (1.9)	Carina	ε
ALNATH (1.7)	Taurus	β	**AZHA** (4.2)	Eridanus	η
ALNILAM (1.7)	Orion	ε	**BATEN KAITOS** (3.9)	Cetus	ζ
ALNITAK (1.7)	Orion	ζ	**BECRUX** (1.3)	Crux	β
ALPHARD (2.0)	Hydra	α	**BEID** (4.1)	Eridanus	o

Greek Alphabet

α alpha
β beta
γ gamma
δ delta
ε epsilon
ζ zeta
η eta
θ theta
ι iota
κ kappa
λ lambda
μ mu
ν nu
ξ xi
o omicron
π pi
ρ rho
σ sigma
τ tau
υ upsilon
φ phi
χ chi
ψ psi
ω omega

[1]The brightest stars in each constellation are designated with a lowercase Greek letter for identification. In astronomy, when a star with a Greek letter is referred to, the Latin genitive form of the constellation name is used in conjunction with the Greek letter designation. For example, the star Betelgeuse in Orion is designated α, so it would be referred to as α Orionis (Alpha Orionis). [1]Alcor does not have a Greek designation, so it is referred to here by its Flamsteed number (see Glossary), which also uses the Latin genitive form.

Commonly Used Names of Stars

Name of Star (Magnitude)	Constellation	Greek Letter Desig[1]	Name of Star (Magnitude)	Constellation	Greek Letter Desig[1]
BELLATRIX (1.6)	Orion	γ	KAUS BOREALIS (2.8)	Sagittarius	λ
BETELGEUSE (0.5)	Orion	α	KAUS MEDIA (2.7)	Sagittarius	δ
BIHAM (3.5)	Pegasus	θ	KEID (4.5)	Eridanus	o
CANOPUS (−0.6)	Carina	α	KITALPHA (4.1)	Equuleus	α
CAPELLA (0.1)	Auriga	α	KOCHAB (2.1)	Ursa Minor	β
CAPH (2.3)	Cassiopeia	β	KORNEPHOROS (2.8)	Hercules	β
CASTOR (1.6)	Gemini	α	KURHAH (4.6)	Cepheus	ξ
CEBALRAI (2.8)	Ophiuchus	β	LESATH (2.7)	Scorpius	υ
CHARA (4.3)	Canes Venatici	β	MARFIK (3.8)	Ophiuchus	λ
CHERTAN (3.3)	Leo	θ	MARKAB (2.5)	Pegasus	α
COR CAROLI (2.9)	Canes Venatici	α	MATAR (2.9)	Pegasus	η
CURSA (2.8)	Eridanus	β	MEBSUTA (3.1)	Gemini	ε
DABIH (3.1)	Capricornus	β	MEGREZ (3.3)	Ursa Major	δ
DENEB (1.3)	Cygnus	α	MEISSA (3.4)	Orion	λ
DENEB ALGEDI (2.9)	Capricornus	δ	MEKBUDA (3.8)	Gemini	ζ
DENEB KAITOS (2.1)	Cetus	β	MENKALINAN (1.9)	Auriga	β
DENEBOLA (2.1)	Leo	β	MENKAR (2.5)	Cetus	α
DUBHE (1.8)	Ursa Major	α	MENKENT (2.1)	Centaurus	θ
EDASICH (3.3)	Draco	ι	MENKIB (4.0)	Perseus	ξ
ENIF (2.4)	Pegasus	ε	MERAK (2.3)	Ursa Major	β
ERRAI (3.2)	Cepheus	γ	MESARTIM (4.8)	Aries	γ
ETAMIN (2.2)	Draco	γ	MIAPLACIDUS (1.7)	Carina	β
FOMALHAUT (1.2)	Piscis Austrinus	α	MINTAKA (2.3)	Orion	δ
FURUD (3.0)	Canis Major	ζ	MIRA (3.0)	Cetus	o
GACRUX (1.6)	Crux	γ	MIRACH (2.1)	Andromeda	β
GIAUSAR (4.1)	Draco	λ	MIRPHAK (1.8)	Perseus	α
GIENAH (3.0)	Corvus	ε	MIRZAM (2.0)	Canis Major	β
GOMEISA (2.9)	Canis Minor	β	MIZAR (2.2)	Ursa Major	ζ
GRAFFIAS (2.6)	Scorpius	β	MUPHRID (2.7)	Bootes	η
GRUMIUM (3.9)	Draco	ξ	MUSCIDA (3.4)	Ursa Major	o
HADAR (0.6)	Centaurus	β	NASHIRA (3.8)	Capricornus	γ
HAMAL (2.1)	Aries	α	NEKKAR (3.5)	Bootes	β
HOMAM (3.4)	Pegasus	ζ	NIHAL (2.8)	Lepus	β
IZAR (2.4)	Bootes	ε	NUNKI (2.1)	Sagittarius	σ
KAUS AUSTRALIS (1.8)	Sagittarius	ε	NUSAKAN (3.7)	Corona Borealis	β

Greek Alphabet

α alpha
β beta
γ gamma
δ delta
ε epsilon
ζ zeta
η eta
θ theta
ι iota
κ kappa
λ lambda
μ mu
ν nu
ξ xi
o omicron
π pi
ρ rho
σ sigma
τ tau
υ upsilon
φ phi
χ chi
ψ psi
ω omega

39

Names of Stars

Commonly Used Names of Stars

Name of Star (Magnitude)	Constellation	Greek Letter Desig[1]	Name of Star (Magnitude)	Constellation	Greek Letter Desig[1]
PEACOCK (1.9)	Pavo	α	SHAULA (1.6)	Scorpius	λ
PHACT (2.7)	Columba	α	SHEDIR (2.2)	Cassiopeia	α
PHAD (2.4)	Ursa Major	γ	SHELIAK (3.5)	Lyra	β
PHERKAD (3.0)	Ursa Minor	γ	SHERATAN (2.6)	Aries	β
POLARIS (2.0)	Ursa Minor	α	SIRIUS (−1.4)	Canis Major	α
POLLUX (1.2)	Gemini	β	SKAT (3.3)	Aquarius	δ
PORRIMA (2.7)	Virgo	γ	SPICA (1.0)	Virgo	α
PROCYON (0.4)	Canis Minor	α	SULAFAT (3.3)	Lyra	γ
PROPUS (3.3)	Gemini	η	SYRMA (4.2)	Virgo	ι
RASALAS (3.9)	Leo	μ	TALITHA (3.1)	Ursa Major	ι
RASALGETHI (2.8)	Hercules	α	TANIA AUSTRALIS (3.1)	UMaj	μ
RASALHAGUE (2.1)	Ophiuchus	α	TANIA BOREALIS (3.5)	Ursa Major	λ
RASTABAN (2.8)	Draco	β	TARAZED (2.7)	Aquila	γ
REGOR (1.7)	Vela	γ	THUBAN (3.6)	Draco	α
REGULUS (1.4)	Leo	α	UNUKALHAI (2.6)	Serpens	α
RIGEL (0.2)	Orion	β	VEGA (0.0)	Lyra	α
RIGIL KENT[2] (−0.0)	Centaurus	α	VINDEMIATRIX (2.9)	Virgo	ε
RUCHBAH (2.7)	Cassiopeia	δ	WASAT (3.5)	Gemini	δ
RUKBAT (4.1)	Sagittarius	α	WAZN (3.1)	Columba	β
SABIK (2.4)	Ophiuchus	η	WEZEN (1.8)	Canis Major	δ
SADACHBIA (4.0)	Aquarius	γ	YED POSTERIOR (3.2)	Ophiuchus	ε
SADALBARI (3.5)	Pegasus	μ	YED PRIOR (2.7)	Ophiuchus	δ
SADALMELIK (−0.2)	Aquarius	α	ZANIAH (4.0)	Virgo	η
SADALSUUD (3.1)	Aquarius	β	ZAURAK (3.0)	Eridanus	γ
SADR (2.2)	Cygnus	γ	ZAVIJAVA (3.8)	Virgo	β
SAIPH (2.1)	Orion	κ	ZOSMA (2.6)	Leo	δ
SARGAS (1.9)	Scorpius	θ	ZUBENELGENUBI (2.8)	Libra	α
SCHEAT (2.4)	Pegasus	β	ZUBENESCHAMALI (2.6)	Libra	β
SEGINUS (3.0)	Bootes	γ			

Greek Alphabet

α alpha
β beta
γ gamma
δ delta
ε epsilon
ζ zeta
η eta
θ theta
ι iota
κ kappa
λ lambda
μ mu
ν nu
ξ xi
ο omicron
π pi
ρ rho
σ sigma
τ tau
υ upsilon
φ phi
χ chi
ψ psi
ω omega

[1]The brightest stars in each constellation are designated with a lowercase Greek letter for identification. In astronomy, when a star with a Greek letter is referred to, the Latin genitive form of the constellation name is used in conjunction with the Greek letter designation. For example, the star Mizar in Ursa Major is designated ζ, so it would be referred to as ζ Ursae Majoris (Zeta Ursae Majoris). [2]Rigil Kent is also known as Rigil Kentaurus.

Brightest Stars

60 Brightest Stars in the Sky

Name of Star (Greek Desig[1])	Constellation	Mag	Name of Star (Greek Desig[1])	Constellation	Mag
SUN		−26.8	ALNAIR (α)	Grus	1.7
SIRIUS (α)	Canis Major	−1.4	ALNITAK (ζ)	Orion	1.7
CANOPUS (α)	Carina	−0.6	REGOR (γ)	Vela	1.7
ARCTURUS (α)	Bootes	−0.1	ALIOTH (ε)	Ursa Major	1.8
RIGIL KENT[2] (α)	Centaurus	−0.0	MIRPHAK (α)	Perseus	1.8
VEGA (α)	Lyra	0.0	KAUS AUSTRALIS (ε)	Sagittarius	1.8
CAPELLA (α)	Auriga	0.1	DUBHE (α)	Ursa Major	1.8
RIGEL (β)	Orion	0.2	WEZEN (δ)	Canis Major	1.8
PROCYON (α)	Canis Minor	0.4	ALKAID (η)	Ursa Major	1.9
ACHERNAR (α)	Eridanus	0.5	AVIOR (ε)	Carina	1.9
BETELGEUSE (α)	Orion	0.5	SARGAS (θ)	Scorpius	1.9
HADAR (β)	Centaurus	0.6	MENKALINAN (β)	Auriga	1.9
ALTAIR (α)	Aquila	0.8	ATRIA (α)	Triangulum Australe	1.9
ACRUX (α)	Crux	0.8	ALHENA (γ)	Gemini	1.9
ALDEBARAN (α)	Taurus	0.9	DELTA VELA (δ)	Vela	1.9
SPICA (α)	Virgo	1.0	PEACOCK (α)	Pavo	1.9
ANTARES (α)	Scorpius	1.1	POLARIS (α)	Ursa Minor	2.0
POLLUX (β)	Gemini	1.2	MIRZAM (β)	Canis Major	2.0
FOMALHAUT (α)	Piscis Austrinus	1.2	ALPHARD (α)	Hydra	2.0
BECRUX (β)	Crux	1.3	NUNKI (σ)	Sagittarius	2.1
DENEB (α)	Cygnus	1.3	ALGOL (β)	Perseus	2.1
REGULUS (α)	Leo	1.4	DENEBOLA (β)	Leo	2.1
ADHARA (ε)	Canis Major	1.5	HAMAL (α)	Aries	2.1
CASTOR (α)	Gemini	1.6	ALPHERATZ (α)	Andromeda	2.1
GACRUX (γ)	Crux	1.6	KOCHAB (β)	Ursa Minor	2.1
SHAULA (λ)	Scorpius	1.6	SAIPH (κ)	Orion	2.1
BELLATRIX (γ)	Orion	1.6	DENEB KAITOS (β)	Cetus	2.1
ALNATH (β)	Taurus	1.7	ALSUHAIL (λ)	Vela	2.2
MIAPLACIDUS (β)	Carina	1.7	ASPIDISKE (ι)	Carina	2.2
ALNILAM (ε)	Orion	1.7	ALPHEKKA (α)	Corona Borealis	2.2

Greek Alphabet

α alpha
β beta
γ gamma
δ delta
ε epsilon
ζ zeta
η eta
θ theta
ι iota
κ kappa
λ lambda
μ mu
ν nu
ξ xi
ο omicron
π pi
ρ rho
σ sigma
τ tau
υ upsilon
φ phi
χ chi
ψ psi
ω omega

[1]The brightest stars in each constellation are designated with a lowercase Greek letter, a system of notation used in astronomy known as the Bayer letters. This nomenclature was introduced by the German astronomer Johann Bayer (1572–1625) in his star atlas, *Uranometria*. Many of the stars in this list are designated with the Greek letter α or β indicating that they are the brightest stars in their respective constellations.
[2]Rigil Kent is also known as Rigil Kentaurus.

Closest Stars

21 Closest Stars to Earth

Name or Designation[1]	Constellation[2]	Distance in Light Years[3]	Visual Magnitude[4]
Sun	—	0.000016[5]	−26.8
Proxima	Centaurus	4.22	11.01
Alpha (α) Centauri A[6]	Centaurus	4.40	−0.01
Alpha (α) Centauri B[6]	Centaurus	4.40	1.35
Barnard's Star	Ophiuchus	5.94	9.54
Wolf 359	Leo	7.79	13.46
2Mass 0253+16	Aries	7.9	15.40
BD +36°2147	Ursa Major	8.31	7.49
Sirius A[6]	Canis Major	8.60	−1.44
Sirius B[6]	Canis Major	8.60	8.44
L 726-8 A[6]	Cetus	8.7	12.56
L 726-8 B[6]	Cetus	8.7	12.96
Ross 154	Sagittarius	9.69	10.37
Ross 248	Andromeda	10.3	12.27
Epsilon (ε) Eridani	Eridanus	10.50	3.72
Lacaille 9352	Piscis Austrinus	10.73	7.35
Ross 128	Virgo	10.89	11.12
L 789-6 ABC[6]	Aquarius	11.2	12.32
61 Cygni A[6]	Cygnus	11.36	5.20
Procyon A[6]	Canis Minor	11.41	0.40
Procyon B[6]	Canis Minor	11.41	10.7

[1]Many of these designations appear "unusual" because of listings in specialized astronomical catalogues. [2]I am not providing the exact location of these stars within their constellations because most cannot be seen with the naked eye. [3]One light year is approximately 6 trillion miles. [4]Most of us can see stars as faint as magnitude 6 with our eyes. A 12-inch diameter telescope increases our ability to see stars as faint as magnitude 14. Any of the stars listed here between magnitudes 10 and 16 would be very difficult to identify in a telescope without experience and detailed star charts. [5]The "fractional" distance in light years that the Earth is from the Sun. [6]All of the A's, B's and C's refer to binary stars, where two or more stars orbit one another.

North Celestial Pole Area

Right Ascension
0 hours to 24 hours

Declination
+40° to +90°

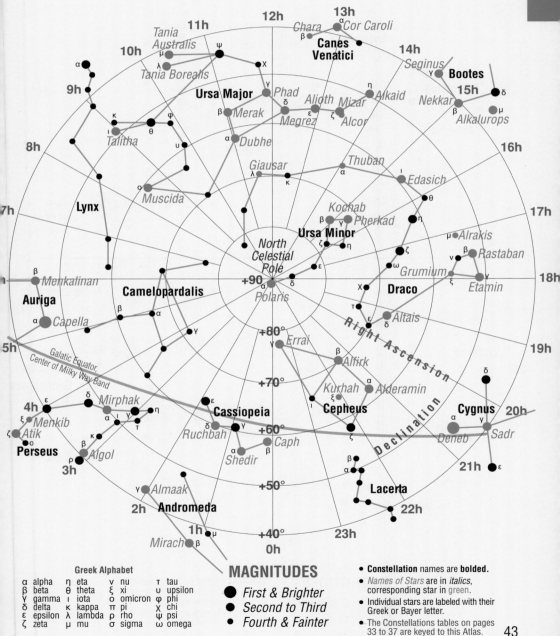

MAGNITUDES

- **First & Brighter**
- *Second to Third*
- *Fourth & Fainter*

Greek Alphabet

α	alpha	η	eta	ν	nu	τ	tau
β	beta	θ	theta	ξ	xi	υ	upsilon
γ	gamma	ι	iota	ο	omicron	φ	phi
δ	delta	κ	kappa	π	pi	χ	chi
ε	epsilon	λ	lambda	ρ	rho	ψ	psi
ζ	zeta	μ	mu	σ	sigma	ω	omega

- **Constellation** names are **bolded**.
- *Names of Stars* are in *italics*, corresponding star in green.
- Individual stars are labeled with their Greek or Bayer letter.
- The Constellations tables on pages 33 to 37 are keyed to this Atlas.

43

Celestial Atlas ✧ 0 Hour
of the 88 Constellations

Right Ascension
21 hours to 3 hours

Declination
−50° to +50°

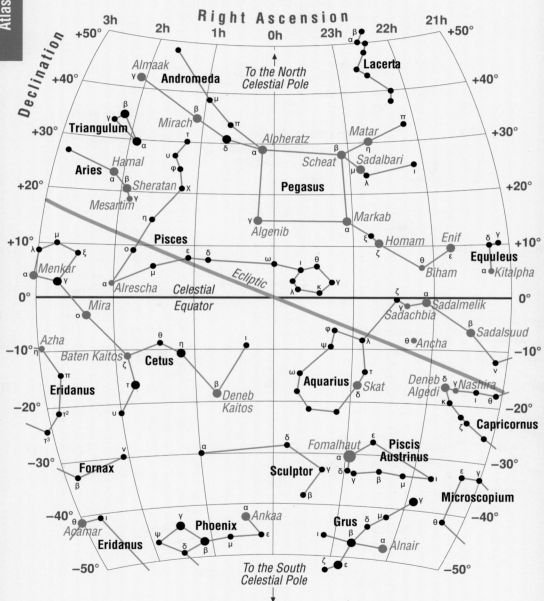

Right Ascension

To the North Celestial Pole

To the South Celestial Pole

MAGNITUDES

● *First & Brighter*
● *Second to Third*
• *Fourth & Fainter*

- **Constellation** names are **bolded**.
- *Names of Stars* are in *italics*, corresponding star in green.
- Individual stars are labeled with their Greek or Bayer letter.
- The Constellations tables on pages 33 to 37 are keyed to this Atlas.

Right Ascension
1 hour to 7 hours

Declination
−50° to +50°

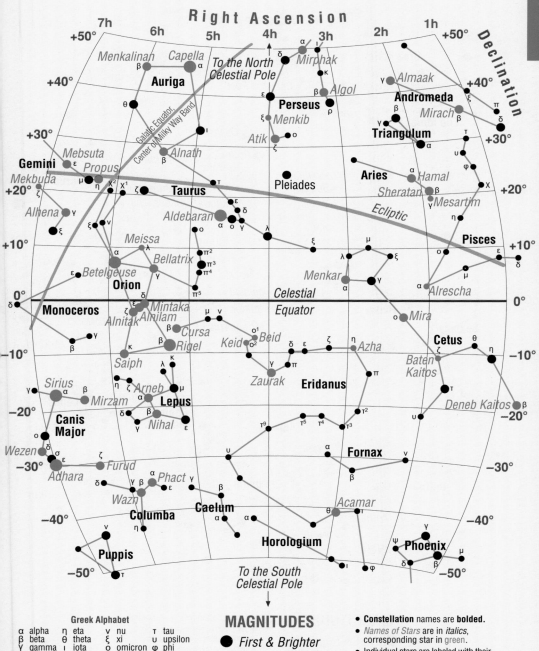

Greek Alphabet

α alpha	η eta	ν nu	τ tau
β beta	θ theta	ξ xi	υ upsilon
γ gamma	ι iota	ο omicron	φ phi
δ delta	κ kappa	π pi	χ chi
ε epsilon	λ lambda	ρ rho	ψ psi
ζ zeta	μ mu	σ sigma	ω omega

MAGNITUDES

● **First & Brighter**

● *Second to Third*

• Fourth & Fainter

- **Constellation** names are **bolded**.
- *Names of Stars* are in *italics*, corresponding star in green.
- Individual stars are labeled with their Greek or Bayer letter.
- The Constellations tables on pages 33 to 37 are keyed to this Atlas.

45

Celestial Atlas ✧ 8 Hour
of the 88 Constellations

Right Ascension
5 hours to 11 hours

Declination
−50° to +50°

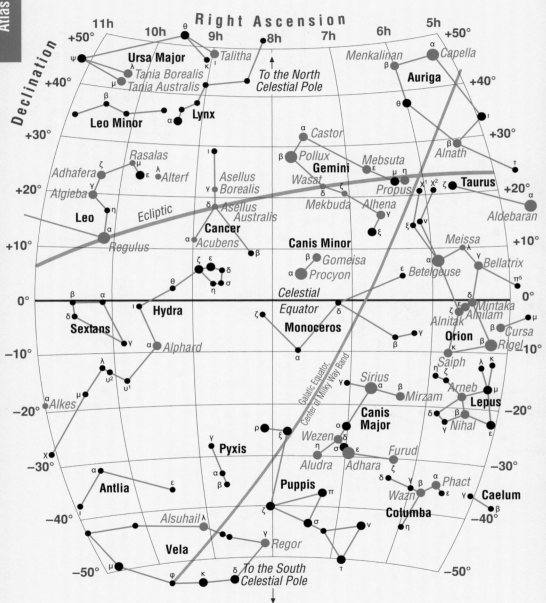

Right Ascension

Declination

11h 10h θ 9h 8h 7h 6h 5h +50°

+50°

ψ Ursa Major Talitha ↑ Menkalinan α Capella

λ Tania Borealis κ ι To the North β Auriga +40°
μ Tania Australis Celestial Pole

+40° β α θ ι

Leo Minor Lynx +30°

+30° α Castor β Alnath

Rasalas β Pollux Mebsuta τ

Adhafera ζ μ λ Gemini ε μ η Taurus

Algieba γ ε Alterf Asellus Wasat χ¹ χ² +20°

+20° η Borealis γ δ ζ Propus ζ α

Leo Ecliptic δ Asellus Mekbuda Alhena ξ ν Aldebaran

α Cancer Australis γ ξ Meissa

Regulus α Acubens β Canis Minor ε λ γ +10°

+10° ζ ε β Gomeisa Betelgeuse Bellatrix

θ δ α Procyon π⁵

σ η δ 0°

β α ι Hydra Celestial ζ ε Mintaka μ

0° δ Equator Alnitak Alnilam

Sextans Monoceros β Cursa

γ α Alphard γ Orion Rigel 10°

−10° β κ Saiph κ λ

λ α Sirius η ζ Arneb μ Lepus

μ² Sirius α Mirzam δ β −20°

−20° α Alkes ρ ξ Canis γ Nihal ε

χ γ Wezen Major δ β

Pyxis η σ ε Furud α Phact

−30° α Aludra Adhara ζ γ β ε γ Caelum

α ε Puppis Wazn Columba β

Antlia π −40°

−40° ι Alsuhail λ ζ σ ν η

Vela γ Regor

μ To the South −50°

−50° φ κ δ Celestial Pole

MAGNITUDES

- ● **First & Brighter**
- ● *Second to Third*
- • *Fourth & Fainter*

- Constellation names are **bolded**.
- *Names of Stars* are in *italics*, corresponding star in green.
- Individual stars are labeled with their Greek or Bayer letter.
- The Constellations tables on pages 33 to 37 are keyed to this Atlas.

12 Hour ✧ Celestial Atlas
of the 88 Constellations

Right Ascension
9 hours to 15 hours

Declination
−50° to +50°

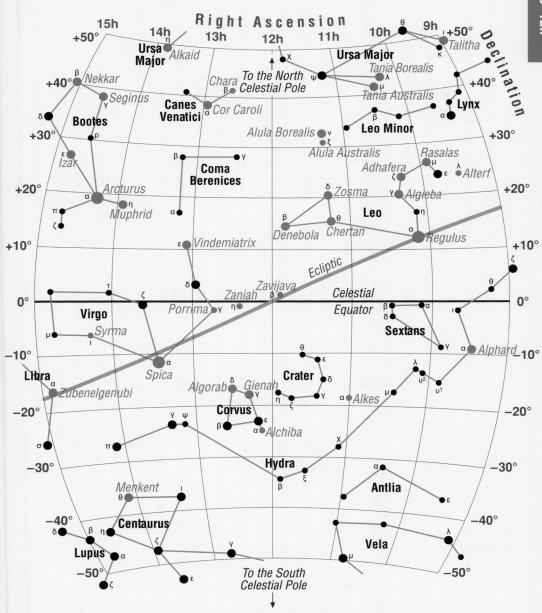

Greek Alphabet

α	alpha	η	eta	ν	nu	τ	tau
β	beta	θ	theta	ξ	xi	υ	upsilon
γ	gamma	ι	iota	ο	omicron	φ	phi
δ	delta	κ	kappa	π	pi	χ	chi
ε	epsilon	λ	lambda	ρ	rho	ψ	psi
ζ	zeta	μ	mu	σ	sigma	ω	omega

MAGNITUDES

● First & Brighter
● Second to Third
• Fourth & Fainter

- **Constellation** names are **bolded**.
- *Names of Stars* are in *italics*, corresponding star in green.
- Individual stars are labeled with their Greek or Bayer letter.
- The Constellations tables on pages 33 to 37 are keyed to this Atlas.

47

Celestial Atlas ✧ 16 Hour
of the 88 Constellations

Right Ascension   **Declination**
13 hours to 19 hours   **−50° to +50°**

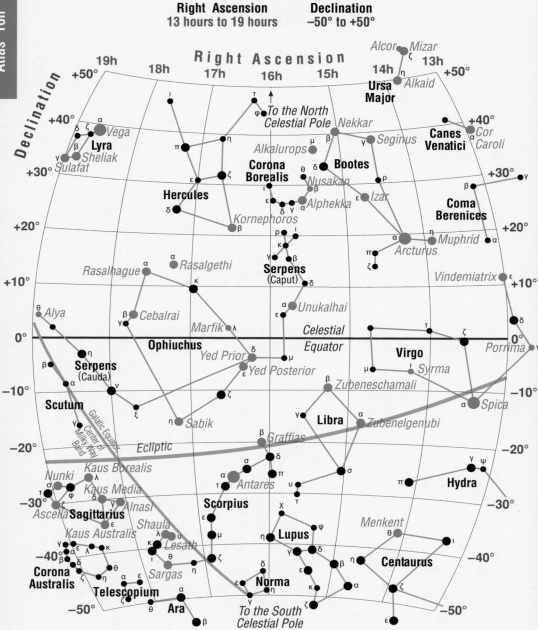

MAGNITUDES

- ⬤ *First & Brighter*
- ● *Second to Third*
- • *Fourth & Fainter*

- **Constellation** names are **bolded**.
- *Names of Stars* are in *italics*, corresponding star in green.
- Individual stars are labeled with their Greek or Bayer letter.
- The Constellations tables on pages 33 to 37 are keyed to this Atlas.

Right Ascension
17 hours to 23 hours

Declination
−50° to +50°

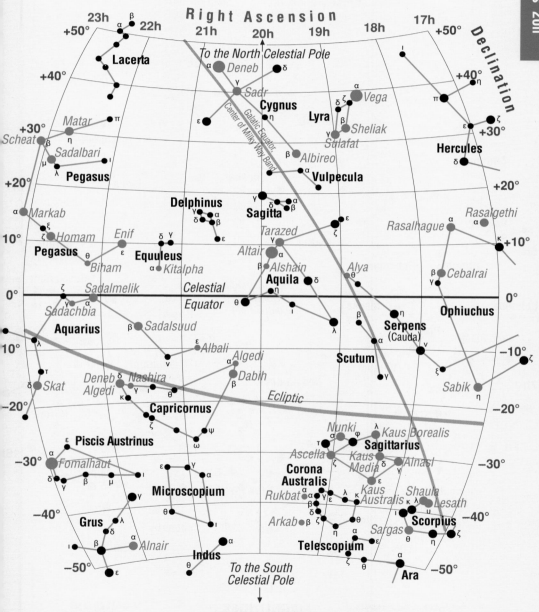

Greek Alphabet

α	alpha	η	eta	ν	nu	τ	tau
β	beta	θ	theta	ξ	xi	υ	upsilon
γ	gamma	ι	iota	ο	omicron	φ	phi
δ	delta	κ	kappa	π	pi	χ	chi
ε	epsilon	λ	lambda	ρ	rho	ψ	psi
ζ	zeta	μ	mu	σ	sigma	ω	omega

MAGNITUDES

● *First & Brighter*

● *Second to Third*

• *Fourth & Fainter*

- **Constellation** names are **bolded**.
- *Names of Stars* are in *italics*, corresponding star in green.
- Individual stars are labeled with their Greek or Bayer letter.
- The Constellations tables on pages 33 to 37 are keyed to this Atlas.

49

Celestial Atlas
of the 88 Constellations

South Celestial Pole Area

Right Ascension
0 hours to 24 hours

Declination
−40° to −90°

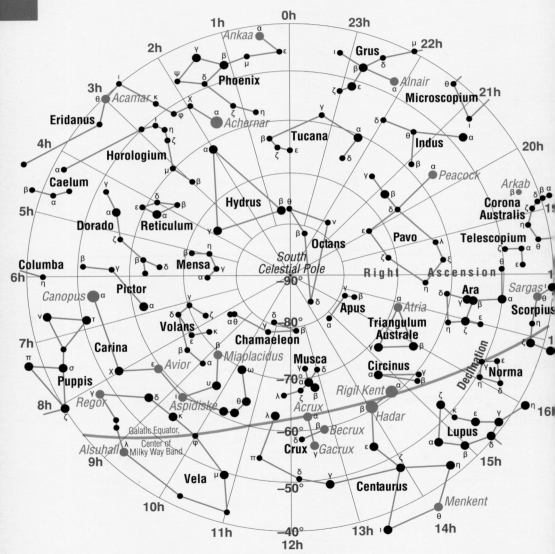

MAGNITUDES

- Constellation names are **bolded**.
- *Names of Stars* are in *italics*, corresponding star in green.
- Individual stars are labeled with their Greek or Bayer letter.
- The Constellations tables on pages 33 to 37 are keyed to this Atlas.

● *First & Brighter*
● *Second to Third*
• *Fourth & Fainter*

Greek Alphabet

α	alpha	η	eta	ν	nu	τ	tau
β	beta	θ	theta	ξ	xi	υ	upsilon
γ	gamma	ι	iota	ο	omicron	φ	phi
δ	delta	κ	kappa	π	pi	χ	chi
ε	epsilon	λ	lambda	ρ	rho	ψ	psi
ζ	zeta	μ	mu	σ	sigma	ω	omega

Stars, the "Atoms" of the Universe

The star *Betelgeuse* in the constellation Orion. This is one of the few images of a star's surface and was taken by the orbiting *Hubble Space Telescope*. This red supergiant is 522 light years away and has a diameter of almost a billion miles.

Red Supergiant

This very small yellow dot is the size of our Sun compared to this red supergiant which has a diameter 1,000 times larger. This makes it slightly smaller than Antares, the brightest star in the constellation Scorpius (visible during the Summer). Red supergiants are very rare and represent "puffed up" stars, a stage at the end of their lives before they explode as supernovae to then become either neutron stars or black holes.

The length of this white line represents the distance from the Earth to the Sun, which is 93 million miles.

Star Facts

Our Sun, the star we are closest to.
Diameter: 865,000 miles
Mass: 333,000 times Earth's
Age: 4.6 billion years

Diameters. *Normal* stars have diameters that vary from about 1/3 to more than 10 times that of our Sun. However, many stars near the end of their lives bloat up to 500 times or more than their original diameters before they collapse down to either hot White Dwarfs (about the size of Earth), Neutron Stars (about 10 miles in diameter) or the even smaller Black Holes. Thus, the very largest and smallest stars are those near the end of their lives.

Mass of stars. The mass or amount of matter stars contain varies from just 1/10 to over 40 times the mass of our Sun.

Life spans. The smallest stars may last a trillion years or more, while the largest may last only a million years because they burn hotter and faster. Stars like our Sun have life spans around 10 billion years.

Element Forging
Normal stars consist of about 75 percent hydrogen and 25 percent helium gas. The nuclear fusion process at their cores fuses hydrogen to helium. Helium is then fused to make carbon and oxygen. Stars like our Sun cannot create or fuse elements "heavier" than oxygen which is the eighth element in the periodic table. More massive stars can fuse about 30 elements of the periodic table. Supernovae explosions account for the heaviest elements.

Interior Circulation
The energy created at the center of stars circulates inside. Depending on their mass, stars' interiors circulate differently. This is one factor that causes different outcomes at their deaths.

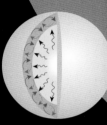

The color of a star depends on its surface temperature. Hotter stars appear blue or white, while cooler stars are red. There are no green stars because green is in the middle of the spectrum and gets washed out.

Identifying the Constellations

If you have never "found" a constellation, it will take practice to orient yourself to the night skies. Even with star charts, your first times may prove frustrating. However, it is not difficult and like with learning any new skill, you *will* become proficient if you practice.

Suggestions for Those Learning to Find the Constellations

1 Jump start by enlisting the help of someone who can identify the constellations. In as little as 30 minutes, he or she can provide a framework that will last a lifetime.

2 Find a dark area and steer clear of cars and other bright or glaring lights.

3 Avoid nights when the Moon shines brightly because this will make the stars more difficult to see.

4 Stay outside at least 15 minutes for your eyes to dark adapt. You will then be able to see more stars (see the next page for information on dark-adapted eyes). Also, use a red-light flashlight to read star charts which will help to preserve your night vision.

5 Initially, always use star charts and face either due north or due south because most charts work best in these directions.

6 Try to correspond the brightest (biggest) stars on the charts with the brightest stars in the sky. *Word of Note:* Don't confuse the Planets with the brightest stars. Venus, Mars, Jupiter and Saturn often outshine the brightest stars. Refer to the Planets at Sunrise and Sunset tables for the Planets that will be out (pages 157 to 187). However, If you practice facing north, you will avoid the Planets.

7 The constellations are bigger than what most people think. With your arm extended, Orion spans one hand length and the Big Dipper over one hand length. See page 62.

8 If you are having difficulty finding the constellations, try to identify a few of the brighter ones, like the Big Dipper, Orion and Sagittarius, then search around these for the others. *And, practice with many short sessions over several days, weeks or months instead of long, drawn out sessions.*

Facing page. *Star trail centered on Polaris. This 20-minute exposure shows the apparent movement of the stars around the North Celestial Pole, which is caused by the Earth's rotation on its axis.*

Night Vision

Dark-Adapted Eyes — Night Vision

One night I mentioned to my wife and six-year-old daughter that I was going out to observe. My daughter immediately perked up and said, "I want to go with you, Daddy." We went downstairs and I set my 4-inch scope on the porch. "I'm going to turn the lights off now," I said to her and we started to observe. After about ten minutes, she remarked, "It's getting lighter out here." I said, "No, it's not getting lighter, your eyes are opening up and you can now see better in the dark." I got no response from this statement and felt that she did not quite understand. About five minutes later, she enthusiastically said, "It's even lighter now." And so, my daughter discovered the process of her eyes "dark-adapting." Of course, I mused with joy in her observations.

It takes about 15 minutes for the eyes to become dark-adapted. You will notice some adaptation in as little as five minutes. If you plan to observe the night sky for an extended period of time, take care to preserve your night vision by using red-light flashlights and avoiding bright lights.

Dark-adapted eyes are essential for observing the fainter deep sky objects (DSOs — pages 239 to 253). You simply will not be able to see these objects if your eyes are not dark adapted.

Use a Red-Light Flashlight to Read Star Charts

A red-light flashlight will help preserve your night vision. Red light works the best because this color does not affect dark-adapted eyes as much as other colors. Ideally, use a red-light flashlight whose light intensity can be varied to accommodate different levels of dark-adapted eyes. Avoid the very bright red-light LED keychains which are no better than white light. Red-light flashlights can be purchased at your local telescope shop or from advertisers in the popular monthly astronomy magazines.

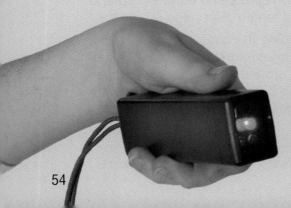

Red-light flashlights are essential for preserving your night vision while you are observing. Models change constantly but I highly recommend one that allows you to vary the light intensity because you will use the lower intensities once your eyes become dark adapted.

Movement of the Stars

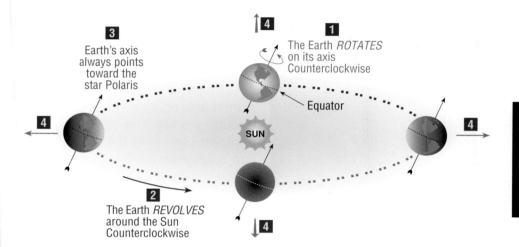

The Basic Movement of the Heavens

Two major factors create most of the movement observed in heavenly bodies: the rotation of the Earth on its axis (causing our day, **1**) and the revolution of the Earth around the Sun (creating our year, **2**). Remember, since the stars are very far away, they appear fixed and stationary in relationship to any movement of the Earth and the Solar System members.

Our day is based on the rotation of the Earth on its axis (**1**). This rotation creates the illusion that the Sun, Moon and stars circle the sky once a day. Also, because the Earth's axis points very close to the star Polaris in the constellation Ursa Minor, all the stars in the sky appear to revolve around Polaris (**3**). The Earth's axis always points in the same direction (toward Polaris). This is because all spinning objects act like gyroscopes in that the spinning axis always points in the same direction even if the gyroscope is moved (like the Earth revolving around the Sun).

The Earth revolves around the Sun once a year (**2**). This movement causes the Earth's nighttime side to face a slightly different direction each night. However, it takes about a month to notice any real difference in the direction that the night side is facing, that is, to see different constellations in the east (**4**).

The Milky Way

The Milky Way is a band, like a ring, of faint light, that divides the whole sky or celestial sphere into halves. Composed of countless

Milky Way & the Ecliptic

Milky Way

The brightest section of the Milky Way Band is near the constellation Sagittarius (outlined) because this part of the band includes the center of our Galaxy, where there is the highest concentration of stars.

stars, all too faint for our eyes to see individually, it represents the majority of stars comprising our Galaxy.

The Milky Way shows considerable irregularity in its path through the sky. The thickest and brightest part, near the constellation Sagittarius, is the direction towards the center of our Galaxy. The Milky Way is not visible in large cities because light pollution easily obscures the band. Outside of metropolitan areas, the Milky Way is prominent.

The Ecliptic: Where the Planets Roam

The ecliptic is a Great Circle (see Glossary) in the sky angled 23½ degrees (the tilt of the Earth) to the celestial equator (a projection of the equator onto the sky). The reason it has a name and is important is because it is the apparent path that the Sun describes against the background of stars over the course of a year. In reality, however, it is the Earth's orbit or movement around the Sun that creates the ecliptic over the course of a year.

The ecliptic is indicated as the yellow arcs on Charts B thru I starting on page 63. Since the ecliptic is tilted in relation to the celestial equator, its most northern point "lands" in the constellation Taurus (Summer Solstice) and its most southern point is in Sagittarius (Winter Solstice). It crosses the celestial equator at Pisces (Vernal Equinox) and Virgo (Autumnal Equinox). The ecliptic is also the path that crosses the 12 constellations known as the zodiac. Historically, there were 12 constellations of the zodiac, one for each month of the year, however, the ecliptic actually crosses 13 constellations, the 13th being Ophiuchus, between Sagittarius and Scorpius.

The Planets are *always* very close to the ecliptic because they orbit the Sun in nearly the same plane as the Earth (see orbit angles on page 134). This makes the ecliptic useful as a guide for locating the Planets. If you know where the ecliptic is, you know that any Planet in the sky will be somewhere near this path.

Legend for Star Charts A–J

"Monthly" Star Charts A thru J

The set of 10 "monthly" star charts A through J on the following pages covers the entire celestial sphere, that is, all the stars and 88 constellations of the northern and southern hemispheres. The charts are, however, orientated for those residing in the northern hemisphere and only need to be turned upside down if you travel south of the equator.

Greek letters next to the stars

The Greek letters next to the stars are called Bayer letters (see Glossary) and are used for identification. Some stars have a number, known as a Flamsteed number (see Glossary).

Star clusters, nebulae, galaxies and the M & NGC catalogues

About 90 Deep Sky Objects (DSOs), that is, star clusters, nebulae and galaxies, are indicated and described on these charts. Many of these objects are easy to find and observe, while others will be downright challenging. These objects should be plenty to keep you busy for a few seasons. **A discussion on finding and observing Deep Sky Objects, as well as explanations of the "M" (Messier) and "NGC" catalogue numbers, begins on page 239.**

Object sizes ★ Arc size or diameter

The size of objects as they appear in the sky is noted in arc minutes. You will need to observe a bit to get a feel for these numbers. Keep in mind that the Moon is about 30 arc minutes in diameter (30'). Many objects are close to the size of the Moon, however, they are much fainter and require optics to see.

Double Stars

Over sixty double stars are indicated on the Charts. These "double stars" are stars so "close" to one another that they casually *appear* as single stars, but when magnified, they separate into two or more stars. **A discussion and table about these double stars begins on page 254.**

Variable Stars

Twenty one variable stars, that is, stars that change in brightness over a period of time are indicated on the Charts. **A discussion and table about these variable stars begins on page 258.** All of these stars can be monitored with the naked eye.

Greek Alphabet

α	alpha
β	beta
γ	gamma
δ	delta
ε	epsilon
ζ	zeta
η	eta
θ	theta
ι	iota
κ	kappa
λ	lambda
μ	mu
ν	nu
ξ	xi
ο	omicron
π	pi
ρ	rho
σ	sigma
τ	tau
υ	upsilon
φ	phi
χ	chi
ψ	psi
ω	omega

Legend for Star Charts A–J

Heavenly coordinates

How are the positions of stars and objects indicated in astronomy? A coordinate system of "Right Ascension" and "Declination" is used that is analogous to longitude and latitude on Earth. Declination uses a similar nomenclature as latitude; however, Right Ascension uses the 24 hours of the day instead of the 180° of east or west longitude.

It is not necessary to know this heavenly coordinate system in order to enjoy the sky or find objects, so I use it "sparingly" on the charts in this book. Along the right hand edges of Charts B through I, the Declination (Dec) is indicated. This ranges from +90° for the North Celestial Pole to 0° at the Celestial Equator, reversing to −90° for the South Celestial Pole. Right Ascension is listed at the top of Charts B through I. These numbers range from 0h to 23h and represent the hours of the day. The small "h" indicates the hour. When observing the sky, the hours of Right Ascension "march by" as the Earth rotates on its axis.

Observing times indicated in the table below and on Charts A–J are reasonably accurate when observing from most North America locations.

Extra-Hour Star Chart Guide

Consult this table to determine which star chart to use for hours other than those listed at the top of each chart. Refer to the instructions on these charts for the correct orientation of the A & J polar charts.

	6 pm	8 pm	10 pm	12 Midnight	2 am	4 am	6 am
January	Chart I	Chart B	Chart B	Chart C	Chart D	Chart E	Chart E
February	Chart B	Chart B	Chart C	Chart D	Chart E	Chart E	Chart F
March	Chart B	Chart C	Chart D	Chart E	Chart E	Chart F	Chart G
April	Chart C	Chart D	Chart E	Chart E	Chart F	Chart G	Chart G
May	Chart D	Chart E	Chart E	Chart F	Chart G	Chart G	Chart H
June	Chart E	Chart E	Chart F	Chart G	Chart G	Chart H	Chart I
July	Chart E	Chart F	Chart G	Chart G	Chart H	Chart I	Chart I
August	Chart F	Chart G	Chart G	Chart H	Chart I	Chart I	Chart B
September	Chart G	Chart G	Chart H	Chart I	Chart I	Chart B	Chart B
October	Chart G	Chart H	Chart I	Chart I	Chart B	Chart B	Chart C
November	Chart H	Chart I	Chart I	Chart B	Chart B	Chart C	Chart D
December	Chart I	Chart I	Chart B	Chart B	Chart C	Chart D	Chart E

Legend for Star Charts A–J

Using the Monthly Star Charts A thru J

These charts were designed specifically to provide undistorted shapes of the constellations.

3 **Chart A** shows the north circumpolar stars. These are the stars that you will always see when facing due north, however their positions change so consult the chart from **1**.

2ª For the Due EAST Constellations
Use the *next* lettered chart of that chosen from **1** and tilt to the left.

Chart A
NORTH Circumpolar Constellations

2ᵇ For the Due WEST Constellations
Use the *previous* lettered chart of that chosen from **1** and tilt to the right.

Top

Constellation names are **Bolded**

Names of Major Stars are in *Italics*

1 **Charts B–I Due SOUTH Constellations**

Start by choosing a "due south" chart for your observing month and time as indicated at the **Top** of these charts, or from the table on page 58.

4 **Chart J**

Chart J provides the southern circumpolar stars. Some stars on this chart are visible from the lower northern latitudes.

Observing from the Southern Hemisphere?
In this case, Charts B thru I must be turned upside down for correct orientation. Additionally, "switch" FACING SOUTH with FACING NORTH.

Chart Legend

59

North Circumpolar Descriptions

Binocular & Telescope Objects
Numbers correspond to those on the Charts

1 In the northern hemisphere, all the constellations appear to revolve around *Polaris*, the North Star, because the Earth's axis is pointed in its direction, thus, this star appears stationary in the night sky. This has not and will not always be the case. Five thousand years ago, the Earth's axis was pointed towards *Thuban* in Draco, and 12,000 years from now it will be pointing close to *Vega* in Lyra. The Earth's axis slowly "wobbles" (this is actually called precession) around a great circle in the sky every 25,800 years, because of tugs from the Moon and Sun.

FEATURED ON PAGE 263

2 & 3 GALAXIES M81 & M82 respectively. Visible in the same eyepiece view at low power, they are separated by about one Moon's diameter. M82 is the one that looks like a cigar. Distances: 9.5 million ly to both. Diameters: 72,000 ly & 30,000 ly. Arc lengths in sky: 26' & 11'. Mag: 6.8 & 8.4. **Favorites. A little challenging to locate, but easy to spot even in mildly polluted skies. Need TELESCOPE, start at 50x.**

4 "Owl" PLANETARY NEBULA M97. Larger, fainter planetary that needs dark skies. In photographs, looks like the face of an owl. Dist: 1,630 ly. Diameter: 1.3 ly. Arc diameter in sky: 3'. Mag: 11. **Difficult to see. Needs dark skies. Use TELESCOPE at 50x to 100x.**

5 A famous DOUBLE STAR. *Alcor* is the "bright" star next to *Mizar* that can be seen with good eyes or binoculars. With a telescope, you can see the much closer, actual binary that takes 10,000 or so years to revolve around *Mizar*. **A favorite.** *Alcor* **just visible with the NAKED EYES, but need TELESCOPE with at least 60x to easily see the actual binary star very close to** *Mizar*.

FEATURED ON PAGE 261

Greek Alphabet
α alpha
β beta
γ gamma
δ delta
ε epsilon
ζ zeta
η eta
θ theta
ι iota
κ kappa
λ lambda
μ mu
ν nu
ξ xi
ο omicron
π pi
ρ rho
σ sigma
τ tau
υ upsilon
φ phi
χ chi
ψ psi
ω omega

6 GALAXY M51 is known as the Whirlpool Galaxy. The "bright" knot off to one side that appears to be interacting with an outer arm is actually a galaxy farther away. Dist: 37 million ly. Diameter: 118,000 ly. Arc size in sky: 11' x 8'. Mag: 8.1. **TELESCOPE object that comes alive in dark skies. Easy to find. 50x to 100x.**

7 Known as *Nu (ν) Draconis*, this is a good example of an easy DOUBLE STAR. **Single star to the eyes, two with BINOCULARS.**

8 A historically famous VARIABLE STAR that helped establish a means to measure distances to stars (see page 259). The magnitude of *Delta (δ) Cephei* varies from 4.4 to 3.5 every 5.4 days. It's also an easy double star. **EYES ONLY to see its change in brightness of 1 magnitude. Need a TELESCOPE at low power to see this star split into two, around 50x.**

9 Pretty CLUSTER NGC 7789. Many equal brightness stars make a faint sprinkle. In our skies, it has an arc diameter of 16', or 1/2 the Moon's width. **A little challenging, but worth it.**

Objects **10 & 11** *listed on page 62.*

Distance to Named Star

Alioth	81 ly
Alkaid	101 ly
Caph	54 ly
Dubhe	124 ly
Etamin	148 ly
Kochab	126 ly
Megrez	81 ly
Merak	79 ly
Mirphak	630 ly
Mizar	78 ly
Navi	613 ly
Phad	84 ly
Polaris	316 ly
Thuban	310 ly

North Circumpolar Stars
View Facing NORTH

This chart is the Northern Extension of Charts B through I

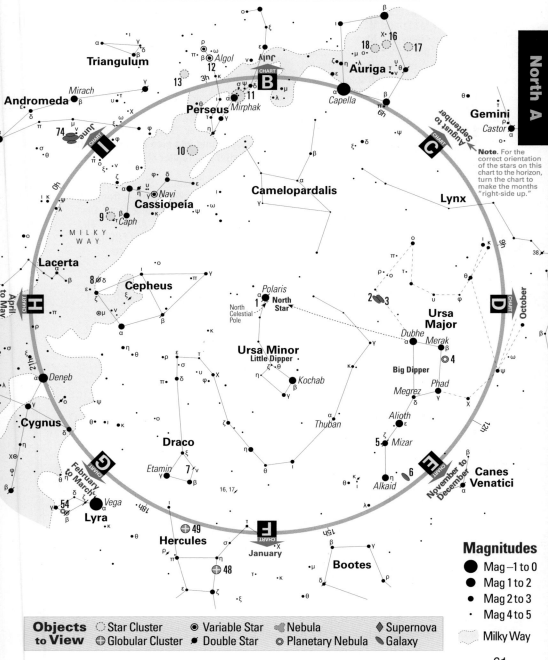

North A

Note. For the correct orientation of the stars on this chart to the horizon, turn the chart to make the months "right-side up."

Triangulum

Andromeda

Perseus

Auriga

Gemini
Castor

Capella
Mirphak
Mirach
Algol

Cassiopeia
Navi
Caph

MILKY WAY

Camelopardalis

Lynx

Lacerta

Cepheus

Polaris
North Star
North Celestial Pole

Ursa Minor
Little Dipper
Kochab

Ursa Major
Dubhe
Merak
Big Dipper
Phad
Megrez
Alioth
Mizar

Canes Venatici

Cygnus
Deneb

Draco
Etamin
Thuban
Alkaid

Hercules

Bootes

Lyra
Vega

Magnitudes
- ⬤ Mag −1 to 0
- ● Mag 1 to 2
- • Mag 2 to 3
- · Mag 4 to 5

Milky Way

Objects to View
- ⬭ Star Cluster
- ⊕ Globular Cluster
- ◉ Variable Star
- ● Double Star
- ◄ Nebula
- ◎ Planetary Nebula
- ♦ Supernova
- ◣ Galaxy

61

January Object Descriptions

Jan B

Binocular & Telescope Objects
Numbers correspond to those on the Charts

10 *On Chart A.* Favorite DOUBLE CLUSTER, NGC 869 & NGC 884 (Honorary M111 and M112), that spans two Moon diameters. Must-see object! M111 has the higher concentration of stars at its center. Clusters are about 7,300 ly away and each spans 65 ly. **A favorite!!! Best with TELESCOPE at about 50x.**

FEATURED ON PAGE 265

11 *On Chart A.* Nice open CLUSTER that can be seen as a haze with the naked eyes. For some unknown reason, it does not have a common name. About 150 ly away. **A favorite. Easy & best with BINOCULARS.**

12 *Algol*, the VARIABLE "Demon Star" which dips in brightness by over 1 magnitude for two hours every 2.87 days. Consult the popular monthly astronomy magazines for times. Dip is caused by a fainter orbiting star passing in "front." **EYES only. Star changes brightness by over 1 magnitude for 2 hours.**

FEATURED ON PAGE 267

13 CLUSTER M34 with fairly bright members totaling 60 stars. Dist: 1,400 ly. Diameter: 14 ly. Arc width in sky: 35'. Mag: 5.2. **Easy object for BINOCULARS or TELESCOPE at low power.**

14 Well-known "Pleiades" CLUSTER M45 is comprised of 100 stars. There is some nebulosity surrounding these stars, but it is difficult to see. Dist: 395 ly. Width: 13 ly. Arc width in sky: 2°. Mag: 1.2. **Wonderful and best with BINOCULARS.**

FEATURED ON PAGE 273

15 The "Hyades" CLUSTER is 20 ly across and 150 ly away. It is the brightest, closest cluster in our skies, spanning over 8° or 16 Moons. **EYES and explore with BINOCULARS.**

16, 17 & 18 CLUSTERS M36, M37 & M38 respectively. In the sky, each

FEATURED ON PAGE 269

is about magnitude 6 and half a Moon's diameter in size. M37 is generally the favorite, housing a red star. They are 3,700, 4,200 & 4,600 ly away, spanning 13 ly with 60 stars, 29 ly with 150 stars and 28 ly with 100 stars. **Easy to find. Best with TELESCOPE starting at 50x.**

19 This favorite CLUSTER M35 contains about 200 stars spanning 23 ly at a distance of 2,800 ly. Covers an area the size of the Moon. Mag: 5. Look for a smaller, fainter cluster, NGC 2158, a Moon's diameter away. **TELESCOPE object. Fairly easy to find and nice at 50x. Look for a smaller and fainter cluster nearby.**

FEATURED ON PAGE 271

20 "Crab Nebula" SUPERNOVA remnant, M1. Needs dark skies away from light population. Shaped like a flame. Dist: 4,000 ly. Length: 7 ly. Arc size in sky: 6' x 4'. Mag: 8. **Need TELESCOPE with dark skies. 50x to 100x.**

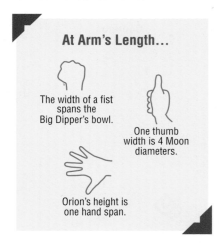

At Arm's Length...

The width of a fist spans the Big Dipper's bowl.

One thumb width is 4 Moon diameters.

Orion's height is one hand span.

Distance to Named Star

Algol	93 ly
Aldebaran	65 ly
Alnath	131 ly
Capella	42 ly
Hamal	66 ly
Menkar	220 ly
Mira	200 ly
Zaurak	170 ly

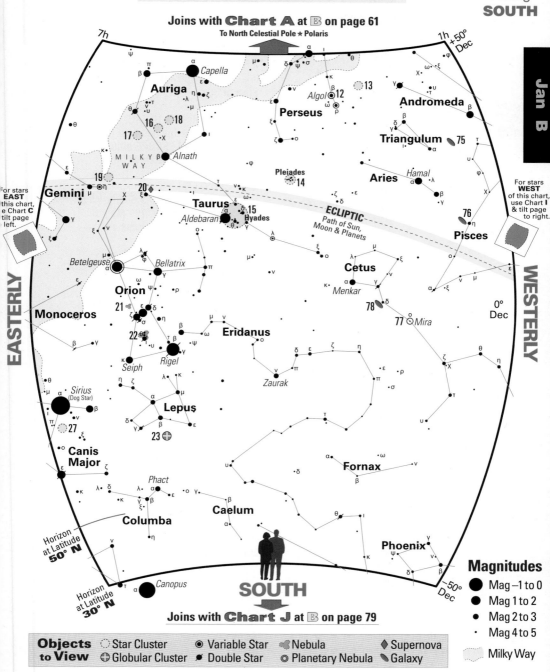

January

| Dec at 11 PM | **Jan at 9 PM** | Feb at 7 PM |

Joins with **Chart A** at Ⓑ on page 61

To North Celestial Pole ★ Polaris

CHART B

View Facing **SOUTH**

Jan B

7h · ψ · π · +50° Dec · 1h

α Capella

Auriga

β · π · ψ

θ · ε · ζ · λ · μ

16 · 18 · 17 · χ

α · δ · ψ · σ · θ

κ · β · 12 · Algol · 13

Perseus

ξ · ζ · ρ

Andromeda · χ · ω · ξ · υ · φ · β

Triangulum · 75 · τ

Aries · δ · γ · Hamal · α · λ · β · υ · φ

MILKY WAY · Alnath

19 · μ · η · **Gemini** · ν

20 · χ · **Taurus** · Pleiades · 14

Aldebaran · Hyades · 15 · τ · ν · κ · ω · λ

ECLIPTIC Path of Sun, Moon & Planets

δ · ⊙ · 76 · τ · η · **Pisces**

ε · γ · ξ · υ

For stars **EAST** of this chart, use Chart C tilt page left.

Betelgeuse · μ · φ · λ · **Bellatrix** · π · μ · ν

Orion · γ · ψ · ρ

21 · ε · δ · η · β · π

22 · ζ · σ · υ

Seiph · κ · β · T · Rigel · ψ

Eridanus · μ · ε · ζ

κ · μ · o · **Cetus** · γ · β · α · μ · ε · ξ · α · υ · μ

Menkar · α · 78 · δ · 77 · Mira

For stars **WEST** of this chart, use Chart I & tilt page to right.

0° Dec

EASTERLY

ε · θ

Sirius (Dog Star) · α · β

27 · π · σ · ξ

Monoceros

β

Canis Major · ζ

o · λ · δ · λ · Phact · α · ε · o · β

κ · γ · ξ · η

Columba

η · ζ · λ · κ · α · μ

Lepus · δ · β · ε

23 ⊕

Zaurak · ν · π · ε · ρ · τ · σ

υ · ω · **Fornax** · ν · α · β · δ

Caelum · θ

ζ · x · θ · ζ

WESTERLY

-50° Dec

Horizon at Latitude **50° N**

Horizon at Latitude **30° N** · α · Canopus

SOUTH

γ · **Phoenix** · ψ · β · δ

Joins with **Chart J** at Ⓑ on page 79

Magnitudes
- ● Mag −1 to 0
- ● Mag 1 to 2
- ● Mag 2 to 3
- · Mag 4 to 5
- Milky Way

Objects to View
- ○ Star Cluster
- ⊕ Globular Cluster
- ◉ Variable Star
- ✱ Double Star
- 🔥 Nebula
- ◎ Planetary Nebula
- ◆ Supernova
- 🌑 Galaxy

63

February ★ March Object Descriptions

Binocular & Telescope Objects
Numbers correspond to those on the Charts

21 NEBULA M78 almost looks like the head of a comet. Dist: 1,600 ly. Length: 4 ly. Arc size in sky: 8' x 6'. Mag: 8. **Fairly easy with a TELESCOPE at 50x. Darker skies helpful.**

22 Great "Orion" NEBULA, M42, is the brightest stellar nursery in the northern sky. Even a small telescope shows considerable detail. Lit up by four central stars known as the Trapezium. Dist: 1,500 ly. Length: 29 ly. Arc size in sky: 1.5° x 1°. Mag: 4. **Favorite, beautiful and bright!!! Use TELESCOPE from 50x to 100x. Look for Trapezium starting at 50x. See more on page 275.**

FEATURED ON PAGE 275

23 GLOBULAR CLUSTER M79. Only globular visible in the winter sky. Dist: 42,000 ly. Diameter: 106 ly. Arc diameter in sky: 9'. Mag: 7.7. **TELESCOPE object fairly easy to find because it is below the two bright stars in Lepus. Start at 50x.**

24 *Castor* is a favorite DOUBLE STAR, somewhat challenging to split because the separation is just 4 arc seconds. These 2nd and 3th magnitude white stars are true binaries that revolve about each other in 445 years. **Classical favorite. Easy to find but need TELESCOPE at 150x to separate easily.**

25 & 26 CLUSTERS M46 and M47 respectively are 1.5° apart, less than two eyepiece views at 50x. M47 has bright members while those of M46 are fainter. With averted vision, look for a faint planetary nebula in M46. Distances: 5,400 ly & 1,800 ly. Widths: 42 ly & 16 ly. Arc widths in sky: 27' & 30'. Mag: 6.1 & 4.4. **Favorites. Fairly easy with a TELESCOPE at 50x.**

27 "Little Beehive" CLUSTER M41. This sprinkle of stars pops out because it is in an area where stars are sparse.

Dist: 2,200 ly. Width: 24 ly. Arc width in sky: 38'. Mag: 4.5. **Fairly easy with a TELESCOPE at 50x because it "pops out."**

28 Pretty orange and blue DOUBLE STAR similar to *Albireo* in Cygnus (object #64), thus sometimes called the "Winter Albireo." Known as *145 Canis Majoris*, it is a true binary. **TELESCOPE object. Start at 50x.**

29 A beautiful CLUSTER, NGC 2362. A bright star surrounded by a triangle of fainter ones. **TELESCOPE object that is fairly easy to find. Start at 50x.**

30 CLUSTER M93 is a nice cluster of about 80 stars. Dist: 3,600 ly. Width: 23 ly. Arc width in sky: 22'. Mag: 6. **Best with TELESCOPE. Pops out. Start at 50x.**

31 CLUSTER NGC 2451 plus surrounding stars. Lower in the sky, but easy to spot with binoculars because it is large with many bright members, including one red. **Nice and easy with BINOCULARS. Pops out.**

The
Winter Triangle
is formed by the stars
Sirius, Betelgeuse & Procyon.

Greek Alphabet

α alpha
β beta
γ gamma
δ delta
ε epsilon
ζ zeta
η eta
θ theta
ι iota
κ kappa
λ lambda
μ mu
ν nu
ξ xi
ο omicron
π pi
ρ rho
σ sigma
τ tau
υ upsilon
φ phi
χ chi
ψ psi
ω omega

Distance to Named Stars

Bellatrix	1,400 ly
Betelgeuse	1,400 ly
Castor	52 ly
Phact	180 ly
Pollux	34 ly
Procyon	11 ly
Rigel	1,400 ly
Seiph	78 ly
Sirius	8.6 ly

February ★ March

Jan at Midnight	**Feb at 10 PM**	Mar at 8 PM

CHART

C

View
Facing
SOUTH

Feb★Mar C

Joins with **Chart A** at Ⓒ on page 61
To North Celestial Pole ★ Polaris

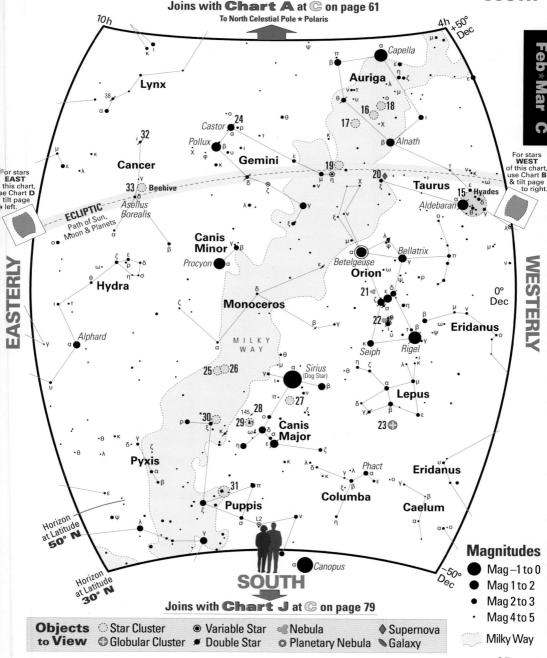

10h

4h +50° Dec

For stars
EAST
of this chart,
use Chart **D**
& tilt page
left.

For stars
WEST
of this chart,
use Chart **B**
& tilt page
to right.

Lynx

α Capella

Auriga

16 18

17

β Alnath

Castor 24

Pollux

Gemini

Cancer

32

33 Beehive

Asellus
Borealis

19

20

Taurus

15 Hyades

Aldebaran

ECLIPTIC
Path of Sun,
Moon & Planets

EASTERLY

WESTERLY

**Canis
Minor**

Procyon α

Hydra

Bellatrix

Betelgeuse

Orion

0°
Dec

21

Monoceros

22

Eridanus

Alphard

MILKY
WAY

Seiph

Rigel

25 26

Sirius
(Dog Star)

Lepus

27

Pyxis

30

28

29

**Canis
Major**

23

31

Puppis

Columba

Phact

Eridanus

Caelum

Horizon
at Latitude
50° N

L2

Horizon
at Latitude
30° N

SOUTH

α Canopus

−50°
Dec

Joins with **Chart J** at Ⓒ on page 79

Magnitudes
- ⬤ Mag −1 to 0
- ● Mag 1 to 2
- • Mag 2 to 3
- · Mag 4 to 5
- Milky Way

**Objects
to View**
- ◌ Star Cluster
- ⊕ Globular Cluster
- ⊙ Variable Star
- • Double Star
- 🌫 Nebula
- ◎ Planetary Nebula
- ◆ Supernova
- 🌀 Galaxy

April ★ May Object Descriptions

Binocular & Telescope Objects
Numbers correspond to those on the Charts

32 Pretty orange and blue optical DOUBLE STAR that is also the "top" star in Cancer. Easy to separate in a telescope at low power. The challenge here is to spot the 5th magnitude top star with your unaided eyes. The distance to the brighter star is 188 ly. **TELESCOPE object that is a little challenging to locate with your unaided eyes. Start at 50x.**

33 "Beehive" CLUSTER M44, also known as the Praesepe. This is a wonderful cluster seen best with binoculars. It is similar in size to the Pleiades but its members are not as bright, so binoculars are needed to bring them to life. M44 is often found by scanning the area halfway between Regulus and Pollux. Dist: 580 ly. Width: 16 ly. Arc width in sky: 1.5°. Mag: 3.1. **A favorite!! Easy & best with BINOCULARS.**

34, 35 & **36** GALAXIES M95, M96 and M105 respectively. All three visible within two eyepiece views at low power. M95 & 96 are spirals, while M105 is an elliptical. Distances: 29 million ly, 29 million ly & 22 million ly. Diameters: 59,000 ly, 59,000 ly & 40,000 ly. Arc sizes in sky: 7' x 5', 7' x 5' & 5' x 4'. Mags: 9.7, 9.2 & 9.3. **Fairly easy with a TELESCOPE at 50x. Easiest to see in dark skies.**

37 & **38** Spiral GALAXIES M65 & M66 respectively. Visible in the same eyepiece view at low power, they are separated by about one Moon's diameter. Distances: 29 million ly & 21.5 million ly. Diameters: 84,000 ly & 65,000 ly. Arc sizes in sky: 10' x 3' & 9' x 4'. Mag: 9.3 & 9. **Fairly easy with a TELESCOPE at 50x if you have dark skies.**

39 CLUSTER of stars in Coma Berenices that can be seen as a haze with the naked eyes. Big loose group best seen with binoculars. **Easy & pops out with BINOCULARS.**

Greek Alphabet
α alpha
β beta
γ gamma
δ delta
ε epsilon
ζ zeta
η eta
θ theta
ι iota
κ kappa
λ lambda
μ mu
ν nu
ξ xi
ο omicron
π pi
ρ rho
σ sigma
τ tau
υ upsilon
φ phi
χ chi
ψ psi
ω omega

40 GLOBULAR CLUSTER M3. Bright, plump cluster. Dist: 35,000 ly. Diameter: 165 ly. Arc diameter in sky: 16'. Mag: 6.2. **TELESCOPE object a little challenging to find but worth it. Start at 50x.**

41 GLOBULAR CLUSTER M53. Smaller and fainter than the nearby M3. Dist: 60,000 ly. Diameter: 220 ly. Arc diameter in sky: 13'. Mag: 7.6. **TELESCOPE object a little challenging to find. Start at 50x.**

42 GALAXY M64 is by far the biggest and brightest-looking galaxy in the area. Known as the "Black-Eye Galaxy," for its resemblance to a black eye. Dist: 13.5 million ly. Width: 35,000 ly. Arc size in sky: 9' x 5'. Mag: 8.5. **TELESCOPE object. Detail shows up better in darker skies. Start at 50x.**

A–D "Virgo" CLUSTER of GALAXIES totalling about 2,500 galaxies. Our "Local Group" of 40 galaxies, which includes the Andromeda Galaxy, is linked to this cluster and others to form the Local Supercluster. The galaxies in the Virgo Cluster are on average 56 million light years away and are centered around M87, a large elliptical galaxy with a diameter of 114,000 ly and a mass estimated at 800 billion Suns (ours). Although M87 appears as a featureless, round fuzzy star through a telescope (see an actual photo at the bottom of page 243), it has an active nucleus, fueled by a supermassive black hole with a mass estimated at

Continues on page 68.

Distance to Named Stars

Algorab	88 ly
Alphard	177 ly
Asellus Borealis	136 ly
Castor	52 ly
Denebola	36 ly
Pollux	34 ly
Procyon	11 ly
Regulus	78 ly
Sirius	8.6 ly

April ★ May

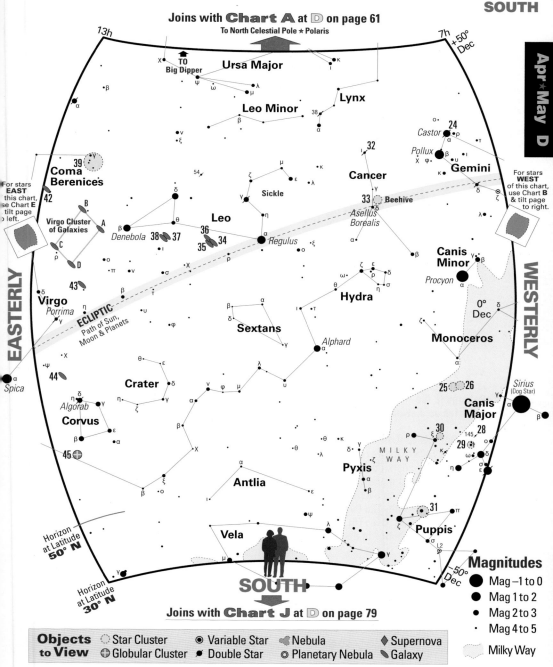

March at 11 PM | **April at 9 PM** | May at 7 PM

Joins with **Chart A** at **D** on page 61

To North Celestial Pole ★ Polaris

13h

7h +50° Dec

TO Big Dipper

Ursa Major

χ ψ ω μ λ

Lynx

ι κ

Leo Minor

38

β

α

Cancer

32

ζ μ κ

Gemini

Castor α ρ τ
Pollux β ι
χ φ
24

54

Sickle

γ

δ

ζ ε λ

δ **33** ○ Beehive

δ ζ

Asellus Borealis

For stars EAST of this chart, use Chart E & tilt page to left.

39 γ

Coma Berenices

42

Virgo Cluster of Galaxies

A B C D ρ

Leo

δ

θ

β **38 37**

Denebola

36

35 34

Regulus ○

η

ξ

λ

Canis Minor

Procyon α

γ

For stars WEST of this chart, use Chart B & tilt page to right.

43

β τ

Virgo

Porrima γ

ECLIPTIC Path of Sun, Moon & Planets

ζ ε
ρ
θ
ω σ
η

Hydra

β

0° Dec δ

Monoceros

ψ χ

44

Spica α

θ ε

Crater

δ

ν φ μ

λ

υ

γ

Alphard

Sextans

ι τ

δ

ζ

α

25 ○ **26**

Sirius (Dog Star)

Canis Major α β

Algorab δ γ

η ζ γ

Corvus β ε α

45 ⊕

χ

ζ

κ α

Antlia

ε

ι

γ

θ κ

δ γ
λ

Pyxis

β α

ρ
ξ **30**
κ
σ

145

28

29 ○

ω σ ε

31

π

Puppis

ζ

σ

L2

M I L K Y W A Y

Horizon at Latitude **50° N**

ψ

Vela

λ

γ

μ

Horizon at Latitude **30° N**

γ

-50° Dec

SOUTH

Joins with **Chart J** at **D** on page 79

Magnitudes
- ● Mag –1 to 0
- ● Mag 1 to 2
- • Mag 2 to 3
- · Mag 4 to 5
- Milky Way

Objects to View
- ○ Star Cluster
- ⊕ Globular Cluster
- ◉ Variable Star
- ✱ Double Star
- ◀ Nebula
- ◎ Planetary Nebula
- ◆ Supernova
- ◣ Galaxy

67

June Object Descriptions

Binocular & Telescope Objects
Numbers correspond to those on the Charts

Continued from page 66.

3 billion Suns (ours). There are 16 Messier galaxies in this area and all are fainter and smaller than M64 (object #42). Fifteen are bounded by the four galaxies lettered A, B, C & D. The 16th is described in #43 below. Arc widths in the sky range from 5' to 10' for these 16 galaxies while their magnitudes vary from 8.4 to 10.2. **TELESCOPE objects that are not difficult to see but more challenging to find because none of them are near any conspicuously bright stars. All are visible in a telescope with a diameter as small as 3 inches and 50x magnification. To find and view these "small" galaxies, I recommend consulting a star atlas like the *Sky Atlas 2000* published by Sky & Telescope or the charts in the book, *The Next Step: Finding & Viewing Messier's Objects* by Ken Graun.**

43 GALAXY M61 is the "last" of the Virgo Cluster galaxies and is typical of the 16 described above. Dist: 56 million ly. Width: 98,000 ly. Arc width in sky: 6'. Mag: 9.7. **TELESCOPE object that is challenging to find. Start at 50x. Belongs to the Virgo Cluster of Galaxies as discussed above.**

44 GALAXY M104. Known as the Sombrero Galaxy for its resemblance to the hat due to a dark dust lane around its perimeter which can just be glimpsed in a small telescope using averted vision. Dist: 48 million ly. Length: 126,000 ly. Arc size in sky: 9' x 4'. Mag: 8.3. **TELESCOPE object that does better in darker skies. Start at 50x.**

45 GLOBULAR CLUSTER M68. Similar in size to M53 farther north (object #41) in Coma Berenices, but with only half the brightness, probably because it is low in the sky, nearer to the horizon. In an area sparse with stars. Dist: 33,300 ly.

Diameter: 115 ly. Arc diameter in sky: 12'. Mag: 8.2. **TELESCOPE object a little challenging to find. Start at 50x.**

FEATURED ON PAGE 295 **46** Largest GLOBULAR CLUSTER (NGC 5139) in our galaxy and brightest in the sky. Designated and called *Omega (ω) Centauri*. To the naked eye, it looks like a faint 5th magnitude star and was identified as such by the ancient Egyptians. In the sky, it has an arc size of 53', almost two Moon diameters across. It is estimated to contain a million stars. Dist: 18,000 ly. Diameter: 281 ly. **Beautiful sight in BINOCULARS or TELESCOPE! Easy to find, but very low in northern hemisphere skies. Start at 50x. Best viewed from the southern hemisphere where it is higher up in the sky.**

(80) "Centaurus A" GALAXY, NGC 5128. The name Centaurus A signifies that it has the "brightest" radio signal coming from any celestial body in the constellation Centaurus. Dist: 23 million ly. Diameter: 120,000 ly. Arc width in sky: 18'. Mag: 7. **Use TELESCOPE starting at 50x. Big & round. Best view from the southern hemisphere where it is higher up in the sky.**

#44. Sombrero Galaxy, M104.

Distance to Named Stars

Algorab	88 ly
Arcturus	37 ly
Menkent	61 ly
Spica	220 ly
Vindemiatrix	102 ly

Greek Alphabet

α	alpha
β	beta
γ	gamma
δ	delta
ε	epsilon
ζ	zeta
η	eta
θ	theta
ι	iota
κ	kappa
λ	lambda
μ	mu
ν	nu
ξ	xi
ο	omicron
π	pi
ρ	rho
σ	sigma
τ	tau
υ	upsilon
φ	phi
χ	chi
ψ	psi
ω	omega

June E

June

May
at
11 PM

June at
9 PM

July
at
7 PM

CHART

E

View
Facing
SOUTH

Joins with **Chart A** at E on page 61

To North Celestial Pole ★ Polaris

June E

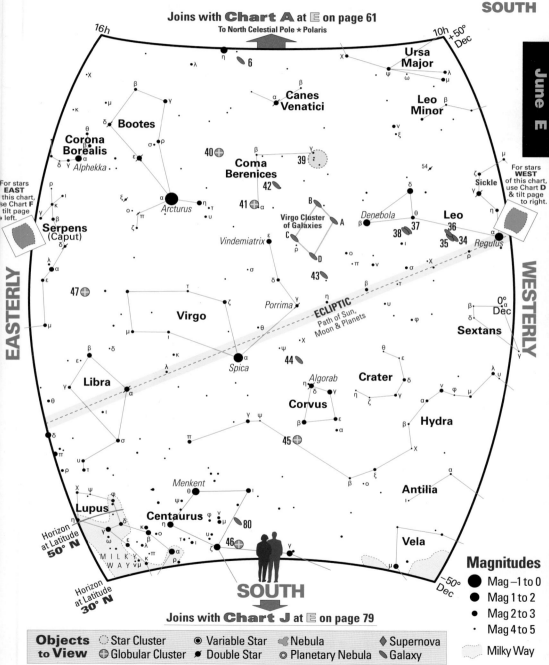

16h

Ursa Major

Canes Venatici

Leo Minor

Bootes

Corona Borealis

Alphekka

Coma Berenices

54

Sickle

For stars EAST this chart, use Chart F tilt page left.

For stars WEST of this chart, use Chart D & tilt page to right.

Serpens (Caput)

Arcturus

Virgo Cluster of Galaxies

Denebola

Leo

Regulus

Vindemiatrix

Porrima

ECLIPTIC
Path of Sun,
Moon & Planets

Sextans

EASTERLY

WESTERLY

0° Dec

Virgo

Spica

Algorab

Crater

Libra

Corvus

Hydra

Menkent

Antilia

Lupus

Centaurus

Vela

Horizon at Latitude **50° N**

MILKY WAY

SOUTH

Horizon at Latitude **30° N**

−50° Dec

Magnitudes
- ● Mag −1 to 0
- ● Mag 1 to 2
- • Mag 2 to 3
- · Mag 4 to 5
- Milky Way

Joins with **Chart J** at E on page 79

Objects to View
- ⬡ Star Cluster
- ⊕ Globular Cluster
- ◉ Variable Star
- ✦ Double Star
- 🌫 Nebula
- ◎ Planetary Nebula
- ◆ Supernova
- 🌊 Galaxy

July Object Descriptions

Binocular & Telescope Objects
Numbers correspond to those on the Charts

47 GLOBULAR CLUSTER M5. Big, bright and pretty globular. Dist: 26,000 ly. Diameter: 132 ly. Arc diameter in sky: 17'. Mag: 6. **BINOCULARS or TELESCOPE object easy to spot because it stands out. Start at 50x.**

48 & **49** GLOBULAR CLUSTERS M13 and M92 respectively. M13 is one of the all-time favorite northern hemisphere globulars. Both are large and bright. Distances: 21,000 & 26,000 ly. Diameters: 104 ly & 85 ly. Arc diameters in sky: 17' & 11'. Mag: 5.8 & 6.4. **Favorites. BINOCULARS or TELESCOPE objects. Fairly easy to find and nice at 50x to 100x. Can see individual stars easily in M13 with smaller telescopes.**

FEATURED ON PAGE 281

50, 51 & **52** Three plumb GLOBULAR CLUSTERS, M12, M10 and M14 respectively that are not far from each other. Distances: 24,000, 20,000 & 29,000 ly. Diameters: 101, 88 & 101 ly. Arc diameters in sky: 15', 15' & 12'. Mags: 6.7, 6.6 & 7.6. **Mainly TELESCOPE objects — start at 50x. You can spot these easily with BINOCULARS at darker locations.**

53 GLOBULAR CLUSTER M4 is known as the Cat's Eye because it is bisected by a faint line of stars that are visible in small telescopes. Dist: 14,000 ly. Diameter: 107 ly. Arc diameter in sky: 26'. Mag: 5.9. **TELESCOPE object. Easy to locate since it is next to the bright star *Antares*. It appears fainter than normal to northern hemisphere observers because it is low in the sky.**

54 Favorite PLANETARY NEBULA M57 known as the Ring Nebula. This is one of the few nebulae that has a definite edge; however it is smaller than most observers initially expect. Dist: 1,140 ly. Length: 0.5 ly. Arc length in sky: 1.3'. Mag: 9. **A favorite. TELESCOPE object that is** easy to locate because it is between the two bottom stars of Lyra (closer to the bottom right star). Magnifications of 100x are best for viewing, but use 50x for locating. Be on the lookout for a small, faintish smoke ring. Visible in some polluted skies.

FEATURED ON PAGE 283

55 M11 CLUSTER of stars nicknamed the "Wild Duck Cluster." Comprised of nearly 700 stars, it is one of my favorites. Dist: 5,600 ly. Width: 23 ly. Arc width in sky: 14'. Mag: 5.8. **BINOCULARS or TELESCOPE object. Stars come alive with telescope. Start at 50x.**

56 The famous M16 "Eagle" NEBULA, contains the "Pillars of Creation," pictured below, as photographed by the Hubble Space Telescope orbiting Earth. Dist: 5,700 ly. Width: 58 ly. Arc width in sky: 35'. Mag: 6. **TELESCOPE object. Requires dark skies to see the Eagle. One of the fainter nebulae in this area. It is easier to find M17 (object #57) first and then move the telescope north to find M16. Start at 50x.**

#56. Pillars of Creation, M16.

Distance to Named Stars

Alphekka	78 ly
Antares	522 ly
Graffias	522 ly
Komephoros	170 ly
Rasalhague	49 ly
Sabik	63 ly
Shaula	330 ly

Greek Alphabet

α	alpha
β	beta
γ	gamma
δ	delta
ε	epsilon
ζ	zeta
η	eta
θ	theta
ι	iota
κ	kappa
λ	lambda
μ	mu
ν	nu
ξ	xi
ο	omicron
π	pi
ρ	rho
σ	sigma
τ	tau
υ	upsilon
φ	phi
χ	chi
ψ	psi
ω	omega

The **"Dog Days" of Summer** refer to *Sirius* rising with the Sun during this season.

July

June at 11 PM	**July at 9 PM**	Aug at 7:30 PM

CHART F

View Facing **SOUTH**

July F

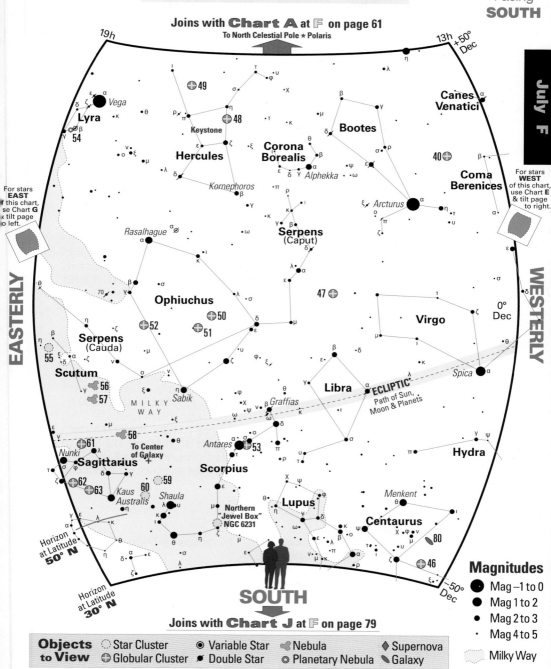

Joins with **Chart A** at **F** on page 61

To North Celestial Pole ★ Polaris

For stars **EAST** of this chart, use Chart **G** & tilt page to left.

For stars **WEST** of this chart, use Chart **E** & tilt page to right.

EASTERLY

WESTERLY

SOUTH

Joins with **Chart J** at **F** on page 79

Magnitudes
- Mag –1 to 0
- Mag 1 to 2
- Mag 2 to 3
- Mag 4 to 5
- Milky Way

Objects to View
- Star Cluster
- Globular Cluster
- Variable Star
- Double Star
- Nebula
- Planetary Nebula
- Supernova
- Galaxy

71

August ★ Sept Object Descriptions

Binocular & Telescope Objects
Numbers correspond to those on the Charts

57 Favorite M17 "Omega" or "Swan" NEBULA that looks similar to the body and neck of a swan. Dist: 3,000 ly. Width: 40 ly. Arc width in sky: 46'. Mag: 7.
A favorite!! Best in a TELESCOPE. The body of the swan shows up well, making it easy to spot. Brightest nebula in the area. Start at 50x. Move the telescope due north to bump into M16 (object #56).

FEATURED ON PAGE 287

58 Favorite M8 "Lagoon" NEBULA and star cluster. Large and easy to find because it is off Sagittarius. Dist: 4,800 ly. Width: 126 ly. Arc width in sky: 90'. Mag: 6. **A favorite. BINOCULARS or TELESCOPE object. Although this nebula is large, it is fainter than you might expect. In binoculars, it looks like a large patch of the Milky Way. Start at 50x.**

FEATURED ON PAGE 289

59 & **60** Star CLUSTERS M6 & M7 respectively. Both are visible to the naked eye as patches but M7 is the lower, larger and brighter one. M6 contains about 330 stars and M7 only 80. Dist: 1,500 ly & 800 ly. Widths: 7 ly & 20 ly. Arc widths in sky: 15' & 80'. Mags: 4.2 & 3.3.
Favorites. BINOCULARS and TELESCOPE objects that are easy to find. M7 will fill any eyepiece field of view.

FEATURED ON PAGE 293

61 Large GLOBULAR CLUSTER M22 is one of my favorites!! Some of the stars are resolvable, that is, they can be seen individually in a small scope. Dist: 10,000 ly. Diameter: 70 ly. Arc diameter in sky: 24'. Mag: 5.1. **BINOCULARS and TELESCOPE object that is easy to locate. Nice in a telescope at 50x to 75x. Also look for a much fainter and smaller globular, NGC 6642, one degree north-west of M22.**

FEATURED ON PAGE 291

62 & **63** GLOBULAR CLUSTERS M54 and M70 are more typical of globulars. Distances: 50,000 & 29,000 ly.

Diameters: 130 & 67 ly. Arc diameters in sky: 9' & 8'. Mag: 7.6 & 8.1. **TELESCOPE objects, start at 50x. M70 is easy to find because it is halfway between a line drawn from the "end" stars of Sagittarius. M54 is on the same line but within two degrees of one end.**

64 Favorite pretty blue and gold DOUBLE STAR *Albireo*. There is some question as to whether this is an actual pair of stars revolving around each other or just two stars near one another. Both stars appear to be about 385 ly away. **Easy and very pretty TELESCOPE object. Start at 50x.**

FEATURED ON PAGE 285

65 "Coathanger" CLUSTER comprised of 10 stars shaped like a bar-type coathanger. It spans about 2° and its stars may be about 150 ly away. Actual name is Brocchi's Cluster. **BINOCULARS object. Easy to spot because the stars pop out. From the northern hemisphere, it looks like an upside-down, bar-type coathanger.**

66 Veil SUPERNOVA remnants. East and west arcs of nebulosity indicated. East arc (NGC 6992) is brightest but west (NGC 6960) has a fairly bright star near its middle. The explosion occurred about 5,000 years ago and it is about 1,500 ly away. Both arcs stretch about 1°. **Challenging TELESCOPE object better viewed with larger scopes of 8-inch diameters or more, *and* dark skies. Arcs are large and faint. Start with 50x.**

Distance to Named Stars

Albireo	380 ly
Altair	16 ly
Dabih	560 ly
Deneb	1,500 ly
Kaus Australis	76 ly
Nunki	170 ly
Vega	25 ly

August ★ September

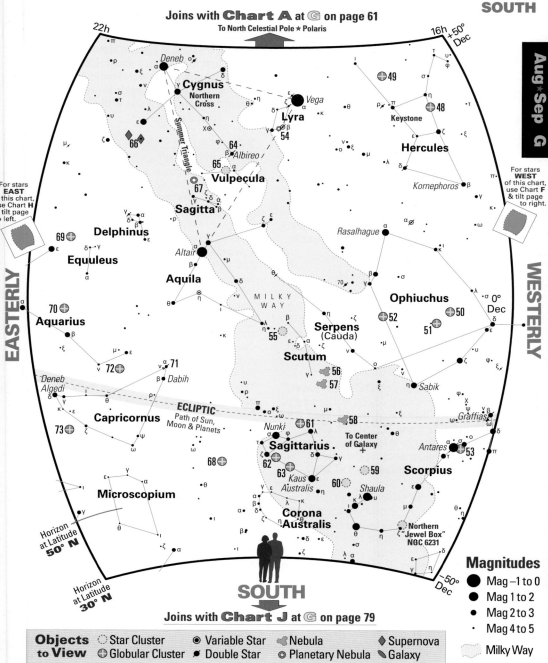

Joins with **Chart A** at Ⓖ on page 61

To North Celestial Pole ★ Polaris

22h
16h +50° Dec

Deneb

Cygnus
Northern Cross

Vega

Lyra

49

48

Keystone

Hercules

Summer Triangle

66

64
54

Albireo

Kornephoros

65

Vulpecula

67

Sagitta

Delphinus

Rasalhague

For stars
EAST
of this chart,
use Chart **H**
& tilt page
left.

69

Equuleus

Altair

Aquila

For stars
WEST
of this chart,
use Chart **F**
& tilt page
to right.

MILKY WAY

Ophiuchus

70
Aquarius

0° Dec

52

50

51

55

Serpens
(Cauda)

Sabik

72

71

Dabih

Scutum

56
57

Deneb Algedi

ECLIPTIC
Path of Sun,
Moon & Planets

61

58

Graffias

Capricornus

Nunki

73

68

To Center
of Galaxy
+

Antares

53

Sagittarius

62

63
Kaus
Australis

60

59

Scorpius

Microscopium

Shaula

**Corona
Australis**

Northern
"Jewel Box"
NGC 6231

Horizon
at Latitude
50° N

EASTERLY

WESTERLY

−50° Dec

Horizon
at Latitude
30° N

SOUTH

Magnitudes
● Mag −1 to 0
● Mag 1 to 2
● Mag 2 to 3
· Mag 4 to 5

Milky Way

Joins with **Chart J** at Ⓖ on page 79

Objects to View	◌ Star Cluster	◉ Variable Star	Nebula	◆ Supernova
	⊕ Globular Cluster	Double Star	◎ Planetary Nebula	Galaxy

October Object Descriptions

Binocular & Telescope Objects
Numbers correspond to those on the Charts

67 M27 PLANETARY NEBULA known as the Dumbbell Nebula for its shape. Dist: 815 ly. Width: 2 ly. Arc width in sky: 8'. Mag: 8. **Best with a TELESCOPE and really "pops" in darker skies. Much larger than the Ring Nebula, M57 (object #54). Appears more roundish than the actual shape of a dumbbell.**

68 GLOBULAR CLUSTER M55 reminds me of a fainter M22 (object #61). Luminosity is even. Can see some of the stars individually in a small scope. Dist: 20,000 ly. Diameter: 111 ly. Arc diameter in sky: 19'. Mag: 7. **TELESCOPE object that has no bright stars for easy location but shows up well in darker skies. This is a very large and nice globular worth coming back to. Start at 50x.**

69 GLOBULAR CLUSTER M15 is big and fairly bright. Dist: 34,000 ly. Diameter: 122 ly. Arc diameter in sky: 12'. Mag: 6.2. **BINOCULARS and TELESCOPE object. Pops out at you in a telescope. Easy to find because it is in line with two "end" stars of Pegasus. Start at 50x.**

70 GLOBULAR CLUSTER M2 is similar to M15 above. Dist: 40,000 ly. Diameter: 151 ly. Arc diameter in sky: 13'. Mag: 6.5. **BINOCULARS and TELESCOPE object that is similar to M15 but may appear a little brighter because the core is slightly more intense. Start at 50x.**

71 "Multiple" STAR *Alpha (α) Capricorni* is also known as *Algedi*. This "corner" star is made up of several stars and is a treat among the faint stars of Capricornus. To the eye, you can *just* discern two stars. These become a golden pair in binoculars while revealing two more stars. Telescopes show a faint star next to the dimmer of the golden pair. **NAKED EYE, BINOCULARS and TELESCOPE at low power.**

72 GLOBULAR CLUSTER M72 is one of the more difficult Messier globulars. Dist: 55,000 ly. Diameter: 96 ly. Arc diameter in sky: 6'. Mag: 9.3. **Challenging TELESCOPE object because it is small and faint and there are no conspicuous markers for locating it easily. If you are viewing this for the first time using a small telescope, you could pass it by several times before realizing that it is a globular because it appears more like a star with a little "fuzz" around it.**

73 GLOBULAR CLUSTER M30 is much bigger and brighter than its northern cousin M72 described above. I specifically included this globular because it is usually the one object that "gets away" from being observed in the very early morning by those participating in a Messier Marathon. What is a **Messier Marathon?** Check out Charles Messier and his DSO catalogue on pages 244–251. A Messier Marathon is the act of viewing all 112 Messier objects in one night (most of us miss M30 though). This can be accomplished around New Moon during March because the Sun is positioned in an area of the sky devoid of Messier objects. Check your local astronomy club for organized participation. Dist: 26,000 ly. Diameter: 33 ly. Arc diameter in sky: 11'. Mag: 7.2. **In dark skies, M30 is fairly easy to spot with a TELESCOPE since it is bright, especially in comparison to nearby M72. How does this object "get away" during a Messier Marathon? It is the last object to rise just before dawn and unless you have a clear view of the eastern horizon, the sky will brighten too much to see it by the time it clears any obstacles blocking the horizon.**

Distance to Named Stars

Alnair	57 ly
Dabih	560 ly
Deneb Algedi	37 ly
Enif	470 ly
Fomalhaut	22 ly
Scheat	220 ly

Greek Alphabet

α	alpha
β	beta
γ	gamma
δ	delta
ε	epsilon
ζ	zeta
η	eta
θ	theta
ι	iota
κ	kappa
λ	lambda
μ	mu
ν	nu
ξ	xi
ο	omicron
π	pi
ρ	rho
σ	sigma
τ	tau
υ	upsilon
φ	phi
χ	chi
ψ	psi
ω	omega

October

Sept at 11:30 PM	Oct at 9:30 PM	Nov at 7:30 PM

Joins with **Chart A** at H on page 61

To North Celestial Pole ★ Polaris

1h

19h +50° Dec

74

Lacerta

MILKY WAY

Deneb

Summer Triangle

Vega

Cygnus
Northern Cross

Lyra
54

Andromeda

Alpheratz

Scheat

66

Albireo 64
65

For stars **EAST** of this chart, use Chart I tilt page to left.

Great Square

Pegasus

67 Vulpecula

Sagitta

For stars **WEST** of this chart, use Chart G & tilt page to right.

Enif 69 Delphinus

Equuleus

Altair

Pisces

70

Aquila

EASTERLY

ECLIPTIC
Path of Sun, Moon & Planets

0° Dec

WESTERLY

Cetus

Aquarius

72 71

Dabih

Deneb Algedi

Deneb Kaitos

Capricornus

73

Fomalhaut

Piscis Austrinus

Sculptor

Microscopium

Nunki

Sagittarius

68

Corona Australis

Grus

Alnair

Phoenix

Horizon at Latitude 50° N

Horizon at Latitude 30° N

-50° Dec

SOUTH

Joins with **Chart J** at H on page 79

Magnitudes
- ● Mag −1 to 0
- ● Mag 1 to 2
- • Mag 2 to 3
- · Mag 4 to 5
- Milky Way

Objects to View
- ○ Star Cluster
- ◉ Variable Star
- Nebula
- ◆ Supernova
- ⊕ Globular Cluster
- Double Star
- ◎ Planetary Nebula
- Galaxy

Nov ★ Dec Object Descriptions

Binocular & Telescope Objects

Numbers correspond to those on the Charts

74 GALAXIES M31, M32 and M110. M31 is the legendary Andromeda Galaxy, a sister to our own Milky Way Galaxy. It is the only galaxy that can be seen easily with the naked eyes (not counting the Small and Large Magellanic Clouds in the southern hemisphere). When you view M31 with binoculars or a telescope, what you actually see is the glow of the core. M32 and M110 are small elliptical companion galaxies next to M31. M32 is easy to spot and is not far from M31's core. On the "opposite" side of the core from M32 is the *much* fainter M110. In pictures of M31, M32 overlaps onto the outer edge (arms) of the galaxy. However, visually through a telescope, M32 appears as a fuzzy star detached from the core's glow. To the eyes, M31 appears as a very pale spot, often better seen using averted vision. It can be glimpsed in some light-polluted skies. Distance to all three: 2.5 million ly. Diameters: 120,000+ ly, 5,600 ly & 12,000 ly. Arc sizes in sky: 178', 8' & 17'. Mags: 3.5, 8 & 9+. **M31 is a NAKED EYE, BINOCULARS and TELESCOPE object. The bright oval core is apparent but the surrounding arms are generally not seen. TELESCOPE needed to see the "fuzzy star" M32 and much fainter M110.**

FEATURED ON PAGE 277

75 Spiral GALAXY M33 is sometimes referred to as the Pinwheel Galaxy because it is "face on," and roundish. I have a difficult time seeing this galaxy in a telescope: even though it is large, it has *very* low "surface" brightness. Dist: 2.2 million ly. Diameter: 40,000 ly. Arc diameter in sky: 60'. Mag: 5.7. **BINOCULARS or TELESCOPE object that requires dark skies. I find it much easier seeing this one with binoculars. In a telescope, you may pass it by several times looking for a brighter object. Start at 30x to 50x, no higher.**

Greek Alphabet

α	alpha
β	beta
γ	gamma
δ	delta
ε	epsilon
ζ	zeta
η	eta
θ	theta
ι	iota
κ	kappa
λ	lambda
μ	mu
ν	nu
ξ	xi
ο	omicron
π	pi
ρ	rho
σ	sigma
τ	tau
υ	upsilon
φ	phi
χ	chi
ψ	psi
ω	omega

76 GALAXY M74, like M33 above, is a faint face-on spiral galaxy. Some have nicknamed this one "The Phantom" because of its elusiveness. Dist: 32 million ly. Diameter: 102,000 ly. Arc diameter in sky: 10'. Mag: 9. **Very challenging TELESCOPE object. This faint galaxy is easy to locate because it is slightly more than a degree away from a "bright" star making up Pisces, but it is more difficult to see because its surface brightness is very low. Needs dark skies. Use 50x to 75x.**

77 The famous VARIABLE STAR *Mira* was one of the first stars recognized to change in brightness by ancient civilizations. This long-term variable star has a cycle averaging 332 days. It stays faint, at magnitude 9, for most of the time and then flares up to magnitude 3.5 or brighter for a week or so. Consult astronomy periodicals for predicted flare-ups. **NAKED EYE monitoring.**

78 GALAXY M77 is within one degree of the star *Delta (δ) Ceti* so it shares a placement similar to galaxy M74 above (object #76). Dist: 52 million ly. Diameter: 106,000 ly. Arc diameter in sky: 7'. Mag: 8.8. **TELESCOPE object. Appears as two "stars," with nebulosity around one, which actually is the galaxy's core, while the other is a star in our Milky Way Galaxy. Needs dark skies. Start with magnifications from 50x to 75x.**

Distance to Named Stars

Alpheratz	97 ly
Deneb Kaitos	96 ly
Hamal	66 ly
Mira	200 ly
Mirach	199 ly
Menkar	220 ly
Zaurak	170 ly

An explanation about the **Star of Bethlehem** is on page 370.

CHART
I
View
Facing
SOUTH

November ★ December

Oct at 12:30 PM   **Nov at 10:30 PM**   Dec at 8:30 PM

Joins with **Chart A** at I on page 61

To North Celestial Pole ★ Polaris

Nov ★ Dec I

1h   α   19h   +50° Dec

δ   ψ   ι   θ   •σ   •ο   φ   κ   M I L K Y   α
ν   κ   χ   ξ   ψ   WAY   **Lacerta**
Perseus   •   •ο

12 ⊙Algol   13   γ   74
ω   π   •σ   •ο   π
ρ   **Andromeda**   β
ξ   •   γ δ   Mirach   π   •τ   η
ζ •   **Triangulum**   75   δ   Alpheratz   Scheat   λ
α   τ   ε   α   β   π
Pleiades   **Aries**   α   λ   υ   •ψ   υ •τ   μ   For stars
⊛ 14   ζ   •ε   Hamal   β   χ φ ψ η   X•   **Pegasus**   ξ λ   **WEST**
of this chart,
δ   •γ   **Pisces**   **Great**   α   use Chart H
For stars   •   76 ◑η   Square   & tilt page
EAST   ξ   μ   ο   ε   δ   γ   ξ ζ   to right.
of this chart,   λ   ν   ω   •ρ
use Chart B   α γ   υ μ   θ   •   Enif
& tilt page   •κ   Menkar   α ξ   ι   γ •λ   θ•   0°α
to left.   78   δ   ν   •   κ   η•   γ Dec
77 ◐Mira   **ECLIPTIC**   δ•
Cetus   θ   Path of Sun,   ψ   •θ
δ   ε ξ η   ζ   Moon & Planets   ω   **Aquarius** τ   •
Zaurak   •ε ρ   X   φ   δ   δ   •
Eridanus   π   •σ   τ   β   α   λ   β
υ   Deneb   **Aquarius**
Kaitos   ω
α   •ω   ν   α   δ   Fomalhaut   ε   **Piscis**
Fornax   **Sculptor**   γ β   **Austrinus**
β   η   β   T μ
υ ι
θ   ι   γ   α   θ •ρ   λ   •γ
Eridanus   κ α   ι   θ •ρ   λ   μ
Phoenix β   ε   **Grus**   δ
ψ   •λ   ι   β   Alnair
κ•   δ   α
Horizon   ζ   ε   −50°
at Latitude   Dec
50° N
SOUTH
Horizon
at Latitude
30° N

Joins with **Chart J** at I on page 79

Magnitudes
● Mag −1 to 0
● Mag 1 to 2
• Mag 2 to 3
· Mag 4 to 5
Milky Way

Objects to View
◌ Star Cluster   ◉ Variable Star   ◣ Nebula   ◆ Supernova
⊕ Globular Cluster   ✹ Double Star   ◎ Planetary Nebula   ◥ Galaxy

South Circumpolar Descriptions

Binocular & Telescope Objects
Numbers correspond to those on the Charts

79 There is no bright star at the South Celestial Pole like there is in the north. Extend the longest length of Crux, the "Southern Cross," 3.5 times to get close to the "down under" celestial pole.

(46) GLOBULAR CLUSTER, NGC 5139, is big and beautiful. Designated and called *Omega (ω) Centauri*. See more on page 68. **Beautiful sight in BINOCULARS or TELESCOPE! Easy to find, but very low in northern hemisphere skies. Start at 50x.**

FEATURED ON PAGE 295

80 "Centaurus A" GALAXY, NGC 5128. Dist: 23 million ly. Diameter: 120,000 ly. Arc width in sky: 18'. Mag: 7. **Use TELESCOPE starting at 50x. Big & round.**

81 *Rigil Kent,* at magnitude –0.3, is the closest, brightest STAR in the sky, at a little more than 4 ly away. **NAKED EYE.**

82 GLOBULAR CLUSTER NGC 6752. Dist: 17,000 ly. Diameter: 208 ly. Arc width in sky: 42'. Mag: 5. **Use BINOCULARS or TELESCOPE starting at 50x.**

83 Well-known *47 Tucanae* GLOBULAR CLUSTER, NGC 104. Dist: 16,000 ly. Diameter: 205 ly. Arc width in sky: 44'. Mag: 5. **Use BINOCULARS or TELESCOPE. Large & bright, start at 50x.**

84 & **85** Small and Large MAGELLANIC CLOUDS (SMC & LMC respectively) are nearby companion galaxies to ours. Dist: 195,000 & 160,000 ly. Span: 14,000 & 18,000 ly. Arc widths in sky: 4° & 6.5°. **NAKED EYE, BINOCULARS and TELESCOPE objects.**

86 "Tarantula" NEBULA, NGC 2070. Distance: 160,000 ly. Width: 1,860 ly. Arc width in sky: 40'. Magnitude: 5. **Use BINOCULARS or TELESCOPE.**

87 Large open CLUSTER of stars, NGC 2516. Dist: 1,300 ly. Width: 11 ly. Arc width in sky: 30'. Mag: 3.8. **Use BINOCULARS or TELESCOPE.**

(31) Large open CLUSTER, NGC 2477. Dist: 4,200 ly. Width: 33 ly. Arc width in sky: 27'. Mag: 6. **Use BINOCULARS or TELESCOPE.**

Greek Alphabet

α alpha
β beta
γ gamma
δ delta
ε epsilon
ζ zeta
η eta
θ theta
ι iota
κ kappa
λ lambda
μ mu
ν nu
ξ xi
ο omicron
π pi
ρ rho
σ sigma
τ tau
υ upsilon
φ phi
χ chi
ψ psi
ω omega

88 *Regor* is actually 4 STARS. **Use TELESCOPE starting at 50x.**

89 GLOBULAR CLUSTER, NGC 2808. Dist: 30,000 ly. Diameter: 166 ly. Arc width in sky: 19'. Mag: 6. **Use BINOCULARS or TELESCOPE starting at 50x.**

90 Large naked-eye CLUSTER, IC 2391. Dist: 600 ly. Spans: 21 ly. Arc size in sky: 2°. Mag: 2.5. **NAKED EYE, BINOCULARS or TELESCOPE.**

91 "Southern Pleiades" CLUSTER, IC 2602. Fainter version of northern counterpart. Dist: 480 ly. Spans: 8 ly. Arc size in sky: 60'. Mag: 1.9. **Use BINOCULARS or TELESCOPE.**

92 Favorite *Eta Carinae* STAR & NEBULA, NGC 3372. Dist: 6,000 ly. Spans: 210 ly. Arc size in sky: 2°. Mag: 3. **Use BINOCULARS or TELESCOPE.**

93 CLUSTER, NGC 3532, pretty sprinkle of stars. Dist: 1,300 ly. Spans: 11 ly. Arc width in sky: 30'. Mag: 3. **Use BINOCULARS or TELESCOPE.**

94 CLUSTER, NGC 3766. Dist: 5,500 ly. Spans: 19 ly. Arc size in sky: 12'. Mag: 5. **Use BINOCULARS or TELESCOPE.**

95 TRIPLE STAR *Acrux.* **Use TELESCOPE starting at 50x.**

96 "Coal Sack" dark NEBULA extends over 7° or 14 Moon diameters. **NAKED EYE, BINOCULARS or TELESCOPE.**

97 Southern "Jewel Box" CLUSTER, NGC 4755 with a red star. Dist: 7,600 ly. Spans: 22 ly. Arc size in sky: 10'. Mag: 4. **Use TELESCOPE starting at 50x. Northern Jewel Box indicated on Charts F & G.**

Distance to Named Stars

Achernar	144 ly
Acrux	321 ly
Atria	415 ly
Canopus	313 ly
Gacrux	88 ly
Hador	526 ly
Miaplacidus	111 ly
Peacock	183 ly
Regor	840 ly
Rigil Kent	4 ly

South Circumpolar Stars
View Facing SOUTH

This chart is the Southern Extension of Charts B through I

Note. For the correct orientation of the stars on this chart to the horizon, turn the chart to make the months "right-side up."

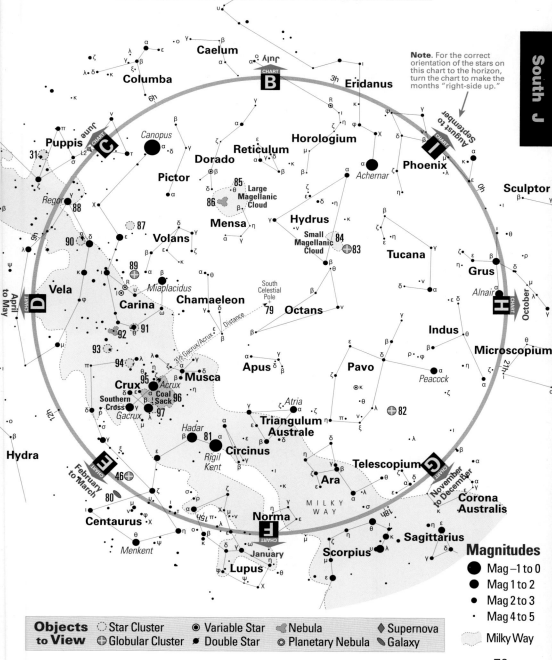

Objects to View
- ○ Star Cluster
- ⊕ Globular Cluster
- ◉ Variable Star
- ✸ Double Star
- 🜲 Nebula
- ◎ Planetary Nebula
- ◆ Supernova
- 🌑 Galaxy
- Milky Way

Magnitudes
- ● Mag −1 to 0
- ● Mag 1 to 2
- • Mag 2 to 3
- · Mag 4 to 5

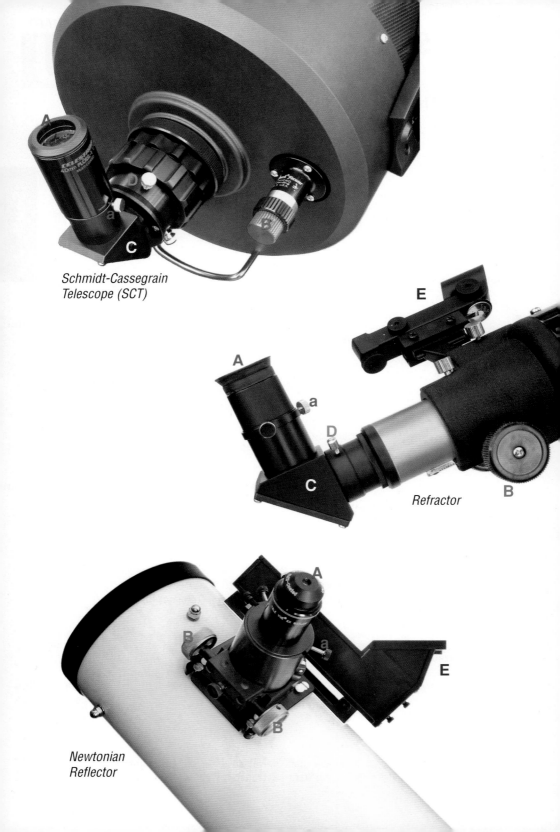

Schmidt-Cassegrain
Telescope (SCT)

Refractor

Newtonian
Reflector

Telescopes & Binoculars

Anyone can participate in and enjoy astronomy without the aid of binoculars or a telescope. However, their use will heighten the experience of exploring the heavens, opening vistas unobtainable in any other manner, revealing a hidden Universe out of reach of the eye alone.

TELESCOPE OVERVIEW

Refractors and reflectors are the two basic types of telescopes; although today, a hybrid of the two has become popular. Refractor telescopes utilize clear optical lenses for focusing light while reflector telescopes use mirrors. The hybrid telescopes use mirrors for focusing light, but also employ a front "correcting lens."

Refractors. Refractors represent the most common notion of a telescope. The front lens used for focusing light is called the objective lens. Common objective diameters range from 2.4 inches (60mm) to 6 inches (150mm). Most are 4 inches (101mm) or less. Refractors are more expensive per inch of aperture than other telescopes. However, small, inexpensive refractors are often purchased for children and since these telescopes do not perform well, they very often taint first impressions of observational astronomy.

Tele Vue 101 Refractor

Facing page. Telescope basics. From top to bottom: SCT or Schmidt-Cassegrain Telescope, Refractor and a Reflector. **A • Eyepieces**. *Telescopes use eyepieces that allow changing the magnification. Eyepieces are secured "lightly" with a thumbscrew,* **a**, *so they do not fall out when the telescope is moved.* **B • Focusing**. *Telescopes are focused by turning a knob. Each observer must focus for his or her eyes.* **C • Diagonal**. *A 90° diagonal is used with SCTs and Refractors to make viewing more comfortable. Diagonals are unnecessary for reflectors.* **D • Swivel**. *Diagonals can be rotated or swiveled to make viewing comfortable by loosening a thumbscrew and rotating. Don't forget to "snugly" retighten the thumbscrew after repositioning.* **E • Reflex-sight Finder**. *It is very difficult to aim a telescope at an object in the sky without some type of "Finder." In the past, these were commonly small-diameter, low-powered telescopes. Today, the Finder of choice is a Reflex-sight that optically projects a red dot or concentric circles onto the night sky.*

Three Popular Telescopes

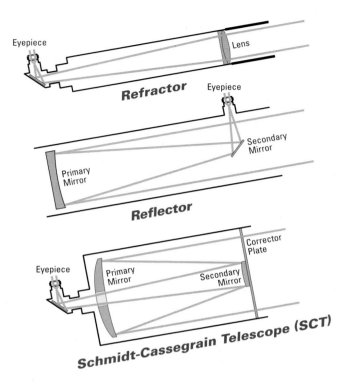

The **Refractor** was the first type of telescope invented, around 1609. And, Galileo was one of the first to make and use this instrument to explore the heavens for a better understanding of our world. Although Galileo's telescopes had apertures averaging about an inch in diameter, most amateur refractors today have diameters of 4 inches or less with the largest around 6 inches.

In 1668, just 60 years after the telescope was introduced to the world, Isaac Newton made the first reflector telescope, utilizing a concave mirror to focus light. His original design is still extensively used today and appropriately called the **Newtonian Reflector**. Although Newton's original mirror measured just 1⅓ inches in diameter, today, common sizes range from 4½ to 12 inches. Many Newtonian reflectors, especially those called "Dobsonians," which are characterized by their simple altazimuth mounts, are manual scopes, that is, designed to be moved by hand. Although this makes them the least expensive per aperture inch of any telescope, they require a greater knowledge of the sky in order to locate objects.

The **Schmidt-Cassegrain Telescope or SCT** uses two mirrors and a front correcting plate to focus light. Although this optical design was introduced in the 1950s, it became popular when Celestron made them for amateurs in the early 1970s.

Telescopes

Reflectors. The Newtonian reflector, patterned after Newton's original design, is the most common reflector telescope. These telescopes use a concave parabolic primary mirror to focus light. Today, the most popular form of the Newtonian telescope is nicknamed a "Dobsonian" (see Glossary). The Dobsonian telescope features a Newtonian telescope on an inexpensive and simple altazimuth mount that allows easy vertical and horizontal movement. These simple mounts have enabled amateurs to purchase larger telescopes for the lowest cost ever. Common diameters of Newtonians reflectors range from 4½ inches to 12 inches, but they max out around 36 inches. The 6 and 8-inch diameters are affordable to own and convenient to use.

Newtonian Reflector, "Dobsonian" Style

SCT

Hybrids. Although there are several types of hybrid telescopes, the Schmidt-Cassegrain Telescope (SCT) is the most popular. The 8-inch diameter is the best-selling size and provides an extremely portable observing system because of its compact "folded" optical system. SCTs have primary mirrors for focusing light, but incorporate a front correcting plate or lens, which also helps seal the optics from the environment. Per aperture inch, SCT telescopes cost less than refractors but more than "Dobsonian" reflectors.

TELESCOPE MOUNTS

Although there are just two basic types of telescope mounts, the **altazimuth** and **equatorial**, there are many variations.

The simplest and most prevalent mount is the **altazimuth**. Everyone is familiar with this type because it is the same mount used with giant binoculars at tourist attractions. Altazimuth mounts allow quick and easy, up-and-down and side-to-side movement. Newtonian reflectors mounted on altazimuth mounts are often referred to as "Dobsonians." I use telescopes on altaz-

Telescopes Mounts

Telescope Mounts

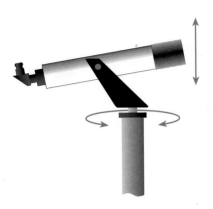

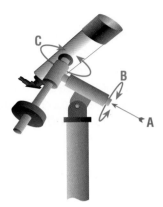

ALTAZIMUTH MOUNT
Simple, easy vertical and horizontal movement.

*For amateurs, a form of the Equatorial mount is required to take photographs of celestial objects requiring **extended** exposures. Altazimuth mounts can be tilted to perform just like Equatorial mounts. The largest professional telescopes are on computer-controlled Altazimuth mounts.*

EQUATORIAL MOUNT
Shown is a traditional German Equatorial Mount. To set up, the Polar Axis, **A**, must be pointed to a Celestial Pole. The telescope is positioned and rotates around the Polar Axis, **B** and the Declination Axis, **C**. A slow moving motor attached to the Polar Axis allows the scope to "follow" celestial objects.

imuth mounts for much of my visual observing. See pictures on pages 81, 83 and 92 of telescopes on this type of mount.

The **equatorial** mount was the traditional astronomical mount before the age of computers because it was the only mount that could be motorized to automatically follow a celestial object across the sky. Equatorial mounts have two axes. One points directly at a celestial pole (close to the star Polaris in the northern hemisphere) and is called the Polar Axis. The other axis, the Declination Axis, is perpendicular to the Polar Axis. A popular design of the equatorial mount is called the German Equatorial (illustrated above), which is recognizable by a counterweight shaft on one end of the Declination Axis.

Advanced Telescope Mounts

The New Mounts — Compliments of the Computer

Computer-controlled telescope mounts have revolutionized astronomy for both the amateur and professional.

Professional astronomers started building and using computer-controlled altazimuth mounts in the early 1970s. They quickly caught on because they were considerably less expensive (and less massive) than equatorial mounts. This technology was eventually adopted to amateur mounts when computer components became affordable in the early 1990s.

Motorized Mounts & GO TO Computerized Telescopes

Slow-moving motors are or can be attached to the axes of many altazimuth and equatorial mounts, allowing telescopes to follow celestial objects. So, instead of nudging the telescope every minute or so to keep a celestial object in view, the motorized mounts do it for you. Many SCTs come with motorized mounts; however, for many telescopes, it is an option or accessory.

One of the greatest technological breakthroughs for amateurs was the introduction of the GO TO computerized/motorized telescopes in the 1990s (it is actually the mount and not the telescope that is motorized and controlled by a computer even though it is often referred to as the telescope having this capability). For the first time, amateurs had telescopes like their professional counterparts — telescopes that could automatically find and follow celestial objects. GO TO telescopes are controlled through hand-controllers that look and work similar to cellular phones. They have a small display screen, where celestial objects, including the Planets, can be chosen from scrollable lists.

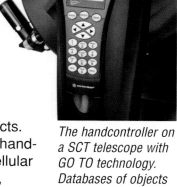

The handcontroller on a SCT telescope with GO TO technology. Databases of objects are accessed through the keypad — similar to phone number lists on cellphones.

All altazimuth GO TO telescopes are easy to set up and use, however, like with any new electronic piece of equipment (VCR or DVD players, etc), they require a short learning curve for their operation to become second nature.

Magnification & f/numbers

How do you get a GO TO mount going? After the mount or "telescope" is turned on, it must first be aligned to two bright stars before it will automatically find, move to, and follow objects. This two-star alignment takes about five minutes and the hand controller displays information that walks you through the process. The telescope will even choose the two bright stars to be used for alignment and it will also move and roughly point the telescope close to them. All you have to do is center the stars in the eyepiece and press a button on the keypad to indicate that you have accomplished each of the alignments. After this has been completed, the telescope will automatically move to any object in the sky (except for objects like new comets) selected from scrollable lists.

MORE ABOUT TELESCOPES

The Myth about Telescope Magnification

Magnification is the least important factor in choosing a telescope! But, unfortunately, the selling and marketing of many telescopes, especially those sold in department, chain or toy stores, has often been based on magnification.

Technically, it is possible to get any magnification out of any optical system, but there are practical limits. *Useful magnification for most observing, independent of objective lens or primary mirror size, is from 30x to 250x. Magnifications higher than 250x often do not provide more detail because the usually turbulent atmosphere limits image quality and resolution.*

The practice of selling "high magnification" does not seem to go away despite the repeated efforts of professional and amateur astronomers to stamp out this idea. The reason for its persistence is simple. Marketers realize that high magnification is a selling point — something that consumers understand, especially when purchasing telescopes for children. Even the largest telescope manufacturers, who should know better, are guilty of using this hyperbole to sell their lower-end telescope line.

What are all those f/numbers about?

The f/numbers (e.g. f/4, f/5.4, f/8) associated with telescopes indicate the ratio of the telescope focal length to its aperture. In other words, the focal length of a telescope, divided by the

Magnification & Eyepieces

Computing Telescope Magnification

Focal Length of TELESCOPE ÷ *Focal Length* of EYEPIECE = Magnification

NOTE: All focal lengths must be expressed in the same units — usually millimeters.

EXAMPLE 1

What magnifications are achieved using 8mm, 15mm & 20mm eyepieces with an 8-inch SCT having a focal length of 2032mm?

2032mm ÷ 8mm = 254x
2032mm ÷ 15mm = 135.5x
2032mm ÷ 20mm = 101.6x

EXAMPLE 2

What magnification is achieved with a 4-inch f/6 telescope and 20mm eyepiece?

1. Compute focal length of the telescope.
   4-inch x 6 (f/6) = 24-inch focal length
2. Change 24-inch focal length into millimeters. 24 x 25.4 (conversion factor) = 610mm focal length
3. Compute Magnification.
   610mm ÷ 20mm = 30.5x

diameter of the objective lens or primary mirror, gives you the f/number. For example, if your telescope has a focal length of 21.5 inches (540mm) and an objective lens diameter of 4 inches (100mm), then your f/number is f/5.4 (21.5 inches ÷ 4 inches = 5.4 *or* 540mm ÷ 100mm = 5.4). Telescopes with f/numbers of 5 or lower are considered rich-field telescopes (RFT) because they provide lower magnifications and wider fields of view (that is, you can see more of the sky through an eyepiece). Most telescopes have f/numbers that range from f/4 to f/15. The f/number is also referred to as the focal ratio and it is the same number used with camera lenses.

Eyepieces, the Barlow Lens, Eyeglasses & Focusing

Quality eyepieces are just as important as a quality objective lens or primary mirror. Low quality eyepieces will render poor quality images. The standard eyepiece is the Plössl eyepiece (Plössl is the name of a specific lens design). Plössls are excellent eyepieces because they provide good imagery across a wide field of view and are reasonably priced.

Plössl Eyepiece Design

Eyepieces are identified by their focal length, which is always expressed in millimeters (mm). Focal lengths range from about 2mm to 55mm (0.08 inches to 2.16 inches). Shorter focal length eyepieces (those with smaller numbers) provide higher magnifications. See the top of this page for computing magnifications.

Computing Magnification

The standard eyepiece barrel diameter is 1¼ inches. There is also a 2-inch size. Some inexpensive telescopes use eyepieces that have barrel diameters of 0.965 inches, but very few eyepieces are available for this smaller barrel diameter.

A **barlow lens** can be used in conjunction with an eyepiece to double (triple or even quadruple) its magnification. A quality barlow will not degrade the performance of an eyepiece. Most barlows look like long eyepieces that fit into the eyepiece holder (focuser) of a telescope. Regular eyepieces are then inserted into the barlow (see photo below).

There are many "specialty" eyepieces that provide different viewing experiences. Mostly, these eyepieces provide a greater field of view, that is, they allow you can see more of the sky, similar to the difference between looking out a small and large window. Unfortunately, these eyepieces are considerably more expensive than the Plössl design, so if possible, try them out before you buy.

Most telescopes come with at least one eyepiece, so be prepared to purchase more. To start, I recommend two Plössls and a 2x barlow. If you start with this combination, the focal length of your "shorter" eyepiece should be ⅔ to ¾ that of your longer focal length eyepiece in order to avoid duplicate magnifications when using the barlow.

If possible, observe without eyeglasses. If you are unsure as to whether or not you can, give it a try. Observing is more pleasant and comfortable without them. If you must wear your glasses, remember that some eyepieces have a rubber guard

The eyepiece on the far left has a barrel diameter of 0.965 inches. The 20mm Plössl eyepiece to its right has the standard barrel diameter of 1¼ inches. The very large eyepiece in the "center," a 55mm Plössl, has the largest commercially made barrel diameter of 2 inches. The 2x Barlow lens at the far right accepts eyepieces with 1¼-inch barrel diameters (they are inserted at the top and secured with a thumbscrew (not visible).

that can be folded back to get you closer to the lens for a better view. Better yet, there are specialty eyepieces designed with "long eye relief" that allow eyeglass users to comfortably look through eyepieces. These designs enable eyeglass wearers to easily see to the edge of the field of view instead of just seeing the middle portion of the image.

Focusing. Everyone needs to focus a telescope to his or her individual eyes. I am always amazed at the difference in focus from one person to another. What may be completely out of focus for one is perfectly focused to another. Although it is a common courtesy to ask the owner or operator of a telescope if you can use the focuser, please do not hesitate to ask for there is nothing worse than viewing an image that is not focused.

Finderscopes & Reflex Sights

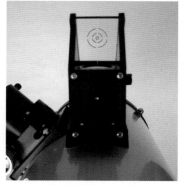

Above. The view through a Telrad, one of the most popular reflex-sight finders. To use, position an eye 6-inches or so behind the slanted glass plate to see the bulls-eye for aiming the scope. These finders are natural and fun to use — kids really like them.

Have you ever tried to point a telescope at a star or Planet? It is not easy without a finderscope. A finderscope is a small, low-powered telescope attached to the main telescope. It usually has cross reticles and is used to steer or target the telescope. Even economically priced finderscopes will help you enormously to guide your telescope.

However, today, there are finders, known as "reflex sights," that project a red dot or concentric circles onto the night sky for guiding the telescope. Reflex sights are wonderful because you can quickly point a telescope to a specific spot in the night sky without having to look through the "narrow" confines of a finderscope. Most amateurs now use reflex sights instead of traditional finderscopes.

Left. A traditional finderscope is nothing more than a small, low-powered telescope with a "generous" field of view.

Binoculars

Upside-Down and Inside-Out Images

Most astronomical telescopes and traditional finderscopes do not provide upright, true-to-life views. For instance, refractors without the 90° diagonal, provide upside down views. With the 90° diagonal, the image is upright but it is a "mirror image" where left and right are reversed. SCTs with a 90° diagonal provide the same view as a refractor with a 90° diagonal. The biggest problem with reversed "mirror-image" views is matching stars in the eyepiece to those printed correctly in star atlases. Newtonian reflectors provide a true-to-life image but its orientation changes depending on your position to the eyepiece, so these telescopes are not the most practical for terrestrial viewing if you require an upright image.

There has always been a toleration for mirrored and upside down images in astronomy because image orientation is generally immaterial when studying the stars.

Modern Optical Quality

At the beginning of this twenty-first century, middle-of-the-line telescopes and other optical instruments perform better than the very high-end telescopes of the 1970s. Modern computer technology, sophisticated production techniques and new materials give us the highest mechanical and optical quality ever.

Unfortunately, not all optics are excellent. Most telescopes sold in department and discount stores, as well as the lower-end line of telescopes sold by the major telescope manufacturers, almost always exhibit lower optical quality. Don't disappoint yourself — if you are in the market to purchase binoculars or a telescope, buy at least middle-of-the-line.

BINOCULARS

Binoculars are an excellent instrument for observing the heavens. They offer the comfort of two-eye viewing and capture greater vistas than can be obtained with telescopes.

Almost all middle-of-the-line binoculars offer good optical performance. The standard configuration, 7x50, is ideal for gazing at the heavens and for daytime use. I do not recommend binoculars smaller than 40mm for astronomical use. My 10x40s provide excellent views of the brighter nebulae and star clusters, however, my 8x20 pair is not adequate for these fainter objects. There are speciality binoculars with magnification above 10x, but I don't recommend them because you can't use them easily, for terrestrial viewing, without a tripod.

Binocular Nomenclature

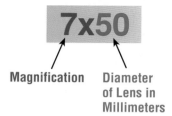

Magnification   Diameter of Lens in Millimeters

Since most binoculars are limited to magnification from 7x to 10x, they cannot provide the detail possible with telescopes. On the other hand, the wide vistas obtainable with binoculars are impossible to capture with telescopes. In my opinion, the most beautiful views of the Pleiades (M45, page 273) and the Praesepe (M44, page 279) are through binoculars. These clusters fill the binoculars' field of view and give the impression that the stars are floating in front of you. Many deep sky objects *are* visible with binoculars, however, they just appear smaller and fainter than through telescopes. About 80 of the Messier Objects (pages 248–251) can be seen through binoculars. For the most part, binoculars serve as observing adjuncts for amateur astronomers.

A tripod is very useful when using binoculars to view the heavens. It steadies your view and gives you the opportunity to study the heavens without making your arms tired. I also lean on the tripod, which makes it more comfortable for me to stand in place for a period of time. Most binoculars sold today have a tripod socket that allows easy attachment to the tripod head. You may

Porro-Prism binoculars (left) represent a proven design and are identified by the offset of the eyepieces from the front lenses. Although this design is bigger and thus bulkier than **Roof-Prism** binoculars (right), they can edge out the performance of roof-prism binoculars for a much lower cost.

Summary & Recommendations

have to get creative to attach older binoculars without tripod sockets to tripod heads. In lieu of a tripod, I often sit or lay on lawn furniture to not only steady my view but to also make my observing more comfortable.

Tripod adapters are used to attach binoculars to tripods.

TELESCOPE RECOMMENDATIONS & CONSIDERATIONS

The best telescope is the one that gets used. Often, this may be the easiest one to set up. Although I have several telescopes ranging in diameters from 4 to 8 inches, I tend to use a lightweight 6-inch Newtonian Reflector on a simple altazimuth mount because it *is* easy to set up and take down.

For casual observing, that is, when I want to go outside for a quick look around, I want it to be simple and fun, so I shy away from my larger and heavier scopes.

On the next page, I have provided summaries on telescopes, binoculars and eyepieces as well as some suggestions about purchasing these optics.

A favorite scope of mine is this 6-inch diameter Newtonian Reflector mounted on a simple altazimuth pipe mount that I made a few years ago. It is quick and easy to set up and fun to use. This is a "manual" scope so I have to move it around by hand.

Telescopes

Summary & Recommendations

REFRACTORS
+ Highest cost per inch of aperture.
+ Practically maintenance-free.
+ Diameters are small, most from 2⅜ to 4 inches. (60 to 100mm). Largest diameters are around 6 inches.
+ Easy set up and take down for 4-inch and smaller sizes.
+ Various mounts available.
+ Smaller "entry level" refractors are inexpensive but are not a good choice for astronomical use.
+ Most expensive refractors (called apochromatic) provide the highest image quality of all telescopes.

NEWTONIAN REFLECTORS — DOBSONIAN STYLE
+ Lowest cost per inch of aperture.
+ Optics need to be realigned frequently and cleaned occasionally.
+ Diameters range from 4½ to 12 and on up to 36 inches.
+ Easy set up and take down for 10-inch and smaller sizes.
+ Mount limited to simple altazimuth.
+ Low-quality components in some commercially produced units.
+ These are mostly manual telescopes that are moved around by hand, so some knowledge of navigating the sky is necessary.
+ Larger diameter provide the brightest and most detailed images of deep sky objects (DSOs). See pages 239 to 253.

HYBRIDS ★ SCHMIDT-CASSEGRAIN TELESCOPES (SCT)
+ Per inch of aperture, SCTs are more expensive than Newtonian Reflectors but less expensive than refractors.
+ Maintenance required occasionally.
+ Common diameters range from 5 to 16 inches.
+ Easy set up and take down for 8-inch and smaller sizes. Those larger than 8-inches get heavy fast.
+ Front correcting plate susceptible to dew.
+ Often have computerized and motorized mounts that find and follow the stars (GO TO).
+ 8-inch is telescope of choice for many amateurs.

Telescopes

Summary & Recommendations

BINOCULARS

+ Purchase at least middle-of-the-line binoculars. These should provide good image quality.
+ 7x40, 10x40, 7x50 or 10x50 or similar are good choices for astronomical and terrestrial use.
+ A tripod or lawn chair is helpful to steady your view when looking at astronomical objects.
+ Older binoculars may not have a tripod socket, so you may have to get creative in latching them to a tripod's head.

EYEPIECES

+ Telescopes are only half of the equation for viewing the heavens. Good quality eyepieces are the other half.
+ Be prepared to purchase a few with your telescope since most telescopes come with only one eyepiece.
+ Plössl is the standard eyepiece of choice.
+ A barlow lens can economically double or triple the magnification range of your set of eyepieces.

Here are some of my suggestions for exploring the heavens with and without your own optical instrument.

Interloper. Do not buy a telescope or binoculars, but instead attend public astronomy events that feature telescope viewing. If you "hang around" at these events, you will see more celestial objects than you ever would by yourself, and see them through larger telescopes than you would have purchased. And you won't have to do any of the work. At such gatherings, I have looked through 2 to 36-inch telescopes and have seen objects that I can't see with my own scopes.

Gathering Dust. Borrow a friend's telescope that is sitting in the garage or basement. They may not want to sell it, but they may let you use it.

Really Want a Telescope. Please take some time to become informed so you can choose the best telescope for your budget and interests. Read about astronomy, subscribe to one of the popular monthly astronomy magazines, visit telescope shops, attend astronomy events, join a club and ask lots of questions

Summary & Recommendations

before you decide to buy. And remember, most amateurs go through several telescopes during their lifetime.

Used Telescopes. Some telescope stores sell used telescopes but they usually go quickly because they are less expensive than new. So, visit www.astromart.com and sign up for their email alerts on used telescopes sold by amateurs across America.

Bottom Line Recommendation. My first recommendation would be a 6 or 8-inch Newtonian Reflector (Dobsonian style) with several quality eyepieces. This will cost around $500 to $600. For around $2,000, you can get an 8-inch GO TO SCT. The 8-inch SCT is the most versatile product for the price. Either of these telescopes can easily be sold or traded if you outgrow them.

Telescopes

Our Moon

Of all the celestial objects, the Sun and the Moon command the most attention. The Sun rules by day, and the Moon by night, waxing and waning through phases that make it visually unique.

The Moon has been an integral part of humanity since the earliest times, gracing our skies with a splendor unmatched by any other celestial body. I have often wondered what people in the past thought of the Moon, ever changing, disappearing and even obliterating. To me, it would have been absolutely haunting and mysterious. So, I am glad I live in a time when mostly rational thought rules and we can appreciate the Moon for what it is, a planetary satellite, inextricably bound to us by gravity, but beautiful to behold.

Where did the Moon come from?

The most accepted theory is that the Moon is the result of a Mars-sized object colliding with Earth "shortly" after the formation of our Solar System 4.6 billion years ago. This catastrophic impact caused the Mars-sized object, along with part of Earth's crust and mantle, to break up into particles that formed a ring orbiting Earth and later coalescing to form the Moon. Crustal and mantle materials from the Earth have been identified in the Moon rocks retrieved from the Apollo landings, lending support to this theory.

Greek myth unknowingly hit upon truth with its story that the goddess of the Moon, Selene, was a descendant of Mother Earth or Gaia.

The Moon can be seen during the day!

An astronomy professor I had in college said he regularly received telephone calls from concerned members of the community. They would ask if something was wrong because the Moon was out during the daytime. He always assured them this was normal and that they had probably never noticed the Moon during the day.

When my daughter was two, we were driving around and I pointed the Moon out to her, plainly visible as a white crescent against the blue daytime sky. Regularly after that, and to my

Facing page. *John Young (pictured) and Charles Duke of the Apollo 16 mission working on instrumentation. The Lunar Roving Vehicle is in the background.*
Above. *The Lunar Prospector spacecraft that orbited the Moon in 1998.*

surprise, she would stretch out her arm and point her finger, and say only as a two-year old can, "Moooon." Her ability to find the Moon during the day became uncanny. Once, I told her, "No, that's not the Moon," but on closer examination, I noticed that she was right.

When you start noticing the Moon during the day, you will see it there often. In fact, about the only time that you cannot see the Moon during the day is around New Moon. From New Moon to Full Moon, the Moon trails the Sun. From Full Moon to New Moon, it precedes the Sun.

The same side always faces us. What's on the back?
Why does the same side of the Moon or **"near side"** as it is often referred to, always face the Earth? Because the Moon's rotation on its axis (Yes, the Moon rotates on its axis just like Earth!) is synchronized with its revolution around the Earth. This is not a coincidence. The gravitational effects of tidal and other forces have "locked in" the heaviest side of the Moon to always face the Earth.

What's on the other side? The back or **"far side,"** as it is often called, is covered heavily with craters. There are a few small maria (dark plains), but they are indistinct. The Earth-facing or near side is by far more interesting.

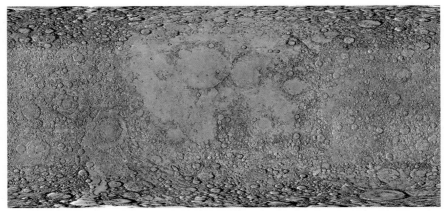

A relief map of the entire Moon. The far side of the Moon, which is comprised of the areas on the left and right sides, is riddled mostly with craters. The middle portion is the near side that faces Earth. The size of the craters along the top and bottom edges are greatly exaggerated because this type of map stretches out the polar regions.

Full Moon Nicknames

There is probably more lore associated with the Moon than any other celestial body. Every culture has its myths and traditions; however, the Moon's most important impact is the division of the year into months.

In the past, the Moon was given 12 nicknames, one for each month of the year. The nicknames that are occasionally used today include Harvest, Hunter, Moon Before Yule and Moon After Yule (Yule refers to Christmas). The Harvest Moon is the Full Moon closest to the Autumnal Equinox (about September 23). The Hunter's Moon follows Harvest; next comes Moon Before Yule, then Moon After Yule.

Once in a Blue Moon

The origin of the phrase "Once in a Blue Moon" is uncertain, however it means very seldom. The modern day definition of a Blue Moon refers to the occurrence of two full Moons in a month. This happens about once every three years. In the past, when the Moon's 12 nicknames were used, "Blue Moon" was the name given to the *third* Full Moon in a season (any of the four seasons) that had four Full Moons. A season, which spans three months, normally has three Full Moons.

Man in the Moon

What about the Man in the Moon? The darker plains (maria) and the lighter cratered areas (terrae) have given rise to people seeing a host of figures in the Full Moon. These include a rabbit, donkey, jack-o'-lantern, woman, man, and a girl reading. Let me caution you that seeing these figures or any other requires a bit of imagination.

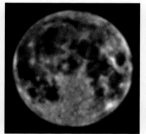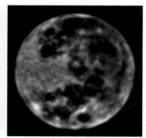

Three orientations of the Moon as it can appear in the sky. Can you see any figures in these Moons? I think a rabbit is the easiest to see. Does this say something about me? These images have been purposely blurred to help you focus on finding a figure.

Moon

Observing the Moon's Phases

The Moon: Bane of Deep Sky Objects (DSOs)

Dark skies are needed for the best viewing of the fainter deep sky objects like star clusters, nebulae and galaxies (see page 239). A bright Moon hinders observing these objects because it "white washes" the sky by scattering its light, preventing us from seeing the fainter celestial objects. Additionally, when the Moon is bright, our eyes cannot fully adapt to the darkness — and night vision is essential for viewing deep sky objects. So, unless you want to observe the Planets, Moon or Double Stars, you must work around the Moon's schedule to view the deep sky objects. There is always a flurry of amateur activity on weekends closest to the New Moon in order to take advantage of a long dark night nestled against a day for sleeping in.

Eclipses

Why don't we have both a solar and lunar eclipse every month? Because the Moon's orbit is tilted 5.1° to the Earth's orbit. This usually places the Moon above or below the Sun and Earth's shadow at Full Moon and New Moon. See page 288 for more information.

OBSERVING THE MOON: Phases & Movement

The Moon appears to cycle through phases because it orbits the Earth. In reality, one-half of the Moon is *always* bathed in sunlight just like with the Earth. So, the phases represent the *portion* of the sunlit side of the Moon that we see from Earth.

I have found that some individuals do not understand why the Moon has phases. I believe that this misunderstanding is partially because people get confused quickly with explanations involving geometry, which is the case with the Moon's phases. So, if you are

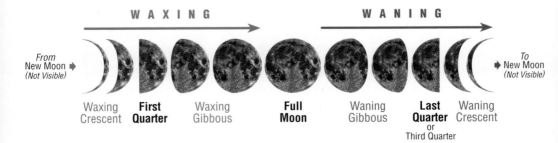

WAXING · WANING

From New Moon (Not Visible) → · → To New Moon (Not Visible)

Waxing Crescent · **First Quarter** · Waxing Gibbous · **Full Moon** · Waning Gibbous · **Last Quarter** or Third Quarter · Waning Crescent

Observing the Moon's Phases

one of these individuals having difficulty understanding the phases of the Moon, I don't know if I can explain it here to your satisfaction, but I will try.

First, study the picture below which might help you to visualize the different angles of view that account for the phases.

Secondly, you can partake in a "down-to-earth" example that mimics the phases of the Moon. On sunny days, when you are out and about walking the city streets, take a closer look at any smooth round pole that is bathed in sunlight. One "side" or half of any such pole is always lit by sunlight (its day side) while the other half is always "dark" (its night side). On a smooth pole, there is usually a fairly well-defined vertical line dividing the sunlit side from the dark side. Now, walk slowly around the pole, observing and noting the amount of "light" to "dark" that you see from different sides. This is the same effect that accounts for the phases of the Moon, except the Moon moves around us instead of us walking around it.

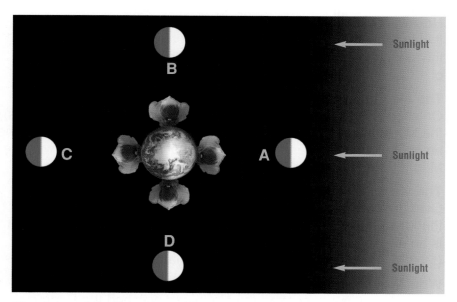

The phases of the Moon are nothing more than seeing the dayside of the Moon from different angles as it circles Earth. Imagine yourself in the center and visualize what phase of the Moon you would see. **A.** New Moon — *the Moon is next to the Sun during the daytime so you will not see it at all.* **B.** First Quarter — *right-half lit.* **C.** Full Moon. **D.** Third Quarter — *left-half lit.*

Observing the Moon's Phases

Observing the Moon's Phases

Phase of Moon	Rises in East	Sets in West	Location During Day
TO FIRST QUARTER))→D	Shortly *after* Sunrise	Shortly *after* Sunset	Visible for most of the day, trailing the Sun
FIRST QUARTER D	At Noon	At Midnight	Noon to Sunset, visible in the eastern or morning half of the sky
FULL MOON ○	At Sunset	At Sunrise	Not visible during the day
LAST QUARTER (	At Midnight	At Noon	Sunrise to Noon, visible in the western or after-noon half of the sky
TO NEW MOON (→(	Shortly *before* Sunrise	Shortly *before* Sunset	Visible for most of the day, preceeding the Sun
NEW MOON ●	*Not visible at all — in "line" or very close to the Sun*		

How much does the Moon move eastwardly in an hour?
It moves slightly more than its own diameter or 0.55 arc degrees in the sky with respect to the stars. This adds up to a daily movement of 13.2 arc degrees or about 27 of its diameters.

The Moon rises an average of 50 minutes later each day
On successive nights, over the course of a lunar month (29½ days), the Moon rises anywhere from 30 to 70 minutes *later* each day. The amount of time varies because of the geometry associated with the Moon's orbit inclined 28½ arc degrees to the Earth's equator.

The visual diameter of the Moon changes slightly
Over the course of a lunar orbit (27⅓ days), the visual diameter of the Moon in the sky changes by as much as 14% because its orbit is an ellipse so its distance from Earth varies by 31,250 miles (50,300 km) which is nearly four Earth diameters.

What would the Earth appear like from the Moon?
If you stayed in one spot on the Moon and watched the Earth over the course of a month, the Earth would cycle through phases like the Moon but it would neither rise nor set, just hover in the same area of the sky. Additionally, the Earth would appear nearly four times larger in diameter and shine 45 or more times brighter than the Moon in our skies.

Observing the Moon

OBSERVING THE MOON: Through a Telescope

The prime time to observe the Moon is during its waxing and waning phases. Waxing means "adding on" and waning means "subtracting from." The terminator, the "line" separating the lighted side from the dark side, is present when the Moon is waxing and waning. Craters appear their best (sharpest) when near the terminator because the contrast from the shadows makes them more pronounced. Magnifications from 40x to 250x are recommended.

The Moon is disappointing to observe around Full Moon. During this time, the entire surface, along with most features, is "washed out." However, at this time, the rays of craters are at their most pronounced. The crater Tycho's rays stretch halfway across the hemisphere.

Want to observe features on the dark or night side of the Moon? Around New Moon, when the Moon is a thin crescent, the dark side of the Moon is slightly lit by reflected light from Earth called **Earthshine**. Some features on the dark side are visible in a telescope at this time. Try observing this night side — it is a pretty sight! See the bottom picture on page 104.

The Moon is very bright and can fatigue your eye when viewing it through a telescope. Many amateurs thread two polarizing filters onto their eyepieces to reduce the intensity. These can be turned to vary the amount of light that gets through.

Major Features of the Moon

The most notable features on the Moon are its brighter cratered highlands called terrae and smoother darker plains known as maria. These and other features are described below.

Terminator. The border or "line" separating the lighted side from the dark side. The terminator is absent during Full Moon. Craters appear at their sharpest near the terminator.

Craters. Huge bowl-like depressions on the Moon. Most of the craters on the Moon were formed from meteoroid or cometary impact that ended about 3½ billion years ago.

Features of the Moon

Moon

Terrae & Maria. Terms coined by Galileo meaning "highlands" and "seas." The lighter-colored terrae have the highest concentration of craters and are older than the maria. The darker maria are smoother areas of the Moon and represent 16% of its surface. They are the result of impacts from large asteroids or comets creating fractures to the once molten interior, releasing dark, iron-rich, basalt lava, which flowed upward and outward to create the great plains. They average 500 to 600 feet thick (150 to 180 meters). There are very few maria on the far side of the Moon.

Rille. A long cliff or split in the maria, up to hundreds of miles or kilometers in length. Rilles can be seen in a telescope. They are the result of cracks, fractures or collapses in the maria.

Rays. Bright streaks that radiate from some craters. They represent lighter, reflective material, ejected during the formation of craters and are most pronounced around Full Moon. The crater Tycho has the longest rays, spanning one-quarter of the globe. It is estimated that rayed craters are less than one billion years old because the rays of older craters have been eroded by micrometeorites (see below).

Regolith. A fine grained "soil" that covers the surface of the Moon. Created from the bombardment of the surface by micrometeorites, the regolith varies in depth from 6½ to 26 feet (2 to 8 meters) in the maria, and to a possible 49 feet (15 meters) in the highlands. The micrometeorites that bombard Earth burn up in the atmosphere.

Top. Rays emanating from the southern crater Tycho, and the low contrast, "washed out" look of a fully illuminated Moon.
Middle. The Straight Wall, a favorite rille (see page 107).
Bottom. Earthshine. This overexposed picture of a Waxing Crescent Moon brings out the dark side of the Moon which is softly lit by reflected Earth light. Try observing this shortly after New Moon.

Index of Moon's Craters

NUMBERED CRATERS ARE ON PAGES 112 & 113

Below is an index of the major craters on the Moon. They are alphabetized and referenced by quadrant for easier identification. Several craters are referenced to two quadrants because these craters fall on the boundary.

1 Abenezra (IV)	39 Bessel (I)	60 Bullialdus (III)
2 Abulfeda (IV)	40 Bettinus (III)	61 Burckhardt (I)
3 Agatharchides (III)	41 Bianchini (II)	62 Bürg (I)
4 Agrippa (I)	42 Biela (IV)	63 Büsching (IV)
5 Albategnius (III)(IV)	43 Billy (III)	64 Byrgius (III)
6 Alexander (I)	44 Birmingham (II)	65 La Caille (III)
7 Alfraganus (IV)	45 Birt (III)	66 Calippus (I)
8 Aliacensis (III)(IV)	46 Blancanus (III)	67 Campanus (III)
9 Almanon (IV)	47 Blanchinus (III)	68 Capella (IV)
10 Alpetragius (III)		
11 Alphonsus (III)		
12 Anaxagoras (II)		

Quadrant Reference

13 Anaximenes (II)		
14 Apianus (IV)		
15 Apollonius (I)		
16 Arago (I)		
17 Archimedes (II)		
18 Archytas (I)		
19 Ariadaeus (I)		
20 Aristarchus (II)		
21 Aristillus (I)		
22 Aristoteles (I)		
23 Arzachel (III)		
24 Asclepi (IV)		
25 Atlas (I)		
26 Autolycus (I)		
27 Azophi (IV)	48 Bode (II)	69 Capuanus (III)
28 Baco (IV)	49 Bohnenberger (IV)	70 Cardanus (II)
29 Bailly (III)	50 G. Bond (I)	71 Carpenter (II)
30 Ball (III)	51 W. Bond (II)	72 Cassini (I)
31 Barocius (IV)	52 Bonpland (III)	73 Catharina (IV)
32 Barrow (I)	53 Borda (IV)	74 Cavalerius (II)
33 Bayer (III)	54 Boscovich (I)	75 Cavendish (III)
34 Beaumont (IV)	55 Bouguer (II)	76 Celsius (IV)
35 Bernouilli (I)	56 Boussingault (IV)	77 Cepheus (I)
36 Berosus (I)	57 Brayley (II)	78 Chacornac (I)
37 Berzelius (I)	58 Briggs (II)	79 Cichus (III)
38 Bessarian (II)	59 Buch (IV)	80 Clairaut (IV)

Index of Moon's Craters

Maria ★ Oceans, Seas, Lakes & Channels

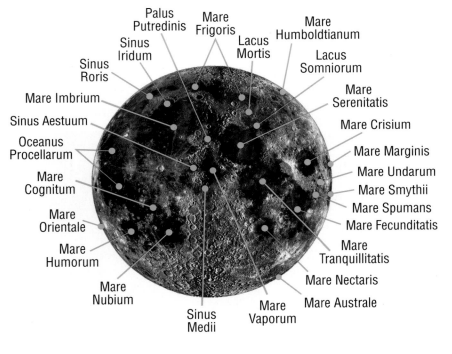

Moon Craters

Index of Moon's Craters

Mountain Ranges & Associated Features

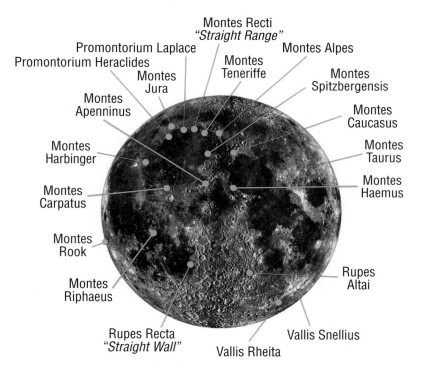

Montes Recti "Straight Range"
Promontorium Laplace
Promontorium Heraclides
Montes Jura
Montes Teneriffe
Montes Alpes
Montes Spitzbergensis
Montes Apenninus
Montes Caucasus
Montes Harbinger
Montes Taurus
Montes Carpatus
Montes Haemus
Montes Rook
Rupes Altai
Montes Riphaeus
Rupes Recta "Straight Wall"
Vallis Rheita
Vallis Snellius

Moon Craters

Index of Moon's Craters

Moon Craters

108

Lunar Surface Elevations

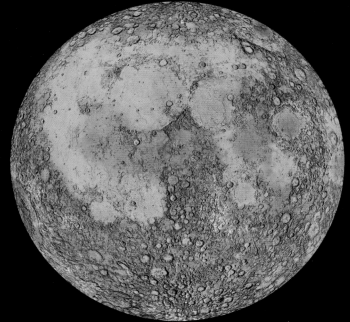

HIGHEST
ELEVATION

LOWEST
ELEVATION

Color-coded elevation maps of the Moon. The difference in elevation from the lowest point on the Moon to the highest is 11 miles (18 km). Both of these points are found on the far side (below).

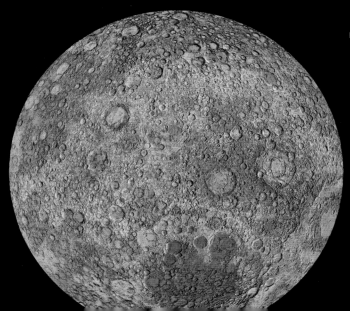

Six Apollo Lunar Missions

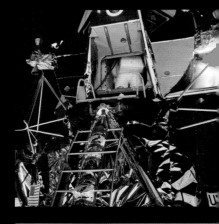

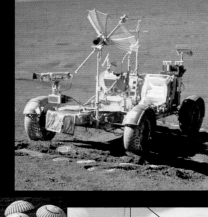

The 364-feet tall Saturn V rockets launched three astronauts on a 4½ day journey to the Moon (see landing locations and crew names on the next page). The Command & Service Modules orbited the Moon with one astronaut aboard while two descended to the surface in the Lunar Module, with stays that lasted 21.6 to 75 hours. The Lunar Roving Vehicle was used on missions 15, 16 & 17 traveling as far as 4.7 miles from the landing site. Only the Command Modules returned to Earth, splashing into an ocean, slowed by three parachutes.

Index of Moon's Craters

Moon Craters

Apollo Lunar Landings 1969 to 1972

Apollo 14
February 5, 1971

Apollo 12
November 19, 1969

Apollo 15
July 30, 1971

Apollo 17
December 11, 1972

Apollo 11
July 20, 1969

Apollo 16
April 21, 1972

MISSION CREWS

Apollo 11	Neil Armstrong[1] Edwin Aldrin *Michael Collins[2]*	Apollo 15	David Scott[1] James Irwin *Alfred Worden[2]*
Apollo 12	Charles Conrad[1] Alan Bean *Richard Gordon[2]*	Apollo 16	John Young[1] Charles Duke *Thomas Mattingly[2]*
Apollo 14	Alan Shepard[1] Edgar Mitchell *Stuart Roosa[2]*	Apollo 17	Eugene Cernan[1] Harrison Schmitt *Ronald Evans[2]*

Apollo 13 Mission aborted en route to Moon because an oxygen tank ruptured. Crewed by James Lovell[1], Fred Haise & John Swigert.

---

[1]Commander. [2]Remained aboard Command Module orbiting Moon.

Moon's Craters

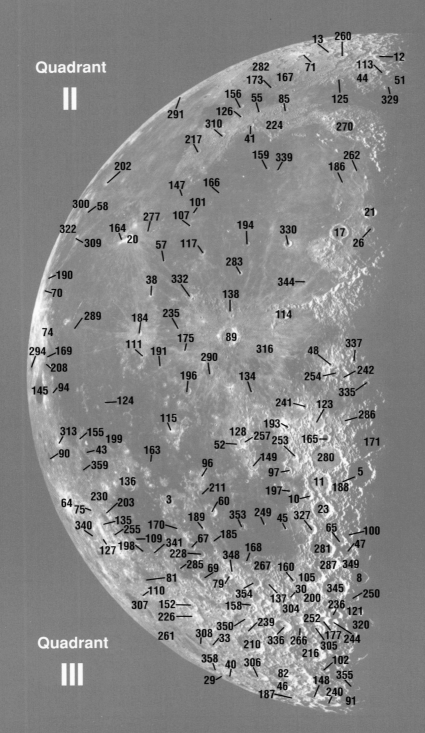

Quadrant II

Quadrant III

Moon's Craters

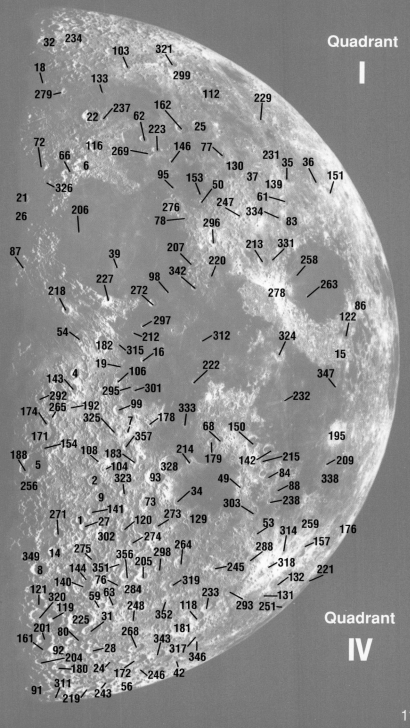

Quadrant
I

Quadrant
IV

Our Moon

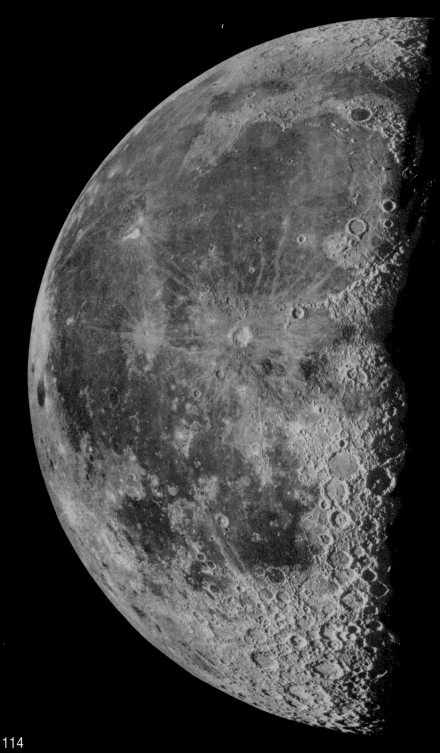

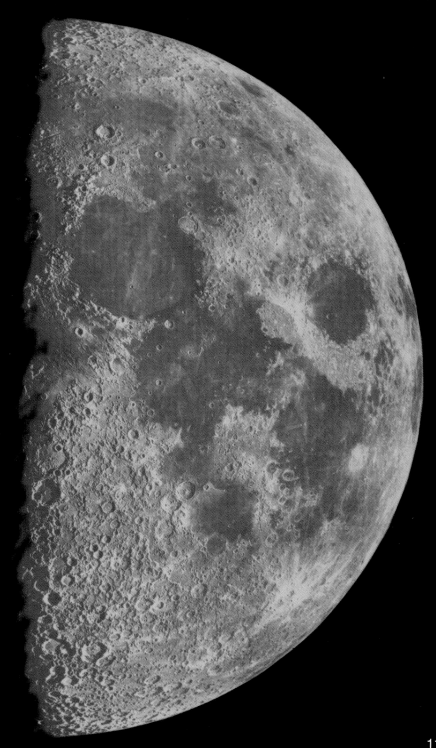

Phases of the Moon 2000 – 2003

Date of Phase Based on Mountain Standard Time

2000	NEW MOON ○	FIRST QTR ◗	FULL MOON ●	LAST QTR ◖
JAN	6	14	❶20	28
FEB	5	12	19	26
MAR	5	12	19	27
APR	4	11	18	26
MAY	3	10	18	26
JUN	2	8	16	24
JUL	1&30❺	8	❶16	24
AUG	29	6	14	22
SEP	27	5	13[1]	20
OCT	27	5	13	20
NOV	25	4	11	18
DEC	❺25	3	11	17

2002	NEW MOON ○	FIRST QTR ◗	FULL MOON ●	LAST QTR ◖
JAN	13	21	28	5
FEB	12	20	27	4
MAR	13	21	28	5
APR	12	20	26	4
MAY	12	19	26	4
JUN	❺10	17	24	2
JUL	10	16	24	2
AUG	8	15	22	1&30
SEP	6	13	21[1]	29
OCT	6	12	21	28
NOV	4	11	19	27
DEC	4	11	19	26

2001	NEW MOON ○	FIRST QTR ◗	FULL MOON ●	LAST QTR ◖
JAN	24	2	9	16
FEB	23	1	8	14
MAR	24	2	9	16
APR	23	1&30	7	15
MAY	22	29	7	15
JUN	21	27	5	13
JUL	20	27	❶5	13
AUG	18	25	3	12
SEP	17	24	2	10
OCT	16	23	2[1]&31[2]	9
NOV	14	22	30	8
DEC	❺14	22	30	7

2003	NEW MOON ○	FIRST QTR ◗	FULL MOON ●	LAST QTR ◖
JAN	2	10	19	25
FEB	1	9	18	23
MAR	2	11	16	24
APR	1	9	18	23
MAY	1&30❺	9	❶15	22
JUN	29	7	14	21
JUL	29	6	13	21
AUG	27	5	11	19
SEP	25	3	10[1]	18
OCT	25	2&31	10	18
NOV	23	30	❶8	16
DEC	23	30	8	16

[1] Harvest Moon. [2] Blue Moon month.
❺ Solar Eclipse. ❶ Lunar Eclipse. *For time and location, see pages 232 to 236.*

Phases of the Moon 2004 – 2007

Date of Phase Based on Mountain Standard Time

		NEW MOON ○	FIRST QTR ◐	FULL MOON ●	LAST QTR ◑
2004	JAN	21	28	7	14
	FEB	20	27	6	13
	MAR	20	28	6	13
	APR	19	27	5	11
	MAY	18	27	4	11
	JUN	17	25	2	9
	JUL	17	24	2&31[2]	9
	AUG	15	23	29	7
	SEP	14	21	28[1]	6
	OCT	13	20	●27	6
	NOV	12	18	26	4
	DEC	11	18	26	4

		NEW MOON ○	FIRST QTR ◐	FULL MOON ●	LAST QTR ◑
2006	JAN	29	6	14	22
	FEB	27	4	12	21
	MAR	29	6	●14	22
	APR	27	5	13	20
	MAY	26	4	13	20
	JUN	25	3	11	18
	JUL	24	3	10	17
	AUG	23	2&31	9	15
	SEP	22	30	7	14
	OCT	21	29	6[1]	13
	NOV	20	27	5	12
	DEC	20	27	4	12

		NEW MOON ○	FIRST QTR ◐	FULL MOON ●	LAST QTR ◑
2005	JAN	10	16	25	3
	FEB	8	15	23	2
	MAR	10	17	25	3
	APR	☉8	16	24	1&30
	MAY	8	16	23	30
	JUN	6	14	21	28
	JUL	6	14	21	27
	AUG	4	12	19	26
	SEP	3	11	17[1]	24
	OCT	3	10	●17	24
	NOV	1	8	15	23
	DEC	1&31	8	15	23

		NEW MOON ○	FIRST QTR ◐	FULL MOON ●	LAST QTR ◑
2007	JAN	18	25	3	11
	FEB	17	24	1	10
	MAR	18	25	●3	11
	APR	17	23	2	10
	MAY	16	23	2&31[2]	9
	JUN	14	22	30	8
	JUL	14	21	30	7
	AUG	12	20	●28	5
	SEP	11	19	26[1]	3
	OCT	10	19	25	3
	NOV	9	17	24	1
	DEC	9	17	23	1&31

[1]Harvest Moon. [2]Blue Moon month.
☉Solar Eclipse. ●Lunar Eclipse. *For time and location, see pages 232 to 236.*

Moon Phases

Phases of the Moon 2008 – 2011

Date of Phase Based on Mountain Standard Time

		NEW MOON ○	FIRST QTR ◗	FULL MOON ●	LAST QTR ◖
2008	**JAN**	8	15	22	29
	FEB	6	13	❶20	28
	MAR	7	14	21	29
	APR	5	12	20	28
	MAY	5	11	19	27
	JUN	3	10	18	26
	JUL	2	9	18	25
	AUG	1&30	8	16	23
	SEP	29	7	15[1]	21
	OCT	28	7	14	21
	NOV	27	5	12	19
	DEC	27	5	12	19

		NEW MOON ○	FIRST QTR ◗	FULL MOON ●	LAST QTR ◖
2010	**JAN**	15	23	29	7
	FEB	13	21	28	5
	MAR	15	23	29	7
	APR	14	21	28	6
	MAY	13	20	27	5
	JUN	12	18	❶26	4
	JUL	11	18	25	4
	AUG	9	16	24	2
	SEP	8	14	23[1]	1&30
	OCT	7	14	22	30
	NOV	5	13	21	28
	DEC	5	13	❶21	28

		NEW MOON ○	FIRST QTR ◗	FULL MOON ●	LAST QTR ◖
2009	**JAN**	26	4	10	17
	FEB	24	2	9	16
	MAR	26	4	10	18
	APR	24	2	9	17
	MAY	24	1&30	8	17
	JUN	22	29	7	15
	JUL	❸21	28	7	15
	AUG	20	27	5	13
	SEP	18	25	4	11
	OCT	17	25	3[1]	11
	NOV	16	24	2	9
	DEC	16	24	2&31[2]	8

		NEW MOON ○	FIRST QTR ◗	FULL MOON ●	LAST QTR ◖
2011	**JAN**	4	12	19	26
	FEB	2	11	18	24
	MAR	4	12	19	26
	APR	3	11	17	24
	MAY	2	10	17	24
	JUN	1	8	15	23
	JUL	1&30	7	14	22
	AUG	28	6	13	21
	SEP	27	4	12[1]	20
	OCT	26	3	11	19
	NOV	24	2	10	18
	DEC	24	2&31	❶10	17

[1]Harvest Moon. [2]Blue Moon month.
❸Solar Eclipse. ❶Lunar Eclipse. *For time and location, see pages 232 to 236.*

Moon Phases

Phases of the Moon 2012 – 2015

Date of Phase Based on Mountain Standard Time

	NEW MOON ○	FIRST QTR ◐	FULL MOON ●	LAST QTR ◑
2012 JAN	23	30	9	16
FEB	21	29	7	14
MAR	22	30	8	14
APR	21	29	6	13
MAY	S20	28	5	12
JUN	19	26	L4	11
JUL	18	26	3	10
AUG	17	24	1&31[2]	9
SEP	15	22	29[1]	8
OCT	15	21	29	8
NOV	13	20	L28	6
DEC	13	19	28	6

	NEW MOON ○	FIRST QTR ◐	FULL MOON ●	LAST QTR ◑
2013 JAN	11	18	26	4
FEB	10	17	25	3
MAR	11	2&31	27	4
APR	10	19	25	2
MAY	S9	17	24	2&31
JUN	8	18	23	29
JUL	8	15	22	29
AUG	6	14	20	28
SEP	5	12	19[1]	26
OCT	4	11	18	26
NOV	3	9	17	25
DEC	2	9	17	25

	NEW MOON ○	FIRST QTR ◐	FULL MOON ●	LAST QTR ◑
2014 JAN	1&30	7	15	23
FEB	—	6	14	22
MAR	1&30	8	16	23
APR	28	7	L15[3]	22
MAY	28	6	14	21
JUN	27	5	12	19
JUL	26	5	12	18
AUG	25	3	10	17
SEP	23	2	8[1]	15
OCT	S23	1&30	L8	15
NOV	22	29	6	14
DEC	21	28	6	14

	NEW MOON ○	FIRST QTR ◐	FULL MOON ●	LAST QTR ◑
2015 JAN	20	26	4	13
FEB	18	25	3	11
MAR	20	27	5	13
APR	18	25	L4	11
MAY	17	25	3	11
JUN	16	24	2	9
JUL	15	23	1&31[2]	8
AUG	14	22	29	6
SEP	12	21	L27[1]	5
OCT	12	20	27	4
NOV	11	18	25	3
DEC	11	18	25	3

[1]Harvest Moon. [2]Blue Moon month. [3]Lunar Eclipse occurs at Midnight on April 14.
S Solar Eclipse. L Lunar Eclipse. *For time and location, see pages 232 to 236.*

Moon Phases

Phases of the Moon 2016 – 2019

Date of Phase Based on Mountain Standard Time

		NEW MOON ○	FIRST QTR ◑	FULL MOON ●	LAST QTR ◐
2016	JAN	9	16	23	1&31
	FEB	☉ 8	15	22	—
	MAR	8	15	23	1&31
	APR	7	13	21	29
	MAY	6	13	21	29
	JUN	4	12	20	27
	JUL	4	11	19	26
	AUG	2	10	18	24
	SEP	1&30	9	16[1]	23
	OCT	30	8	15	22
	NOV	29	7	14	21
	DEC	28	7	13	20

		NEW MOON ○	FIRST QTR ◑	FULL MOON ●	LAST QTR ◐
2017	JAN	27	5	12	19
	FEB	26	3	☾ 10	18
	MAR	27	5	12	20
	APR	26	2	10	19
	MAY	25	2	10	18
	JUN	23	1&30	9	17
	JUL	23	30	8	16
	AUG	☉ 21	29	7	14
	SEP	19	27	6	12
	OCT	19	27	5[1]	12
	NOV	18	26	3	10
	DEC	17	26	3	10

		NEW MOON ○	FIRST QTR ◑	FULL MOON ●	LAST QTR ◐
2018	JAN	16	24	1&31[2] ☾	8
	FEB	15	23	—	7
	MAR	17	24	1&31[2]	9
	APR	15	22	29	8
	MAY	15	21	29	7
	JUN	13	20	27	6
	JUL	12	19	27	6
	AUG	11	18	26	4
	SEP	9	16	24[1]	2
	OCT	8	16	24	2&31
	NOV	7	15	22	29
	DEC	7	15	22	29

		NEW MOON ○	FIRST QTR ◑	FULL MOON ●	LAST QTR ◐
2019	JAN	5	13	☾ 20	27
	FEB	4	12	19	26
	MAR	6	14	20	27
	APR	5	12	18	26
	MAY	4	11	17	26
	JUN	3	9	17	25
	JUL	2&31	9	16	24
	AUG	30	7	15	23
	SEP	28	5	13[1]	21
	OCT	27	5	13	21
	NOV	26	4	12	19
	DEC	25	4	11	18

[1] Harvest Moon. [2] Blue Moon month.
☉ Solar Eclipse. ☾ Lunar Eclipse. *For time and location, see pages 232 to 236.*

Phases of the Moon 2020 – 2023

Date of Phase Based on Mountain Standard Time

		NEW MOON ○	FIRST QTR ◗	FULL MOON ●	LAST QTR ◖
2020	JAN	23	2	10	17
	FEB	24	1	9	15
	MAR	24	2	9	16
	APR	22	1&30	7	14
	MAY	22	29	7	14
	JUN	20	28	5	12
	JUL	20	27	4	12
	AUG	18	25	3	11
	SEP	17	23	1	10
	OCT	16	23	1^1&31^2	9
	NOV	14	21	30	8
	DEC	14	21	29	7
2021	JAN	12	20	28	6
	FEB	11	19	27	4
	MAR	13	21	28	5
	APR	11	20	26	4
	MAY	11	19	◐26	3
	JUN	◉10	17	24	2
	JUL	9	17	23	1&31
	AUG	8	15	22	30
	SEP	6	13	20^1	28
	OCT	6	12	20	28
	NOV	4	11	◐19	27
	DEC	4	10	18	26

		NEW MOON ○	FIRST QTR ◗	FULL MOON ●	LAST QTR ◖
2022	JAN	2&31	9	17	25
	FEB	—	8	16	23
	MAR	2&31	10	18	24
	APR	30	8	16	23
	MAY	30	8	◐15	22
	JUN	28	7	14	20
	JUL	28	6	13	20
	AUG	27	5	11	18
	SEP	25	3	10^1	17
	OCT	25	2&31	9	17
	NOV	23	30	◐8	16
	DEC	23	29	7	16
2023	JAN	21	28	6	14
	FEB	20	27	5	13
	MAR	21	28	7	14
	APR	19	27	5	13
	MAY	19	27	5	12
	JUN	17	26	3	10
	JUL	17	25	3	9
	AUG	16	24	1&30	8
	SEP	14	22	29^1	6
	OCT	◉14	21	28	6
	NOV	13	20	27	5
	DEC	12	19	26	4

Moon Phases

[1] Harvest Moon. [2] Blue Moon month.
◉ Solar Eclipse. ◐ Lunar Eclipse. *For time and location, see pages 232 to 236.*

Phases of the Moon 2024 – 2027

Date of Phase Based on Mountain Standard Time

	NEW MOON ○	FIRST QTR ◐	FULL MOON ●	LAST QTR ◑
2024 JAN	11	17	25	3
FEB	9	16	24	1
MAR	20	16	◐ 25[3]	3
APR	⑤ 8	15	23	1
MAY	7	15	22	1&30
JUN	6	13	21	28
JUL	5	13	21	27
AUG	2	12	19	26
SEP	2	10	17[1]	24
OCT	⑤ 2	10	17	24
NOV	1&30	8	15	22
DEC	30	8	15	22

	NEW MOON ○	FIRST QTR ◐	FULL MOON ●	LAST QTR ◑
2025 JAN	29	6	13	21
FEB	27	5	12	20
MAR	29	6	◐ 13	22
APR	29	4	12	20
MAY	26	4	12	20
JUN	25	2	11	17
JUL	24	2	10	18
AUG	22	1&30	9	15
SEP	21	29	7	14
OCT	21	29	6[1]	13
NOV	20	27	5	11
DEC	19	27	4	11

	NEW MOON ○	FIRST QTR ◐	FULL MOON ●	LAST QTR ◑
2026 JAN	18	25	3	10
FEB	17	24	1	9
MAR	18	25	◐ 3	11
APR	17	23	1	9
MAY	16	23	1[1]&31[2]	9
JUN	14	21	29	8
JUL	14	21	29	7
AUG	⑤ 12	18	◐ 27	5
SEP	10	3	26[1]	4
OCT	10	18	25	3
NOV	9	17	24	1&31
DEC	8	16	23	30

	NEW MOON ○	FIRST QTR ◐	FULL MOON ●	LAST QTR ◑
2027 JAN	7	15	22	29
FEB	6	14	20	27
MAR	8	15	22	29
APR	6	13	20	28
MAY	6	12	20	28
JUN	4	11	18	26
JUL	3	10	18	26
AUG	2&31	8	17	24
SEP	29	7	15[1]	23
OCT	29	7	15	22
NOV	27	6	13	20
DEC	27	5	13	20

Moon Phases

[1] Harvest Moon. [2] Blue Moon month. [3] Lunar Eclipse occurs at Midnight on March 24.
⑤ Solar Eclipse. ◐ Lunar Eclipse. *For time and location, see pages 232 to 236.*

Facing page. *The solitude of the Moon comes across in this Apollo 17 picture.* 123

Phases of the Moon 2028 – 2031

Date of Phase Based on Mountain Standard Time

2028	NEW MOON ○	FIRST QTR ◑	FULL MOON ●	LAST QTR ◐
JAN	⑤ 26	4	ⓛ 11	18
FEB	25	3	10	17
MAR	25	4	10	17
APR	24	2	9	16
MAY	24	1&31	8	16
JUN	22	29	6	14
JUL	21	28	6	14
AUG	20	26	5	13
SEP	18	25	3	11
OCT	17	24	3[1]	11
NOV	16	23	2	9
DEC	15	23	1&31[2] ⓛ	8

2029	NEW MOON	FIRST QTR	FULL MOON	LAST QTR
JAN	⑤ 14	22	29	7
FEB	13	21	28	5
MAR	14	23	29	7
APR	13	21	28	5
MAY	13	20	27	5
JUN	⑤ 11	19	ⓛ 25	3
JUL	11	18	25	3
AUG	9	16	23	2&31
SEP	8	14	22[1]	30
OCT	7	14	22	30
NOV	5	12	20	28
DEC	5	12	20	28

2030	NEW MOON ○	FIRST QTR ◑	FULL MOON ●	LAST QTR ◐
JAN	3	11	19	26
FEB	2	10	17	24
MAR	3	12	19	26
APR	2	10	17	24
MAY	2&31	10	17	23
JUN	30	8	15	22
JUL	30	8	14	22
AUG	28	6	13	20
SEP	27	4	11[1]	19
OCT	26	3	11	19
NOV	24	2	11	18
DEC	24	1&31	ⓛ 9	19

2031	NEW MOON	FIRST QTR	FULL MOON	LAST QTR
JAN	22	30	8	16
FEB	21	28	7	14
MAR	22	30	8	15
APR	21	29	7	14
MAY	21	29	6	13
JUN	19	27	5	11
JUL	19	27	4	11
AUG	17	25	2	9
SEP	16	23	1&31[1&2]	8
OCT	16	23	30	8
NOV	⑤ 14	21	28	7
DEC	14	20	28	6

[1] Harvest Moon. [2] Blue Moon month.
⑤ Solar Eclipse. ⓛ Lunar Eclipse. *For time and location, see pages 232 to 236.*

Phases of the Moon 2032 – 2035

Date of Phase Based on Mountain Standard Time

		NEW MOON ○	FIRST QTR ◐	FULL MOON ●	LAST QTR ◑
2032	**JAN**	12	19	27	5
	FEB	10	17	26	4
	MAR	11	18	26	4
	APR	9	17	❶25	3
	MAY	9	17	24	2&31
	JUN	7	15	23	29
	JUL	7	15	22	29
	AUG	5	14	20	27
	SEP	4	12	19[1]	26
	OCT	4	11	18	25
	NOV	2	10	16	24
	DEC	2	9	16	24
2033	**JAN**	1&30	7	15	23
	FEB	—	6	14	22
	MAR	1&30 ❸	7	15	23
	APR	28	6	14	22
	MAY	28	5	14	21
	JUN	26	4	12	19
	JUL	26	4	12	18
	AUG	24	3	10	17
	SEP	23	1	8[1]	15
	OCT	23	1&30	❶8	14
	NOV	21	29	6	13
	DEC	21	29	6	13

		NEW MOON ○	FIRST QTR ◐	FULL MOON ●	LAST QTR ◑
2034	**JAN**	20	27	4	12
	FEB	18	25	3	11
	MAR	20	26	4	12
	APR	18	25	3	11
	MAY	17	24	3	11
	JUN	16	23	1	8
	JUL	15	23	1&30[2]	9
	AUG	13	21	29	6
	SEP	12	20	27[1]	5
	OCT	12	20	27	4
	NOV	10	18	25	2
	DEC	10	18	25	2
2035	**JAN**	9	16	23	1&30
	FEB	8	15	22	—
	MAR	9	16	23	1&31
	APR	8	14	22	30
	MAY	7	14	21	30
	JUN	5	12	20	28
	JUL	5	12	20	27
	AUG	3	10	❶18[1]	26
	SEP	❸1	9	17	24
	OCT	1&30	9	16	23
	NOV	29	7	15	21
	DEC	29	7	14	21

[1]Harvest Moon. [2]Blue Moon month.
❸Solar Eclipse. ❶Lunar Eclipse. *For time and location, see pages 232 to 236.*

Moon Phases

Phases of the Moon 2036 – 2039

Date of Phase Based on Mountain Standard Time

2036	NEW MOON ○	FIRST QTR ☽	FULL MOON ●	LAST QTR ☾
JAN	28	6	13	21
FEB	26	5	11	18
MAR	27	5	12	19
APR	26	3	10	18
MAY	25	2	10	18
JUN	23	1&30	8	16
JUL	23	29	8	16
AUG	Ⓢ21	28	Ⓛ6	14
SEP	19	26	5	13
OCT	19	26	5[1]	12
NOV	17	25	3	10
DEC	17	25	3	10

2038	NEW MOON ○	FIRST QTR ☽	FULL MOON ●	LAST QTR ☾
JAN	Ⓢ5	13	20	27
FEB	3	12	19	26
MAR	5	13	20	27
APR	4	12	19	25
MAY	4	11	18	25
JUN	2	10	16	24
JUL	Ⓢ2&31	9	16	23
AUG	30	7	14	22
SEP	28	5	13[1]	21
OCT	27	5	12	21
NOV	26	3	11	19
DEC	25	3	11	19

2037	NEW MOON ○	FIRST QTR ☽	FULL MOON ●	LAST QTR ☾
JAN	16	24	1&31 Ⓛ	8
FEB	14	22	—	6
MAR	16	24	1&31	8
APR	15	22	29	7
MAY	14	22	28	6
JUN	13	20	27	5
JUL	12	19	Ⓛ26	5
AUG	11	17	25	4
SEP	9	16	24[1]	2
OCT	8	15	23	2&31
NOV	7	14	22	29
DEC	6	14	22	29

2039	NEW MOON ○	FIRST QTR ☽	FULL MOON ●	LAST QTR ☾
JAN	24	2&31	10	17
FEB	22	—	8	15
MAR	24	2	10	17
APR	23	1	8	15
MAY	22	1&30	8	14
JUN	Ⓢ21	29	6	13
JUL	21	28	5	12
AUG	19	26	4	11
SEP	18	24	2	10
OCT	17	24	2[1]&31[2]	10
NOV	15	22	Ⓛ30	8
DEC	15	22	30	8

[1] Harvest Moon. [2] Blue Moon month.
Ⓢ Solar Eclipse. Ⓛ Lunar Eclipse. *For time and location, see pages 232 to 236.*

Phases of the Moon 2040 – 2043

Date of Phase Based on Mountain Standard Time

2040	NEW MOON ○	FIRST QTR ◐	FULL MOON ●	LAST QTR ◑
JAN	13	20	29	7
FEB	12	19	27	5
MAR	12	20	28	6
APR	11	19	26	4
MAY	10	19	❶26	3
JUN	9	17	24	1
JUL	9	17	23	1&30
AUG	9	15	22	29
SEP	6	13	20[1]	27
OCT	5	13	19	27
NOV	⑤4	11	18	26
DEC	4	10	18	26

2042	NEW MOON ○	FIRST QTR ◐	FULL MOON ●	LAST QTR ◑
JAN	21	28	6	14
FEB	20	26	4	13
MAR	21	28	6	14
APR	⑤19	26	❶5	13
MAY	19	26	4	12
JUN	17	25	2	10
JUL	16	24	3	11
AUG	15	23	1&30	8
SEP	14	22	29[1]	6
OCT	13	21	28	7
NOV	12	20	26	4
DEC	12	19	26	4

2041	NEW MOON ○	FIRST QTR ◐	FULL MOON ●	LAST QTR ◑
JAN	2&31	9	17	25
FEB	—	7	15	23
MAR	2&31	9	17	25
APR	30	8	16	23
MAY	29	7	❶15	22
JUN	28	6	14	20
JUL	27	6	13	20
AUG	26	4	11	18
SEP	25	3	10[1]	16
OCT	⑤24	2	9	16
NOV	23	1&30	❶7	15
DEC	23	29	7	15

2043	NEW MOON ○	FIRST QTR ◐	FULL MOON ●	LAST QTR ◑
JAN	10	18	24	2
FEB	9	16	23	1
MAR	11	17	❶25	3
APR	⑤9	16	24	2
MAY	8	15	23	2&31
JUN	7	14	22	29
JUL	6	13	21	29
AUG	4	12	20	27
SEP	3	11	❶18[1]	25
OCT	2	11	18	24
NOV	1	11	16	23
DEC	1&31	9	16	22

Moon Phases

[1]Harvest Moon. [2]Blue Moon month.
⑤Solar Eclipse. ❶Lunar Eclipse. *For time and location, see pages 232 to 236.*

Phases of the Moon 2044 – 2047

Date of Phase Based on Mountain Standard Time

		NEW MOON ○	FIRST QTR ◗	FULL MOON ●	LAST QTR ◖
2044	JAN	29	7	14	21
	FEB	28	6	12	20
	MAR	29	6	13	21
	APR	27	4	12	20
	MAY	26	4	13	19
	JUN	25	2	10	18
	JUL	24	1&31	9	17
	AUG	Ⓢ 22	30	8	16
	SEP	21	29	● 7	14
	OCT	20	28	7[1]	13
	NOV	19	27	5	12
	DEC	19	27	4	11
2045	JAN	17	25	3	9
	FEB	Ⓢ 16	24	1	8
	MAR	18	25	3	10
	APR	17	24	30	9
	MAY	16	23	30	8
	JUN	14	21	29	7
	JUL	14	20	28	7
	AUG	Ⓢ 12	19	27	5
	SEP	10	17	25[1]	4
	OCT	10	17	25	3
	NOV	8	16	24	1
	DEC	8	16	23	1&30
2046	JAN	6	15	22	28
	FEB	Ⓢ 5	13	20	27
	MAR	7	15	22	29
	APR	6	13	20	27
	MAY	5	13	19	27
	JUN	4	11	18	26
	JUL	3	10	● 17	25
	AUG	2&31	8	16	24
	SEP	29	7	14[1]	23
	OCT	29	6	14	22
	NOV	27	5	13	20
	DEC	27	5	13	20
2047	JAN	25	3	● 11	18
	FEB	24	2	10	16
	MAR	26	4	11	18
	APR	24	3	10	16
	MAY	24	2	9	16
	JUN	23	1&30	7	15
	JUL	22	29	● 7	14
	AUG	21	27	5	13
	SEP	19	26	4	12
	OCT	18	25	3[1]	11
	NOV	17	24	2	10
	DEC	16	23	2&31[2] ●	10

[1] Harvest Moon. [2] Blue Moon month.
Ⓢ Solar Eclipse. ● Lunar Eclipse. *For time and location, see pages 232 to 236.*

Phases of the Moon 2048 – 2051

Date of Phase Based on Mountain Standard Time

2048	NEW MOON ○	FIRST QTR ◗	FULL MOON ●	LAST QTR ◖
JAN	15	22	30	8
FEB	13	21	29	6
MAR	14	22	29	7
APR	12	21	28	5
MAY	12	20	27	4
JUN	⑤11	19	●25	3
JUL	10	18	25	2
AUG	9	16	23	1&31
SEP	7	14	21[1]	29
OCT	7	14	21	29
NOV	5	12	20	28
DEC	5	12	●19	28

2049	NEW MOON ○	FIRST QTR ◗	FULL MOON ●	LAST QTR ◖
JAN	3	10	18	26
FEB	2	9	17	25
MAR	3	11	19	26
APR	2	10	17	24
MAY	1&31⑤	9	17	23
JUN	29	8	15	22
JUL	29	8	14	21
AUG	28	6	13	20
SEP	26	4	11[1]	18
OCT	26	4	10	18
NOV	24	2	9	17
DEC	24	1&31	9	17

2050	NEW MOON ○	FIRST QTR ◗	FULL MOON ●	LAST QTR ◖
JAN	22	29	7	15
FEB	21	28	6	14
MAR	22	29	8	16
APR	21	28	7	14
MAY	20	28	6	13
JUN	19	27	5	11
JUL	18	26	4	11
AUG	17	25	2	9
SEP	15	23	1&30[1,2]	7
OCT	15	23	●29	7
NOV	⑤14	21	28	6
DEC	13	20	27	5

2051	NEW MOON ○	FIRST QTR ◗	FULL MOON ●	LAST QTR ◖
JAN	12	19	26	4
FEB	10	17	25	3
MAR	12	19	27	5
APR	⑤10	17	●25	4
MAY	10	17	25	3
JUN	8	15	23	1
JUL	7	15	23	1&30
AUG	6	14	21	28
SEP	4	13	20[1]	26
OCT	4	12	19	26
NOV	3	11	17	24
DEC	3	10	17	24

[1] Harvest Moon. [2] Blue Moon month.
⑤ Solar Eclipse. ● Lunar Eclipse. *For time and location, see pages 232 to 236.*

Moon Phases

Observing the Planets

Like the Earth, asteroids and comets, the Planets are part of our Solar System, all gravitationally bound to the star that we call the Sun.

In ancient times, the Planets were known as five wandering stars because their true nature was not understood. These "stars" did not stay put like the others and even changed brightness. It took the invention of the telescope in the early 1600s for scientists like Galileo to make observations and conclude that the Planets were companions of Earth and all circled the Sun.

The dawning of the space age in the 1960s opened the doors to our Solar System. Our knowledge of the Planets took off, as exploratory spacecraft encountered every Planet except Pluto. We received unprecedented close-up images of the Planets and their moons, revealing detail that no telescope could approach. For the first time, humankind was seeing the Solar System as it actually existed. Centuries of speculation and conjecture were over.

Then, during the 1990s, astronomers found planets orbiting other stars. It is now known that planets are commonplace. However, the question still begging to be answered is, "Is there life in any of these solar systems?" Answers may be found during the next 50 years.

> **In ancient times, the five Planets were puzzling stars because they did not stay in place like the others but wandered among them.**

Planets

How are planets formed?
Planets form with stars, condensing out of protoplanetary disks. These disks, which have been imaged by the Hubble Space Telescope and are pictured on page 6, are gigantic clouds of hydrogen and other elements, including ices and minerals, that slowly condense by gravity into a star and planets. Our Sun is known as a second-generation star because it contains heavier elements, like gold, that can only be

Facing page. *A beautiful picture of Jupiter that clearly shows the complexity of its cloud belts. Twenty-seven images were captured by the Cassini Orbiter spacecraft on its way to Saturn in December 2000 to form this mosaic. Yes, that giant "eye" is the Great Red Spot which is bigger than Earth.*

Planet Position Terms

created by a supernova explosion of a large star that burned fast. Our Sun's protoplanetary disk contained debris from such explosions.

OBSERVING THE PLANETS: SOME TERMINOLOGY

Elongation. The arc angle distance in the sky that separates a Planet from the Sun. This term is often applied to the Inferior Planets — Mercury and Venus. These Planets are at Greatest Eastern Elongation or Greatest Western Elongation when they appear, from Earth, the farthest away from the Sun. Elongation is a perspective view from the Earth.

Mercury or Venus at Greatest Elongations and Inferior & Superior Conjunction

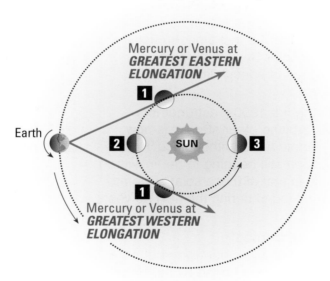

1 **Greatest Eastern or Western Elongation** is the farthest Mercury or Venus appears from the Sun in the sky. See pages 193 to 203.

2 **Inferior Conjunction.** Neither Mercury nor Venus are visible at this time because they are in line with the Sun. Both rise and set with the Sun. Usually these Planets are slightly "above" or "below" the Sun.

3 **Superior Conjunction.** Neither Mercury nor Venus are visible at this time because they are in line with the Sun. Both rise and set with the Sun. Usually these Planets are slightly "above" or "below" the Sun.

Planet Position Terms

Opposition. Refers to the Superior Planets, Mars through Pluto. A Superior Planet is at opposition if it is rising in the east as the Sun is setting; that is, it is on the opposite side of the Earth from the Sun. The Superior Planets are closest to the Earth at opposition; hence they will appear their largest in a telescope and be at their brightest. Opposition places a Superior Planet at its highest in the sky (near the zenith) around midnight.

The Superior Planets at Opposition

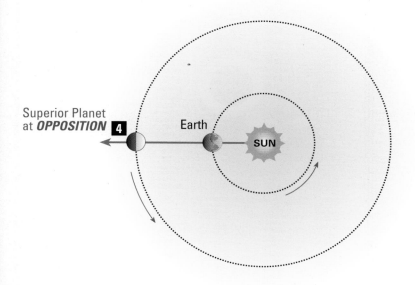

4 The Superior Planets are the Planets Mars through Pluto. These Planets are at opposition when they are directly opposite the Sun from Earth. At opposition, the Planets appear their largest and brightest. They rise in the east as the Sun sets in the west and are overhead at midnight. See pages 189 to 191.

Conjunction. Term often used to indicate when two or more Planets, or a Planet and the Moon appear close to one another in the sky. Conjunctions are beautiful sights, as little can compare to the brilliant glow of Venus standing next to a crescent Moon. Conjunctions are a perspective alignment as viewed from Earth and do not represent the Planet(s) and/or Moon *(Continues on page 136)*

Solar System Comparisons

Comparative Orbit Sizes of Our Nine Planets

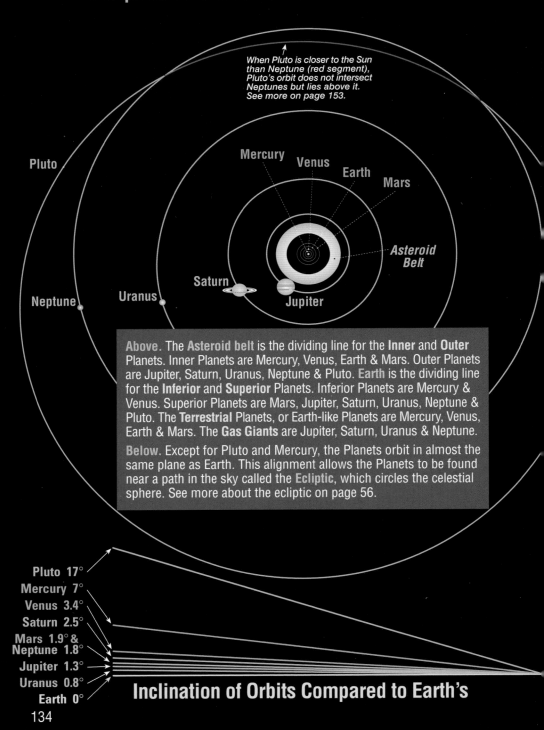

When Pluto is closer to the Sun than Neptune (red segment), Pluto's orbit does not intersect Neptunes but lies above it. See more on page 153.

Pluto

Mercury Venus
Earth
Mars

Asteroid Belt

Neptune Uranus Saturn Jupiter

Above. The Asteroid belt is the dividing line for the **Inner** and **Outer** Planets. Inner Planets are Mercury, Venus, Earth & Mars. Outer Planets are Jupiter, Saturn, Uranus, Neptune & Pluto. **Earth** is the dividing line for the **Inferior** and **Superior** Planets. Inferior Planets are Mercury & Venus. Superior Planets are Mars, Jupiter, Saturn, Uranus, Neptune & Pluto. The **Terrestrial** Planets, or Earth-like Planets are Mercury, Venus, Earth & Mars. The **Gas Giants** are Jupiter, Saturn, Uranus & Neptune.

Below. Except for Pluto and Mercury, the Planets orbit in almost the same plane as Earth. This alignment allows the Planets to be found near a path in the sky called the **Ecliptic**, which circles the celestial sphere. See more about the ecliptic on page 56.

Pluto 17°
Mercury 7°
Venus 3.4°
Saturn 2.5°
Mars 1.9° &
Neptune 1.8°
Jupiter 1.3°
Uranus 0.8°
Earth 0°

Inclination of Orbits Compared to Earth's

Solar System Comparisons

Sun

Prominence

Pictured here is what the Sun looks like when viewed through a special narrow-band, hydrogen-alpha filter which allows prominences to be seen. See more on page 223.

Our Moon's orbit

Comparative sizes of the Sun and Planets

Mercury

Venus

Earth

Mars

Jupiter

Saturn

Uranus

Neptune

Pluto

QUICK COMPARISON
of Solar System Members

	Distance from Sun Earth=1	Diameter Earth=1	Mass Earth=1	Volume Earth=1
SUN	–	109	333,000	1,300,000
MERCURY	0.4	0.4	0.06	0.06
VENUS	0.7	0.95	0.8	0.9
EARTH	1	1	1	1
MARS	1.5	0.5	0.1	0.15
JUPITER	5.2	11.2	318	1,326
SATURN	9.5	9.5	95	771
URANUS	19	4	15	63
NEPTUNE	30	3.8	17	58
PLUTO	39.5	0.2	0.003	0.006

See page 29 for an expanded table with explanatory notes.

Sunspot complex

Observing Considerations

physically getting close to one another. See listings on pages 205 to 207 and the Glossary for an expanded definition of Conjunction.

Retrograde Motion. An apparent backward movement of the Superior Planets (Mars through Pluto). Normally, these Planets move slowly eastward in the sky (against the stationary background stars) because of their counterclockwise revolutions around the Sun. However, as the Earth "passes" them in their orbits, they appear to travel backwards or westward for several months before resuming their eastward course. This backward, retrograde motion is a perspective view from Earth, and occurs because the Earth travels around the Sun more quickly than the Superior Planets. It is similar to the view seen from one automobile that is passing another.

OBSERVING THE PLANETS: SOME CONSIDERATIONS

Binoculars. Most binoculars will not be useful to view any detail of the Planets, however, with well-focused binoculars, you may be able to see Venus when crescent and the four Galilean moons of Jupiter. Additionally, binoculars are helpful for locating Mercury and Uranus.

Telescope Magnification. Useful magnifications for observing the Planets are from 60x to 300x. Depending on your telescope size, quality of the optics and atmospheric conditions, magnifications from 150x to 300x may not provide good images.

Viewing/Seeing Conditions. Because of changing weather conditions, some nights are just better than others to view the Planets. Observing them as often as possible will increase your chance of encountering good seeing conditions.

However, the best "views" of the Planets generally occur during **moments of clarity** when, for just a instant, you can clearly see details on the Planets. These moments last just a fraction of a second but occur frequently and are the portal to studying the Planets.

Seeing conditions are poor near the horizon because light passes through more atmosphere and turbulence. Through a telescope, Planets near the horizon look like they are bubbling.

No Dark-Adapted Eyes Needed. The Planets are bright enough that dark-adapted eyes are not a requirement for viewing, so the Moon and outdoor lights will not readily interfere with observing them.

Observing Tips

Relative Sizes & Brightness of the Planets

Planet Size/Detail. When I show the Planets to others, a comment I often hear is, "It's pretty small." Don't expect any of the Planets to appear large in smaller telescopes. The amount of detail will also be limited. However, through repetitive viewing, the occasional crystal clear night, moments of clarity and familiarity, you will be able to see much more than you think.

Planet Comparisons

1. Relative Sizes of the Planets at 100x Magnification
Smallest & Largest Appearances

MERCURY VENUS MARS JUPITER SATURN URANUS NEPTUNE PLUTO

MOON
30' or 1800"

⊢⊣ *20 Arc Angle Seconds*

2. Arc Angle Sizes of Planets in Sky
Smallest & Largest Appearances

Planet	Smallest / Largest Arc Angle Size[1]	Planet	Smallest / Largest Arc Angle Size[1]
MERCURY	5" / 13"	SATURN	15" / 21" (Rings 35"/50")
VENUS	10" / 64"	URANUS	3.4" / 4"
MARS	4" / 25"	NEPTUNE	2.2" / 2.4"
JUPITER	31" / 50"	PLUTO	0.16" / 0.28"

[1]Indicated in arc seconds ("). The Moon extends an arc angle of 1,800" or 30' (minutes) or about 1/2 degree. There are 60 arc seconds in an arc minute and 60 arc minutes in an arc degree. The Planets appear their smallest when they are away from Earth, on the other side of the Sun, and appear their largest near inferior conjunction (for Mercury and Venus) or at opposition (for Mars through Pluto).

3. Magnitude of Planets at their Faintest/Brightest
Corresponds with Smallest & Largest Appearances

Planet	Magnitude	Planet	Magnitude
MERCURY	5/–1.9	SATURN	1.1/–0.4
VENUS	–3.7/–4.6	URANUS	5.9/5.6
MARS	2.3/–2.8	NEPTUNE	8.0/7.6
JUPITER	–1.2/–2.5	PLUTO	15.9/13.7

Observing Mercury

OBSERVING THE PLANETS

THE PLANET MERCURY

 Mercury is the one Planet that is best viewed by eye or with binoculars. It is never far from the Sun — so when it is visible, it is always low in the sky — making it difficult to view its disk through a telescope because of atmosphere turbulence. The farthest it gets from the Sun is about 28°, less than one-third the distance from the horizon to the zenith. For me, the most exciting part about observing Mercury is finding it in the sky.

The little that was known about Mercury before *Mariner 10* visited this Planet in 1974 and 1975 was through telescopic observations made during the day. It is possible to observe, through a telescope, the brighter stars and Planets during the day if you know where to look. During the day, Mercury can more easily be studied in the higher and sometimes steadier sky.

> **WARNING:** Permanent eye damage can result from using binoculars or a telescope near the Sun!
> Use these instruments to find or observe
> Mercury ONLY when the Sun is below the horizon!

Locating Mercury

1 Consult the Mercury at Greatest Elongation tables to find the best observing dates (**bolded entries** on pages 193 to 199). Mercury can only be seen around the time of Greatest Eastern or Western Elongation, when it is farthest from the Sun. And, it cannot be viewed at every elongation. Some elongations place Mercury farther above the horizon than others. Mercury's distance above the horizon varies depending on your latitude, the Sun's inclination to the horizon and where Mercury is in its highly inclined orbit.

2 Start your search for Mercury about one week prior to Greatest Eastern or Western Elongation. Also, the window of opportunity to see Mercury is about one week on either side of the elongation date. Low-lying clouds and an obstructed horizon can easily foil your attempt to locate Mercury.

Observing Mercury & Venus

3 **For Eastern Elongations**, search for Mercury in the evening. Start about 30 minutes after sunset. You will have about 1/2 hour to see Mercury.

4 **For Western Elongations**, search for Mercury in the morning. Start about one hour and fifteen minutes prior to sunrise.

5 Mercury will appear as bright as magnitude –2 above and near the sunrise/sunset point. Since it is visible during twilight, it will most likely be the only visible "star," making it difficult to confuse with anything else. At times Mercury is plainly visible to the naked eye, but more often, you will need *binoculars* to help locate it because it is easily missed unless you are looking *directly* at it. Mercury will be *as much as* a pencil height above the horizon when your arm is fully extended.

Observing Mercury. Since Mercury is always low in the sky where atmospheric turbulence is the greatest, it does not make for good viewing through a telescope where it appears as a bright, bubbling, color-changing spot of light (pretty in its own right). Because of the turbulence, it will be difficult to discern its disk or phase.

THE PLANET VENUS

 One cold, moonless, winter night in Milwaukee, I went outside to look at the stars. Snow covered the back yard and Venus was high and bright. Something that night seemed different. I noticed the shadows of the lilac branches, plainly visible on the snow. Venus was casting shadows!

Venus has the distinction of being the brightest Planet in our sky, reaching magnitude –4.6. It is often referred to as the morning or evening star because it hugs close to the Sun's rising and setting. Since Venus orbits inside Earth's orbit, it also cycles through phases.

In the past, Venus was referred to as Earth's sister Planet because the diameters of the two Planets are almost the same. This connotation vanished when we discovered that Venus is totally inhospitable to life; so much so, that even scientific probes can last only several minutes on its surface. Its atmosphere is 96% carbon dioxide with temperatures soaring over 900° F (482° C). This temperature is more than hot enough to melt lead, zinc or tin. Its atmospheric

Observing Venus & Mars

pressure is 90 times Earth's, equivalent to water pressure at 3,000 feet (915 meters) below sea level. Venus' day is longer than its year, and in comparison to all the other Planets, it rotates on its axis almost upside down.

Locating Venus. Venus is very easy to find in the sky because of its brightness and close proximity to the rising or setting Sun. Reaching magnitude –4.6, Venus easily outshines all the other stars and Planets. See the Planets at Sunrise and Sunset tables (pages 157 to 187) to locate Venus. The Venus at Greatest Elongation tables (pages 201 to 203) provide the dates when Venus appears the farthest from the Sun in the sky.

Observing Venus. With a small telescope (4-inch) and moderate magnifications of 50x to 100x, Venus appears brilliantly white and featureless because of its thick cloud cover. Since this Planet is inside Earth's orbit, it cycles through phases just like the Moon. However, unlike the Moon, it varies in size. Venus is at its largest and brightest when a crescent. This occurs about a month after Greatest Eastern Elongation and a month before Greatest Western Elongation. The crescent phase of Venus can be seen in well-focused binoculars. At Greatest Eastern or Western Elongation, Venus' phase is about half.

THE PLANET MARS

 We identify with Mars more than any other Planet because Mars might have or still may harbor life. In the first half of this century, the United States and other countries will deluge Mars with numerous exploratory vehicles and possibly a manned mission to answer this question. Additionally, Mars is the second most hospitable Planet in the Solar System — the only Planet that humankind might be able to colonize. It has an abundance of frozen water at its North Pole, a major element needed to sustain a colony.

What happened to the canals? Mars never had any canals! During the late 1800s and early 1900s, several astronomers thought they saw a network of lines interlacing the surface of Mars, which became known as "canals." Maps of the canals were even drawn and published. However, no evidence was ever found

Observing Mars

Valles
Marineris

Mars Facts

✦ Next to Earth, Mars is the **most hospitable Planet** in our Solar System

✦ **Temperatures** range from –207° F to 80° F

✦ **Atmosphere** is 95% Carbon Dioxide, 2.7% Nitrogen, 1.6% Argon and 0.2% Oxygen. Carbon Dioxide comprises .03% of Earth's atmosphere. Mars' atmospheric **pressure** is 1/100 of Earth's. **Dust devils** are common as well as the less frequent planet-wide **dust storms**.

✦ **Rotates** on its axis in 24 hours, 37 minutes

✦ **Revolves** around the Sun in 1.9 years or 687 days

✦ **Tilt on its axis** is 25.2° (compared to Earth's 23.4°)

✦ **Gravity** is 1/3 of Earth's

✦ Mars' **moons**, Phobos and Deimos, are most likely **captured asteroids**.

✦ Mars has the **largest inactive volcano** in the Solar System, named Olympus Mons (page 144), and the **longest grand canyon**, Valles Marineris, which is 4 miles deep and stretches 2,500 miles.

✦ Mars' surface, like the Moon's, **appears to be geologically inactive.**

✦ Mars' **north polar cap is made mostly of water ice and its southern polar cap, frozen carbon dioxide or dry ice.**

✦ At one time, Mars had massive quantities of **water** on its surface which may have soaked into the ground.

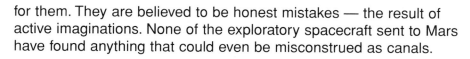

Southern
Polar Cap

for them. They are believed to be honest mistakes — the result of active imaginations. None of the exploratory spacecraft sent to Mars have found anything that could even be misconstrued as canals.

Observing Mars

Locating Mars. Mars is easy to find in the sky near opposition because it is bright and "red" in color, shining steadily around magnitude –2. When Mars is not at opposition, its magnitude and conspicuousness fade to +2. See the Planets at Sunrise and Sunset tables (pages 157 to 187) to locate Mars.

Most Favorable Times to View Mars. Mars is small, so it is best observed around opposition when it is closest to the Earth and appears its largest. **Oppositions** with Mars occur about every 26 months, however, some oppositions bring us much closer to Mars than others because of the elliptical shape of orbits. The distance between Earth and Mars at opposition can vary from 35,000,000 to 63,000,000 miles (56,000,000 to 101,000,000 km). This difference effectively doubles the size of Mars in a telescope. The table below indicates the *most favorable* oppositions from 2000 to 2052 to view Mars. All of Mars' oppositions are listed in the table beginning on page 189.

Best Viewing of Mars ★ When Mars is Largest

These are the dates when Mars is closest to Earth and will appear its largest. The optimal viewing period is from three weeks before to three weeks after these opposition dates. Mars will be at it brightest during these times.

	Date	Arc Angle Size of Mars[1]		Date	Arc Angle Size of Mars[1]
2001	June 13	**21"**	**2033**	June 27	**22"**
2003	August 28	**25"**	**2035**	September 15	**25"**
2005	November 7	**19"**	**2048**	June 3	**19"**
2018	July 26	**24"**	**2050**	August 14	**25"**
2020	October 13	**23"**	**2052**	October 28	**21"**

[1]Indicated in arc seconds ("). See page 137 for a comparison of Planet sizes as they appear in the sky. Magnifications of 150x to 300x are recommended to see the most detail on Mars.

Features on Mars. Although the polar caps and surface coloration can be seen in small telescopes (4-inch to 6-inch), they can be subtle, especially the surface coloration. For this reason, Mars is often disappointing to first-time observers. **So, here are some suggestion to help maximize your viewing of Mars' surface features.**

Observing Mars

1 Try to observe Mars often from one month before to one month after opposition. Repetitive viewing will increase your familiarity with this Planet and increase your chance of observing on a good night. Additionally, you will be able to see the different sides and all of the surface markings on Mars if you observe over a period of time.

2 Use a minimum magnification of 100x, but 200x to 300x is preferable. Achieving higher magnifications is dependent on your telescope and atmospheric conditions.

3 Observe Mars when it is highest in the sky in order to minimize atmospheric disturbance. This will occur around midnight during opposition. It is more difficult to see the surface markings when Mars is low in the sky. The worst part about observing later is staying up or waking up. But, it is worth it. Mars is only at opposition every couple of years.

4 When you are looking at Mars through a telescope, you will notice that there are split-second moments when the view of the surface appears clear. It is during these moments of clarity that the best glimpses will occur. It is a rare night when you can look directly at Mars and plainly see the subtleties of the surface markings for an extended period of time.

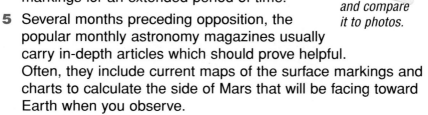

Sketch Mars and compare it to photos.

5 Several months preceding opposition, the popular monthly astronomy magazines usually carry in-depth articles which should prove helpful. Often, they include current maps of the surface markings and charts to calculate the side of Mars that will be facing toward Earth when you observe.

6 If you follow the suggestions above and still cannot see surface markings, here are some possible reasons why. a) Wind storms on Mars could be kicking up dust and obliterating the surface markings. Search the internet to check on Mars' weather. b) Your telescope optics may not be properly aligned. Ask an astronomy club member or a telescope store to check out your telescope. c) The turbulence in Earth's atmosphere may be affecting telescope image quality, so keep trying. d) Finally, remember that if you take your telescope from the warm interior of your home to the cold outside, it will take up to an hour for the telescope optics to cool and settle down. The image of Mars during this time will be blurry. Keep your telescope outside or in an unheated space before observing.

Features on Mars

Longitude centered on **285°**   Longitude centered on **195°**   Longitude centered on **110°**   Longitude centered on **25°**

Rotation ⟶   *Rotation* ⟶   *Rotation* ⟶   *Rotation* ⟶

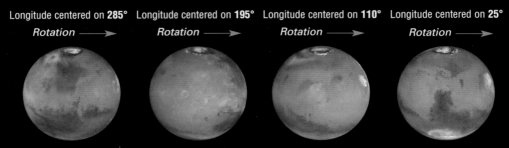

These four photos show the entire surface of Mars, views that can be glimpsed with amateur telescopes. When the North Polar Cap is tilted toward Earth, as shown here, it is easily and clearly visible at the top of Mars. The South Pole is smaller than the North Pole and is not visible in these images. The 25° longitude image shows a whitish area near the southern polar region. This is not the Southern Polar Cap, but a scar, called Hellas, created from a asteroid or cometary impact. Clouds often hang above this depression. The dark appendage above Hellas is named Syrtis Major. Mars' surface colors represent slight differences in the color of its sand and rock and are not a distinction in features as with Earth's Moon. They also change somewhat from planet-wide duststorms that kick up from time to time. *Note: If you use a 90° diagonal with your telescope (see page 90), then the above images will be mirror-reversed and the direction of rotation will be reversed.*

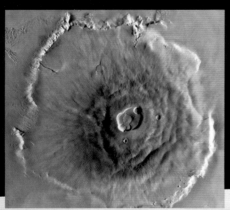

Left. Olympus Mons, the largest inactive volcano in our Solar System (letter A on the next page). The central cauldron rises 15 miles high and measures 56 miles across. The area of the lava flow is the same as the state of Arizona.

Below. A panoramic view from the surface of Mars taken in March 2004 by the rover Spirit at the rim of the crater Bonneville.

Features on Mars

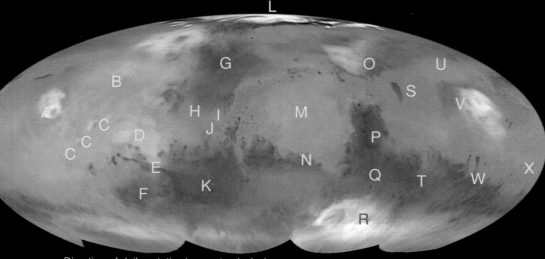

Direction of daily *rotation* is counterclockwise ⟶

Major Surface Features of Mars

A. Clouds atop Mars' highest point and largest volcano, *Olympus Mons*
B. *Arcadia* Plain
C. Chain of three large volcanos
D. *Tharsis* Plain
E. *Valles Marineris* chasm
F. *Solis Lacus*
G. *Mare Acidalium*
H. Landing site of *Viking 1*, 1976
I. Landing site of *Pathfinder*, 1997
J. *Chryse*
K. *Mare Erythraeum*
L. North Pole of Mars
M. Plain of *Arabia*
N. *Sinus Sabaeus*

O. *Utopia*
P. *Syrtis Major* (some report this as being bluish in color)
Q. *Iapygia*
R. *Hellas*, a giant impact crater that is covered with clouds. This is Mars' lowest elevation.
S. *Alcyonius Nodus*
T. Mare *Tyrrhenum*
U. Landing site of *Viking 2*, 1976
V. *Stymphalius Lacus*
W. *Mare Cimmerium*
X. Memmonia Plain

Notes: In the above picture, the South Pole is shrouded in polar clouds. Names of features vary slightly among reference sources.

Moon Comparisons

Pictures are shown to scale, except for Phobos and Deimos.

Mercury is smaller than the moons Ganymede and Titan. Diameter: 3,032 miles.

Our Moon is one of the larger moons in the Solar System. Diameter: 2,160 miles.

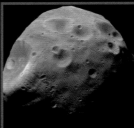

Phobos, the closest moon to Mars is irregular in shape, measuring 17 x 13 miles.

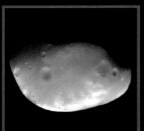

Deimos, the farthest moon from Mars measures 10 x 8 miles.

Io of Jupiter has very active volcanoes. Diameter: 2,255 miles.

Europa of Jupiter may have an ocean under its icy surface. Diameter: 1,950 miles.

Ganymede is Jupiter's and the Solar System's largest moon with a diameter of 3,270 miles.

Callisto of Jupiter is the most distant Galilean moon and has a diameter of 2,980 miles.

Titan of Saturn is the only moon to have an atmosphere. Diameter: 3,200

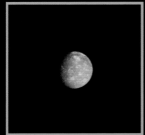

Titania, the largest moon of Uranus has a diameter of exactly 1,000 miles.

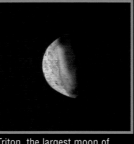

Triton, the largest moon of Neptune has a surface that resembles a cantaloupe. Diameter: 1,678 miles.

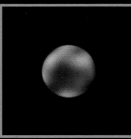

Pluto is smaller than any of the "major" moons, measuring in at 1,433 miles in diameter.

Observing Jupiter

THE PLANET JUPITER

 Jupiter was given its kingly name because it is consistently the brightest Planet in the sky, and unlike Venus, it can be seen throughout the night. It is just a coincidence that Jupiter turned out to be our largest Planet.

Galileo became the first scientist to study this Planet early in 1610. It was his observations of the revolution of Jupiter's four brightest moons that validated the heliocentric or Sun-centered concept of the Solar System. In his honor, these four moons are called the Galilean moons.

Jupiter is the largest of the four Gas Giants, namely Jupiter, Saturn, Uranus and Neptune. The Gas Giants do not have a familiar surface like the Earth and other Terrestrial Planets. They are mainly balls of hydrogen gas, creating enormous pressures that increase with depth, eventually turning the hydrogen into a liquid. And because Jupiter is so large, near its core, the liquid hydrogen is finally compressed to make "solid" metallic hydrogen.

Jupiter is almost synonymous with the Great Red Spot, a giant hurricane-type cloud structure located at the South Equatorial Belt. Its width is about 14,000 miles (22,500 km) and wind speeds top 270 miles/hour (435 km/hour). The "eye" has been a feature of this

Galilean Moons

Moon[1]	Average Distance from Planet[2]	Revolution Period[3]	Diameter	Visual Magnitude[4]
IO (I)	262,000 miles 421,600 km	1.77 days	2,255 miles 3,629 km	5.0
EUROPA (II)	416,900 miles 670,900 km	3.55 days	1,950 miles 3,138 km	5.3
GANYMEDE (III)[5]	664,900 miles 1,070,000 km	7.16 days	3,270 miles 5,261 km	4.6
CALLISTO (IV)	1,171,000 miles 1,885,000 km	16.69 days	2,980 miles 4,800 km	5.6

[1]The Roman numeral designation frequently used for these moons is also noted. [2]Distance measured from center of Planet. [3]Orbit around Planet. [4]Visual magnitude from Earth at Jupiter's closest approach (opposition). The Galilean moons are visible with binoculars and would be visible to the naked eye if they were not close to Jupiter's bright glare. [5]Ganymede is the largest moon in our Solar System and is larger than Mercury and Pluto.

Jupiter

Observing Jupiter

Planet since it was noticed around 1665. It is thought that this vortex could dissipate but it would probably form again. The spot itself is higher than surrounding clouds. Its "color," size and shape do vary.

In July of 1994, comet Shoemaker-Levy 9 slammed into Jupiter's atmosphere, creating dark patches in the clouds. This collision provided direct evidence that Jupiter may have served as a "cometary magnet" during the early evolution of our Solar System, sparing Earth from huge impacts and giving life the chance to develop.

Jupiter's Belts & Spot

North Temperate Belt

North Equatorial Belt

South Equatorial Belt

Great Red Spot which can appear "whitish"

Locating Jupiter. This amber jewel is easy to find in the sky because it is always bright and prominent. It shines boldly above magnitude –2 most of the time. See the Planets at Sunrise and Sunset tables (pages 157 to 187) to locate Jupiter. The Superior Planet Oppositions table beginning on page 189 indicates when Jupiter appears its brightest and largest in the sky, however, Jupiter varies little in size and magnitude compared to some of the other Planets.

The Galilean Moons. The four Galilean moons are easily visible with well-focused binoculars. They are recapped on page 147.

The brightness of the Galilean moons combined with their rapid revolution around Jupiter creates beautiful, ever changing patterns. Movement of these inner moons can be noticed in as little as 15 minutes. There are also transits, that is, the passing of these moons in front of Jupiter. During a transit, the moon's shadow can be seen moving across the cloud belts; however, the actual moon is usually more difficult to see. When Jupiter is visible in the sky, the popular monthly astronomy magazines publish a graph indicating the daily positions of the four moons. However, planetarium software programs like *Starry Night* provide positions accurate to the minute.

Observing Saturn

THE PLANET SATURN

 The magnificent rings of Saturn make this Planet visually unique. Although we now know that all the Gas Giants have ring systems, none are as spectacular as Saturn's.

When Galileo first looked upon Saturn with his 30 power, 1-inch diameter refractor telescope, he thought he saw three orbs, two smaller orbs on opposite sides of a larger one. Galileo's optics were marginal and he had no concept of a Planet surrounded by rings, so he drew what seemed to make the most sense at the time.

In 1980 and 1981, the *Voyager* missions provided close up views of Saturn's rings that answered long-standing questions. The rings were thinner than expected, varying from 33 to 330 feet (10 to 100 meters). They are composed of countless ringlets, made of small chunks of ice, most less than an inch across. The entire ring system, which extends beyond the visible rings, has a diameter of about 596,000 miles (960,000 km).

Why does Saturn have an extensive ring system? This is still a mystery but one thought is that Saturn's rings may represent

Saturn's Brightest Moons

Moon	Average Distance from Planet[1]	Revolution Period[2]	Diameter	Visual Magnitude[3]
ENCELADUS	147,900 miles	1.4 days	311 miles	11.8
	238,000 km		500 km	
TETHYS	183,300 miles	1.9 days	659 miles	10.3
	295,000 km		1,060 km	
DIONE	234,900 miles	2.7 days	699 miles	10.4
	378,000 km		1,120 km	
RHEA	326,800 miles	4.5 days	951 miles	9.7
	526,000 km		1,530 km	
TITAN[4]	758,100 miles	15.9 days	3,200 miles	8.4
	1,221,000 km		5,150 km	

[1]Distance measured from center of Planet. [2]Orbit around Planet. [3]Visual magnitude from Earth at Saturn's closest approach (opposition). The visual limit of a 4-inch telescope is magnitude 12. [4]Titan is the second largest moon in our Solar System and is larger than Mercury and Pluto. Titan is the only moon in the Solar System that has an atmosphere. It is composed of 95% nitrogen and 5% methane.

Observing Saturn

the remains of a gravitationally roped-in comet, since the amount of material in the rings is equivalent to a body about 60 miles (97 km) in diameter. The rings are positioned "close" to the Planet where the tidal or gravitational forces of Saturn would tear apart a comet. Ring systems are most likely a natural feature of larger gaseous Planets that can gravitationally capture objects passing by.

Locating Saturn. This yellowish/amber colored Planet is easy to find in the sky with the naked eye because it shines steadily with an average magnitude of 0. See the Planets at Sunrise and Sunset tables (pages 157 to 187) to locate Saturn. The Superior Planet Oppositions table beginning on page 189 indicates when Saturn will appear its brightest and largest in the sky.

Saturn's Moons. Titan, Saturn's largest moon, is also the second largest moon in our Solar System after Jupiter's Ganymede. Titan is easy to see but can appear fairly far away from Saturn. Much closer to Saturn are four moons which can be glimpsed with a small telescope. These moons are much fainter than the Galilean moons of Jupiter and are close to the ring system, resembling little specs of light. Facts about these moons are provided on page 149. When Saturn is visible in the sky, the popular monthly astronomy magazines publish a graph indicating the daily position of the five moons. However, planetarium software programs like *Starry Night* provide positions accurate to the minute.

Rings of Saturn

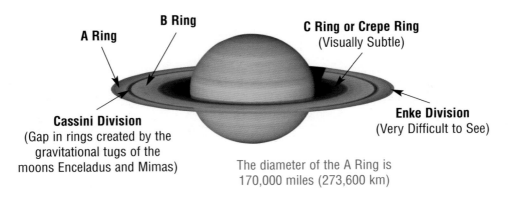

A Ring

B Ring

C Ring or Crepe Ring
(Visually Subtle)

Cassini Division
(Gap in rings created by the
gravitational tugs of the
moons Enceladus and Mimas)

Enke Division
(Very Difficult to See)

The diameter of the A Ring is
170,000 miles (273,600 km)

150

Observing Saturn

The Rings. Saturn's rings are easily seen in a small telescope with magnification as low as 40x. Higher magnifications will reveal more detail.

When Galileo first observed Saturn in 1610, the rings were visible. But several years later in 1612, the rings were edge-on and could not be seen. This no doubt created a stir and was, to say the least, puzzling. Although Saturn is syn-onymous with its ring system, these rings do turn edge-on every 14 years and effectively disappear for about a year. This is not the best time to show your friends Saturn because they will not believe that what they are looking at is the ringed Planet.

Orientation of Saturn's Rings

Date	Orientation of Rings
2000 – 2005	Rings Open Southward
January 2009[1]	Rings Edge-On
2014 – 2020	Rings Open Northward
July 2024[1]	Rings Edge-On
2030 – 2035	Rings Open Southward
April 2039[1]	Rings Edge-On
2040 – 2053	Rings Open Northward
April 2054[1]	Rings Edge-On

[1]Rings not "visible" for about 4 months before and after these dates.

Why does the orientation of Saturn's rings change so much? First, Saturn and its rings are tilted 25.3° on its axis. Secondly, Earth orbits inside Saturn's orbit. Thirdly, as Saturn orbits the Sun, it keeps its axis pointed in the same direction, just like Earth's. So, as Saturn circles us during its 29 year revolution, it presents a 360° view of the rings. This also displays a "top" view of the rings for one-half of Saturn's revolution and a "bottom" view for the other half.

There are three major divisions in the visible rings, labeled from outermost to innermost A, B and C. Between the A and B rings, there is a 2,900 mile (4,700 km) gap, called the Cassini Division. This gap is visible in small telescopes and most apparent when the rings are opened. The middle B ring is the widest and brightest of the three rings and overwhelms the innermost C ring (known as the "Crepe" ring), making it difficult to see in smaller telescopes.

Cloud Belts. Saturn's cloud belts are not as distinct as Jupiter's. Close up pictures of Saturn by *Voyager 1* and *2* also revealed that the clouds are not as complex. You should, however, be able to see several light colored belts when observing Saturn with a small telescope.

Saturn

Observing Uranus & Neptune

THE PLANET URANUS

Uranus is the seventh Planet and shines at about 6th magnitude, making it just visible to the naked eye. Since it is just visible to the eye, I have, over the years, encountered references suggesting that some ancient civilizations knew of Uranus. Nevertheless, in 1781, the English astronomer William Herschel officially discovered Uranus.

Uranus is a Gas Giant similar in size and composition to its farther neighbor Neptune. It is blue-green in color from a small amount of methane in its atmosphere. One unusual characteristic of Uranus is that it rotates on its "side." Its axis is tilted 98° from a perpendicular to its orbit.

Locating Uranus. Although Uranus can just be seen with the unaided eye, it is indistinguishable from other 5th and 6th magnitude stars. The easiest way to find Uranus is to use a GO TO telescope as described on page 85. Otherwise, use a planetarium software program like *Starry Night* to find its location. During the years 2000 to 2050, Uranus moves east from the constellation Capricornus to Leo.

Observing Uranus. Uranus' pale blue color slightly distinguishes it from surrounding stars, however, this Planet appears starlike since magnifications of about 100x are required to discern even a small disk. Uranus' rings and any atmospheric clouds cannot be seen in amateur telescopes.

THE PLANET NEPTUNE

Neptune is the farthest gas giant in our Solar System. Like Uranus, it has a blue-green tinted atmosphere from a small quantity of methane. Neptune was discovered or found in the fall of 1846 by German astronomer Johann Galle from a predicted position calculated by Urbain Le Verrier of France. The existence of Neptune was discerned from anomalies in Uranus' orbit.

Locating Neptune. Neptune requires some persistence to find since it is not visible to the naked eye. The easiest way to find it is to use a GO TO telescope as described on page 85. Otherwise,

Uranus/Neptune

Observing Neptune & Pluto

use a planetarium software program like *Starry Night* to find its location. During the years 2000 to 2050, Neptune moves east from the constellation Capricornus to just inside the boundary of Taurus.

Observing Neptune. Neptune is an 8th magnitude object and cannot be seen with the unaided eye. It is just visible with binoculars but more easily seen with a small telescope.

Neptune has slightly more blue coloring than Uranus. Except for its color, it can appear indistinguishable from other stars since magnifications of about 200x are required to discern a hint of a disk. Neptune's narrow rings, which contain areas of concentrated particles called ring arcs, and its atmospheric clouds cannot be seen in amateur telescopes.

THE PLANET PLUTO

 Pluto is difficult to locate because it is so faint, about magnitude 14, and requires at least a 12-inch telescope. Pluto does not appear as a disk and its moon, Charon cannot be seen. A large telescope, detailed star charts and three to four days of comparative viewing are required to ferret Pluto out from a background of faint stars. Once a year, the popular monthly astronomy magazines provide a star chart to help locate Pluto. Needless to say, Pluto is an object for the better equipped and more experienced observer.

During the years 2000 to 2050, Pluto slowly moves east from the constellation Ophiuchus to Aquarius.

As shown on page 134, Pluto's orbit is highly inclined to the other Planets. Also, its orbit is *not* concentric with the other Planets. Instead, for about 20 of the 248 years that it takes to circle the Sun, Pluto's orbit is closer in than Neptune's. The last period when Pluto was closer to the Sun than Neptune was from 1979 to 1999.

Pluto was found by Clyde Tombaugh in 1930 after an exhaustive photographic search (see next page). Little is known about Pluto because of its distance and small size. It is smaller than many of the moons in our Solar System. Until the flyby of the *New Horizons* spacecraft in 2015, its secrets will remain out of reach.

The Story of Pluto's Discovery

Tombaugh next to comet hunter David Levy's childhood telescope.

Clyde Tombaugh (pronounced Tom-Bah), the discoverer of Pluto, was born in 1906 and raised on farms in Streator, Illinois and later; Burdett, Kansas. His interest in astronomy came early but was piqued at age 12 when he observed through his uncle's telescope. After high school, Clyde stayed to help on the Kansas farm. In 1928, he made drawings of Jupiter's cloud belts and Mars' surface colorations with a 9-inch diameter telescope mirror that he had ground and polished. Always inquisitive, he sent these drawings off, with questions, to the Lowell Observatory in Flagstaff, Arizona. They were so impressed with the drawings and his interest in astronomy that they offered him a job! So, on January 15, 1929, at the age of 22, Clyde Tombaugh arrived by train in Flagstaff as an astronomer's assistant.

At the time, Lowell Observatory was gearing up to search for a ninth planet, code named "Planet X" by its founder, Percival Lowell. A new and special 13-inch photographic refractor had been ordered and arrived a month after Tombaugh. In April, Clyde started the arduous and systematic search for the planet, photographing the night sky around the ecliptic, the path in the sky subscribed by the Sun over the course of a year but also the path where the other Planets roamed. He took two photographs of the same area of the sky on glass plates a week apart, then compared them in a special-type microscope called a blink comparator. This instrument allowed viewing a superimposed image of the two plates while it alternated the view between them about three times a second. Any "star" that moved from one plate to the other would appear blinking in the "combined" image.

Pluto and its largest moon Charon imaged by the Hubble Space Telescope. Charon was discovered in 1978.

Over the course of the year, the Planet X project became Tombaugh's sole responsibility.

On February 18, 1930, Clyde resumed blinking plates having a very high density of stars, taken from a section of the Milky Way in the constellation Gemini, near the star Delta Geminorum. The going was slow, but in the early afternoon, Clyde noticed a star blinking on and off, an indication that it had moved. He checked and double checked before calling it to the attentions of the staff astronomers. However, he did not need their verification to know that he had found Lowell's Planet X.

Planet X was named Pluto after soliciting suggestions from the public. The winning entry came from an 11-year-old girl from England. Pluto, the Greek god of the Underworld was an appropriate name for a Planet in the outer reaches of the Solar System.

Pluto and Beyond

Is Pluto a Planet?

Ironically, the word, "Planet" has no formal scientific definition. "Planet" is an ancient Greek word that simply means "wandering star." To the ancients, the Planets consisted of five naked-eye stars that changed in brightness and wandered among the fixed stars in the sky. They represented a true mystery until the invention of the telescope in 1609 when individuals like Galileo were able to study and discern their true nature.

Pluto is currently classified as a Planet by the International Astronomical Union (IAU), the official organization that keeps track of discoveries, categories and names of objects, however, it may be reclassified from this status.

Why? Because some astronomers who specialize in planetary studies argue convincingly that Pluto is not in the same category as the Terrestrial Planets and Gas Giants, but is rather a large piece of icy-rock debris in a "band" of similar type material surrounding our Solar System. This material, like that of the asteroid belt, is leftover material from when the Solar System formed 4.6 billion years ago.

What evidence is there for this conclusion? Around 1950, a planetary astronomer, Gerard Kuiper (pronounced KYE-per) hypothesized the existence of a belt of icy-rock debris beyond Neptune. Since 1992, hundreds of small, icy-rock bodies have been found in this region, now called the **Kuiper Belt**. But the real surprises began in 2002, when **Quaoar** (pronounced KWAH-wor), a 750 mile diameter (1,200 km) object was found between Neptune and Pluto, lending support that large objects are part of these outer remnants. Then in 2003, **Sedna**, similar in size, but much farther than Pluto was discovered. But the "king" came in 2005, when **Xena** (and its moon Gabriella) was announced, an object closer in than Sedna but with a diameter slightly greater than Pluto's!*

There is no doubt anymore that Pluto is one of many icy-rock Kuiper-belt objects, however, in my heart, Pluto will always remain the ninth Planet of our Solar System, discovered by Clyde Tombaugh on that cold February afternoon in 1930.

The *Lowell Observatory*, located in Flagstaff, Arizona is open to the public and gives tours of the grounds including Lowell's large 24-inch refractor and Tombaugh's telescope used to discover Pluto. I enjoyed the tour and highly recommend it.

The orbits of Neptune, Pluto, Quonar, Xena and Sedna. Sedna's orbit may reach to the outer limits of the Kuiper Belt.

* Xena's diameter is estimated at 1,489 miles (2,397 km) which is about 50 miles greater than Pluto's.

Depictions of the Solar System from books published in 1708 (top) and 1748 (bottom

Using the SUNRISE/SET Planet Tables

Please follow these Guidelines to get the most out of using the Planets at SUNRISE/SUNSET tables.

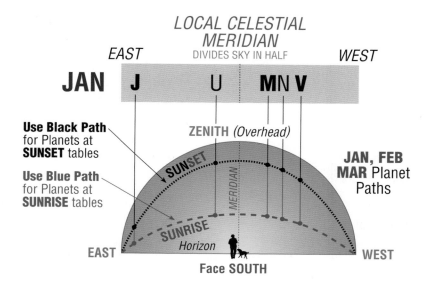

LOCAL CELESTIAL MERIDIAN
DIVIDES SKY IN HALF

EAST   WEST

JAN   J   U   MN V

Use Black Path for Planets at **SUNSET** tables

Use Blue Path for Planets at **SUNRISE** tables

ZENITH (Overhead)

SUNSET

MERIDIAN

SUNRISE

Horizon

EAST   WEST

Face SOUTH

JAN, FEB MAR Planet Paths

INSTRUCTIONS

INSTRUCTIONS: The illustration above shows how the positions of the Planets on the bar correspond to the arced Planet Paths in the sky. The arcs in the above "sky" support January, February and March while those below cover the remainder of the year. This correspondence will become apparent as you become familiar with using the tables. The Planet Path or Ecliptic is also indicated on the Monthly Star Charts.

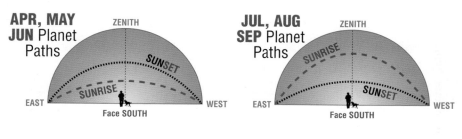

APR, MAY JUN Planet Paths

ZENITH

SUNSET

SUNRISE

EAST   WEST

Face SOUTH

JUL, AUG SEP Planet Paths

ZENITH

SUNRISE

SUNSET

EAST   WEST

Face SOUTH

HEIGHT OF PLANET PATHS. Planet Paths are drawn for the mid-latitude of 39° N (Kansas City). They will arc higher in the sky for lower latitudes and lower in the sky for higher latitudes.

MOVEMENT OF PLANETS. Depending on your location and time of year, it can take a few to 6 or more hours for a Planet to move from the horizon to the meridian.

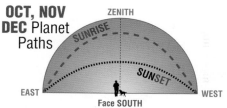

OCT, NOV DEC Planet Paths

ZENITH

SUNRISE

SUNSET

EAST   WEST

Face SOUTH

157

Planets at SUNRISE 2000 – 2003

Relative Positions on the 1st of Each Month
FACING SOUTH

2000 — EAST ← CELESTIAL MERIDIAN (DIVIDES SKY IN HALF) → WEST

Month	Positions (East → West)
JAN	V
FEB	V
MAR	VN
APR	U N
MAY	U N
JUN	JS · · U N
JUL	JS · · U N
AUG	J S · · U N
SEP	M · J S
OCT	M · · J S
NOV	M · · J S
DEC	M · · · J

2002 — EAST ← CELESTIAL MERIDIAN (DIVIDES SKY IN HALF) → WEST

Month	Positions (East → West)
JAN	J
FEB	
MAR	N
APR	U N
MAY	U N
JUN	U N
JUL	S · · U N
AUG	S · · U N
SEP	J · S · · U
OCT	M J · S
NOV	M · J · S
DEC	VM · · J · S

See Instructions on Page 155

2001 — EAST ← CELESTIAL MERIDIAN (DIVIDES SKY IN HALF) → WEST

Month	Positions (East → West)
JAN	M
FEB	M
MAR	N · M
APR	U N · M
MAY	V U N · · M
JUN	V · U N · · M
JUL	S V · · U N
AUG	JV S · · · U N
SEP	V J S
OCT	V · J · S
NOV	V · · J · S
DEC	· · · J S

2003 — EAST ← CELESTIAL MERIDIAN (DIVIDES SKY IN HALF) → WEST

Month	Positions (East → West)
JAN	VM · · J
FEB	V · M · · J
MAR	N V · M
APR	VU N · M
MAY	V U N M
JUN	V · · U MN
JUL	M U · N
AUG	S · · M U N
SEP	S · · · MU
OCT	J · S
NOV	J · · S
DEC	J · · S

Planets.SunRISE

V=Venus, **M**=Mars, **J**=Jupiter, **S**=Saturn, **U**=Uranus, **N**=Neptune
Uranus and ***Neptune*** *are very faint compared to the other Planets listed in these tables.* For **Mercury**, see tables starting on page 193.

Planets at SUNSET 2000 – 2003

Relative Positions on the 1st of Each Month
FACING SOUTH

See Instructions on Page 155

2000 — LOCAL MERIDIAN (DIVIDES SKY IN HALF), EAST ← → WEST

Month	East	West
JAN	S J	M U N
FEB		S J M
MAR		S J M
APR		S J M
MAY		M
JUN		
JUL		
AUG	U N	
SEP	U N	V
OCT	U N	V
NOV	U N	V
DEC	J S	U N V

2001 — LOCAL MERIDIAN (DIVIDES SKY IN HALF), EAST ← → WEST

Month	East	West
JAN	J S	V U N
FEB	J S	V
MAR		J S V
APR		J S
MAY		J S
JUN		
JUL	M	
AUG	U N M	
SEP	U N	M
OCT	U N	M
NOV	U	N M
DEC	S	M U N

2002 — LOCAL MERIDIAN (DIVIDES SKY IN HALF), EAST ← → WEST

Month	East	West
JAN	J S	M U N
FEB	J S	M
MAR		J S M
APR		J S M V
MAY		J S M V
JUN		J V M
JUL		V
AUG	U N	V
SEP	U N	V
OCT	U N	V
NOV	U N	
DEC		U N

2003 — LOCAL MERIDIAN (DIVIDES SKY IN HALF), EAST ← → WEST

Month	East	West
JAN	S	U N
FEB	J S	U
MAR	J S	
APR		J S
MAY		J S
JUN		J S
JUL		J
AUG	N	
SEP	M U N	
OCT	M U N	
NOV	M U N	V
DEC		M U N V

V=Venus, **M**=Mars, **J**=Jupiter, **S**=Saturn, U=Uranus, N=Neptune
Uranus and ***Neptune*** *are very faint compared to the other Planets listed in these tables.* For **Mercury**, see tables starting on page 193.

159

Planets at SUNRISE 2004 – 2007

Relative Positions on the 1st of Each Month
FACING SOUTH

2004 — CELESTIAL MERIDIAN DIVIDES SKY IN HALF (EAST … WEST)

Month	Positions (East → West)
JAN	J S
FEB	J
MAR	N … J
APR	U N
MAY	U N
JUN	U N
JUL	V … U N
AUG	S V … U N
SEP	SV … U
OCT	V S
NOV	M J V … S
DEC	MV J … S

2006 — CELESTIAL MERIDIAN DIVIDES SKY IN HALF (EAST … WEST)

Month	Positions (East → West)
JAN	J S
FEB	V J S
MAR	N V J
APR	U VN J
MAY	VU N J
JUN	V U N
JUL	V U N
AUG	V U N
SEP	VS U
OCT	S
NOV	S
DEC	M S

2005 — CELESTIAL MERIDIAN DIVIDES SKY IN HALF (EAST … WEST)

Month	Positions (East → West)
JAN	V M J S
FEB	M J
MAR	N M J
APR	U NM J
MAY	U MN
JUN	M U N
JUL	M U N
AUG	M U N
SEP	S M U
OCT	S M
NOV	S M
DEC	J S

2007 — CELESTIAL MERIDIAN DIVIDES SKY IN HALF (EAST … WEST)

Month	Positions (East → West)
JAN	MJ S
FEB	M J S
MAR	M J
APR	U MN J
MAY	MU N J
JUN	M U N J
JUL	M U N
AUG	M U N
SEP	V M U
OCT	SV M
NOV	V S M
DEC	V S M

See Instructions on Page 155

NOTE Planet Positions are for 1 hour before Sunrise and 1 hour after Sunset

V=Venus, M=Mars, J=Jupiter, S=Saturn, U=Uranus, N=Neptune
Uranus and *Neptune* are very faint compared to the other Planets listed in these tables. For **Mercury**, see tables starting on page 193.

Planets SunRISE

Planets at SUNSET 2004 – 2007

Relative Positions on the 1st of Each Month
FACING SOUTH

LOCAL MERIDIAN DIVIDES SKY IN HALF (EAST — WEST)

2004 (East → West)

Month	Positions
JAN	S · M U V N
FEB	S · M V U
MAR	J S · M V
APR	J · S MV
MAY	J · S MV
JUN	J · MS
JUL	J M
AUG	N · J
SEP	U N
OCT	U N
NOV	U N
DEC	U N

2006 (East → West)

Month	Positions
JAN	M · U N V
FEB	S · M U
MAR	S · M
APR	S M
MAY	J · S M
JUN	J · S M
JUL	J · MS
AUG	N · J M
SEP	U N · J
OCT	U N · J
NOV	U N
DEC	U N

2005 (East → West)

Month	Positions
JAN	S · U N
FEB	S · U
MAR	S
APR	J · S
MAY	J · S
JUN	J · S V
JUL	J · V
AUG	N · J V
SEP	U N · JV
OCT	U N · V
NOV	M U N · V
DEC	M · U N V

2007 (East → West)

Month	Positions
JAN	U N V
FEB	S · U V
MAR	S · V
APR	S · V
MAY	S V
JUN	J · S V
JUL	J · SV
AUG	N · J
SEP	U N · J
OCT	U N · J
NOV	U N · J
DEC	U · N J

See Instructions on Page 155

V=Venus, M=Mars, J=Jupiter, S=Saturn, U=Uranus, N=Neptune
Uranus and *Neptune* are very faint compared to the other Planets listed in these tables.* For **Mercury**, see tables starting on page 193.

Planets at SUNRISE 2008 – 2011

Relative Positions on the 1st of Each Month
FACING SOUTH

CELESTIAL MERIDIAN — DIVIDES SKY IN HALF

Positions listed East → West.

2008

Month	Planets (East → West)
JAN	V ... S
FEB	VJ ... S
MAR	V J ... S
APR	N J
MAY	U N J
JUN	U N ... J
JUL	U N ... J
AUG	U N
SEP	U
OCT	S
NOV	S
DEC	S

2009

Month	Planets (East → West)
JAN	S
FEB	S
MAR	J ... S
APR	M N J ... S
MAY	M V U N J
JUN	M V U JN
JUL	V M U JN
AUG	V M U NJ
SEP	V M U
OCT	V M
NOV	V S M
DEC	S M

2010

Month	Planets (East → West)
JAN	S M
FEB	S M
MAR	S
APR	J N ... S
MAY	UJ N
JUN	UJ N
JUL	JU N
AUG	JU N
SEP	JU N
OCT	UJ
NOV	S
DEC	V S

2011

Month	Planets (East → West)
JAN	V S
FEB	V S
MAR	V S
APR	V N ... S
MAY	VU N
JUN	VMJ U N
JUL	M J U N
AUG	M J U N
SEP	M J U N
OCT	M J U
NOV	S M J
DEC	S M

See Instructions on Page 155

NOTE Planet Positions are for 1 hour before Sunrise and 1 hour after Sunset

V=Venus, **M**=Mars, **J**=Jupiter, **S**=Saturn, U=Uranus, N=Neptune
Uranus and Neptune are very faint compared to the other Planets listed in these tables. For **Mercury**, see tables starting on page 193.

Planets SunRISE

Planets at SUNSET 2008 – 2011

Relative Positions on the 1st of Each Month
FACING SOUTH

2008 — EAST ← CELESTIAL MERIDIAN (DIVIDES SKY IN HALF) → WEST

Month	Positions (East → West)
JAN	M · · · · U N
FEB	· M · · · · U
MAR	S · M
APR	· S · M
MAY	· · S · M
JUN	· · · S M
JUL	J · · · · · SM
AUG	N · J · · · · M S
SEP	U N · · J · · · MV
OCT	· U N · · J · · V
NOV	· · U N · · J V
DEC	· · · · U · N VJ

2009 — EAST ← CELESTIAL MERIDIAN (DIVIDES SKY IN HALF) → WEST

Month	Positions (East → West)
JAN	U · · VN · J
FEB	· · · V U
MAR	S · · · V
APR	· S
MAY	· · S
JUN	· · · S
JUL	· · · S
AUG	NJ · · · · · S
SEP	U · NJ
OCT	· U · NJ
NOV	· · U · NJ
DEC	· · · · U · NJ

2010 — EAST ← CELESTIAL MERIDIAN (DIVIDES SKY IN HALF) → WEST

Month	Positions (East → West)
JAN	· · · · · U JN
FEB	M · · · · · U J
MAR	· M · · · · · U
APR	S · M · · · · · V
MAY	· S · M · · · V
JUN	· · S · M · V
JUL	· · · S M V
AUG	N · · · · MS V
SEP	JU N · · · · VMS
OCT	UJ · N · · · · VM
NOV	· UJ · N · · · · M
DEC	· · · UJ · N

2011 — EAST ← CELESTIAL MERIDIAN (DIVIDES SKY IN HALF) → WEST

Month	Positions (East → West)
JAN	· · · · JU · N
FEB	· · · · · JU · N
MAR	· · · · · J U
APR	S
MAY	· S
JUN	· · S
JUL	· · · S
AUG	N · · · · · S
SEP	N · · · · · · S
OCT	U · N
NOV	J · U · N · · V
DEC	· J · U · N · · V

V=Venus, **M**=Mars, **J**=Jupiter, **S**=Saturn, U=Uranus, N=Neptune
Uranus and ***Neptune*** *are very faint compared to the other Planets listed in these tables.* For **Mercury**, see tables starting on page 193.

See Instructions on Page 155

163

Planets at SUNRISE 2012 – 2015

Relative Positions on the 1st of Each Month
FACING SOUTH

Positions listed East → West across the sky; the Celestial Meridian divides the sky in half.

2012

Month	Positions (EAST → WEST)
JAN	S M
FEB	S M
MAR	S M
APR	N … S
MAY	U N … S
JUN	U N
JUL	VJ U N
AUG	VJ U N
SEP	V J U N
OCT	V J U
NOV	V J
DEC	VS … J

2013

Month	Positions (EAST → WEST)
JAN	V S
FEB	S
MAR	S
APR	N … S
MAY	U N … S
JUN	U N
JUL	M U N
AUG	MJ U N
SEP	M J U N
OCT	M J U
NOV	M J
DEC	S M J

2014

Month	Positions (EAST → WEST)
JAN	S M … J
FEB	V S M
MAR	V S M
APR	NV S M
MAY	U V N … S
JUN	V U N
JUL	V U N
AUG	V U N
SEP	V J U N
OCT	J … U
NOV	J
DEC	S J

2015

Month	Positions (EAST → WEST)
JAN	S … J
FEB	S … J
MAR	S
APR	N S
MAY	U N … S
JUN	U N … S
JUL	U N
AUG	U N
SEP	MV U N
OCT	JMV U
NOV	MVJ
DEC	V M J

See Instructions on Page 155

Planets SunRISE

NOTE Planet Positions are for 1 hour before Sunrise and 1 hour after Sunset

V=Venus, **M**=Mars, **J**=Jupiter, **S**=Saturn, U=Uranus, N=Neptune
Uranus and *Neptune* are very faint compared to the other Planets listed in these tables.* For **Mercury**, see tables starting on page 193.

Planets at SUNSET 2012 – 2015

Relative Positions on the 1st of Each Month
FACING SOUTH

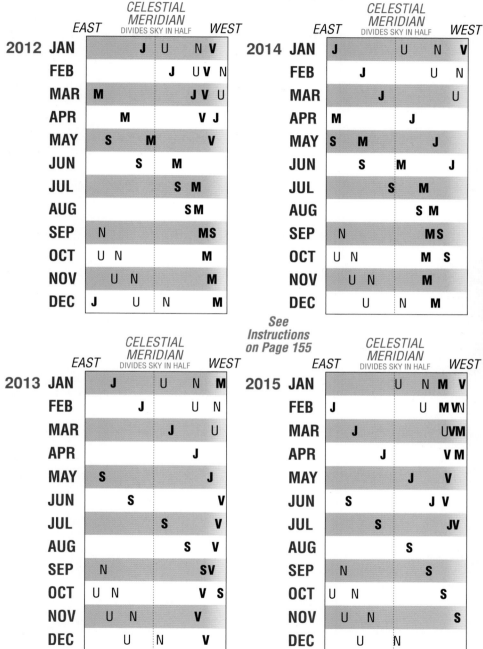

2012 — EAST → CELESTIAL MERIDIAN (DIVIDES SKY IN HALF) → WEST

Month	Positions (East → West)
JAN	J U N V
FEB	J U V N
MAR	M J V U
APR	M V J
MAY	S M V
JUN	S M
JUL	S M
AUG	S M
SEP	N M S
OCT	U N M
NOV	U N M
DEC	J U N M

2014 — EAST → CELESTIAL MERIDIAN (DIVIDES SKY IN HALF) → WEST

Month	Positions (East → West)
JAN	J U N V
FEB	J U N
MAR	J U
APR	M J
MAY	S M J
JUN	S M J
JUL	S M
AUG	S M
SEP	N M S
OCT	U N M S
NOV	U N M
DEC	U N M

2013 — EAST → CELESTIAL MERIDIAN (DIVIDES SKY IN HALF) → WEST

Month	Positions (East → West)
JAN	J U N M
FEB	J U N
MAR	J U
APR	J
MAY	S J
JUN	S V
JUL	S V
AUG	S V
SEP	N S V
OCT	U N V S
NOV	U N V
DEC	U N V

2015 — EAST → CELESTIAL MERIDIAN (DIVIDES SKY IN HALF) → WEST

Month	Positions (East → West)
JAN	U N M V
FEB	J U M V N
MAR	J U V M
APR	J V M
MAY	J V
JUN	S J V
JUL	S J V
AUG	S
SEP	N S
OCT	U N S
NOV	U N S
DEC	U N

See Instructions on Page 155

Planets SunSET

Pages 166 & 167. *Page 166: Jupiter's icy moon Europa imaged by the Galileo spacecraft in 1998. Page 167: Saturn by the Cassini spacecraft in 2004.*

Planets at SUNRISE 2016 – 2019

Relative Positions on the 1st of Each Month
FACING SOUTH

CELESTIAL MERIDIAN DIVIDES SKY IN HALF (EAST ← → WEST)

2016

Month	Positions (EAST → WEST)
JAN	S V M J
FEB	V S M J
MAR	V S M J
APR	N S M J
MAY	N S M
JUN	U N S M
JUL	U N
AUG	U N
SEP	U N
OCT	U
NOV	J
DEC	J

2018

Month	Positions (EAST → WEST)
JAN	JM
FEB	S M J
MAR	S M J
APR	N SM J
MAY	N M S J
JUN	U N M S
JUL	U N M S
AUG	U N M
SEP	U N
OCT	U
NOV	U
DEC	V

2017

Month	Positions (EAST → WEST)
JAN	S J
FEB	S J
MAR	S J
APR	N S J
MAY	V N S
JUN	UV N S
JUL	V U N
AUG	V U N
SEP	V U N
OCT	MV U
NOV	V M
DEC	J M

2019

Month	Positions (EAST → WEST)
JAN	J V
FEB	S V J
MAR	V S J
APR	V S J
MAY	V N S J
JUN	VU N S J
JUL	U N S
AUG	U N
SEP	U N
OCT	U
NOV	M U
DEC	M

See Instructions on Page 155

See Instructions on Page 155

NOTE
Planet Positions are for 1 hour before Sunrise and 1 hour after Sunset

V=Venus, M=Mars, J=Jupiter, S=Saturn, U=Uranus, N=Neptune
Uranus and *Neptune* are very faint compared to the other Planets listed in these tables. For **Mercury**, see tables starting on page 193.

Planets SunRISE

Planets at SUNSET 2016 – 2019

Relative Positions on the 1st of Each Month
FACING SOUTH

Planet positions shown East → West, with the CELESTIAL MERIDIAN dividing the sky in half.

2016

Month	Positions (EAST → WEST)
JAN	U N
FEB	U N
MAR	J U
APR	J
MAY	J
JUN	S M J
JUL	S M J
AUG	S M J
SEP	N M S V
OCT	U N M S V
NOV	U N M VS
DEC	U N M V

2017

Month	Positions (EAST → WEST)
JAN	U M N V
FEB	U M V N
MAR	M U V
APR	J M
MAY	J M
JUN	S J M
JUL	S J M
AUG	S J M
SEP	N S J
OCT	U N S
NOV	U N S
DEC	U N S

2018

Month	Positions (EAST → WEST)
JAN	U N
FEB	U N
MAR	U
APR	V U
MAY	J V
JUN	J V
JUL	S J V
AUG	M S J V
SEP	N M S J V
OCT	N M S J V
NOV	U N M S
DEC	U NM S

2019

Month	Positions (EAST → WEST)
JAN	U M N
FEB	U M N
MAR	M U
APR	M U
MAY	M
JUN	J M
JUL	S J M
AUG	S J
SEP	N S J
OCT	N S J
NOV	U N S J V
DEC	U N S VJ

See Instructions on Page 155

V=Venus, **M**=Mars, **J**=Jupiter, **S**=Saturn, U=Uranus, N=Neptune
Uranus and **Neptune** are very faint compared to the other Planets listed in these tables. For **Mercury**, see tables starting on page 193.

Planets at SUNRISE 2020 – 2023

Relative Positions on the 1st of Each Month
FACING SOUTH

EAST ← CELESTIAL MERIDIAN (DIVIDES SKY IN HALF) → WEST

2020 (East → West)

Month	Positions (East → West)
JAN	M
FEB	J M
MAR	S J M
APR	M J S
MAY	N M S J
JUN	U N M S J
JUL	V U M N S J
AUG	V U M N S
SEP	V U M N
OCT	V U M
NOV	V U
DEC	V

2022 (East → West)

Month	Positions (East → West)
JAN	M
FEB	V M
MAR	V M
APR	V S M
MAY	V J N M S
JUN	U V M J N S
JUL	V U M J N S
AUG	V U M J N S
SEP	V M U J N
OCT	M U J
NOV	M U
DEC	M

2021 (East → West)

NOTE: Planet Positions are for 1 hour before Sunrise and 1 hour after Sunset

Month	Positions (East → West)
JAN	V
FEB	
MAR	J S
APR	J S
MAY	N J S
JUN	U N J S
JUL	U N J S
AUG	U N J S
SEP	U N
OCT	U
NOV	U
DEC	M

2023 (East → West)

Month	Positions (East → West)
JAN	
FEB	
MAR	
APR	S
MAY	N S
JUN	U J N S
JUL	U J N S
AUG	U J N S
SEP	V U J N S
OCT	V U J N
NOV	V U J
DEC	V

See Instructions on Page 155

V=Venus, **M**=Mars, **J**=Jupiter, **S**=Saturn, U=Uranus, N=Neptune
Uranus and **Neptune** are very faint compared to the other Planets listed in these tables. For **Mercury**, see tables starting on page 193.

Planets SunRISE

Planets at SUNSET 2020 – 2023

Relative Positions on the 1st of Each Month
FACING SOUTH

2020 — EAST ← CELESTIAL MERIDIAN (DIVIDES SKY IN HALF) → WEST

Month	Positions (EAST → WEST)
JAN	U N V
FEB	U VN
MAR	U V
APR	V U
MAY	V
JUN	
JUL	J
AUG	S J
SEP	N S J
OCT	M N S J
NOV	U M N S J
DEC	U M N S J

2022 — EAST ← CELESTIAL MERIDIAN (DIVIDES SKY IN HALF) → WEST

Month	Positions (EAST → WEST)
JAN	U N J S
FEB	U N J
MAR	U
APR	U
MAY	
JUN	
JUL	
AUG	S
SEP	N S
OCT	J N S
NOV	U JN S
DEC	M U JN S

2021 — EAST ← CELESTIAL MERIDIAN (DIVIDES SKY IN HALF) → WEST

Month	Positions (EAST → WEST)
JAN	U M N JS
FEB	M U N
MAR	M U
APR	M U
MAY	M
JUN	M V
JUL	MV
AUG	J S VM
SEP	N J S V
OCT	N J S V
NOV	U N J S V
DEC	U N J S V

2023 — EAST ← CELESTIAL MERIDIAN (DIVIDES SKY IN HALF) → WEST

Month	Positions (EAST → WEST)
JAN	M U J N S V
FEB	M U J N V
MAR	M U VJ N
APR	M VU
MAY	M V
JUN	MV
JUL	MV
AUG	M
SEP	N S M
OCT	N S
NOV	UJ N S
DEC	UJ N S

See Instructions on Page 155

V=Venus, **M**=Mars, **J**=Jupiter, **S**=Saturn, **U**=Uranus, **N**=Neptune
Uranus and ***Neptune*** *are very faint compared to the other Planets listed in these tables.* For **Mercury**, see tables starting on page 193.

171

Planets at SUNRISE 2024 – 2027

Relative Positions on the 1st of Each Month
FACING SOUTH

2024 — CELESTIAL MERIDIAN (DIVIDES SKY IN HALF), EAST ← → WEST

```
     EAST          |meridian|          WEST
JAN  V
FEB  MV
MAR  VM
APR  SM
MAY  MN S
JUN   M N S
JUL  JUM    N S
AUG  JM U       N S
SEP    MJ  U         N S
OCT       M    J  U        N
NOV          M      J  U
DEC              M      J
```

2025 — CELESTIAL MERIDIAN (DIVIDES SKY IN HALF), EAST ← → WEST

```
     EAST          |meridian|          WEST
JAN                    M
FEB                       M
MAR
APR  V
MAY  VNS
JUN  V NS
JUL  UV  NS
AUG  JV U    NS
SEP  V J  U        NS
OCT  V   J    U      NS
NOV  V      J     U
DEC              J    U
```

2026 — CELESTIAL MERIDIAN (DIVIDES SKY IN HALF), EAST ← → WEST

```
     EAST          |meridian|          WEST
JAN                                   J
FEB
MAR
APR
MAY  SN
JUN  M SN
JUL  UM    S N
AUG   M U     S N
SEP  J M   U      S N
OCT   J M        U     S N
NOV  V     JM       U
DEC  V       M J       U
```

2027 — CELESTIAL MERIDIAN (DIVIDES SKY IN HALF), EAST ← → WEST

```
     EAST          |meridian|          WEST
JAN  V             M J
FEB  V                 M J
MAR  V                   MJ
APR  V
MAY  VN
JUN  V S N
JUL  U  S N
AUG   U   S N
SEP     U     S N
OCT  J        U     S N
NOV  J          U
DEC   J             U
```

See Instructions on Page 155

V=Venus, **M**=Mars, **J**=Jupiter, **S**=Saturn, U=Uranus, N=Neptune
Uranus and *Neptune* are very faint compared to the other Planets listed in these tables. For **Mercury**, see tables starting on page 193.

Planets at SUNSET 2024 – 2027

Relative Positions on the 1st of Each Month
FACING SOUTH

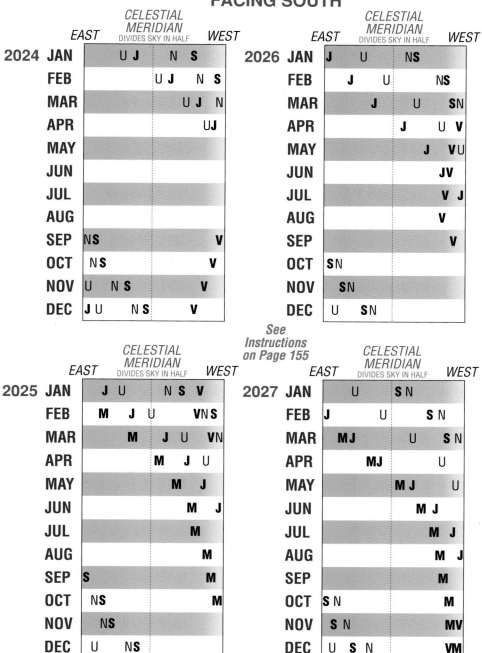

See Instructions on Page 155

V=Venus, **M**=Mars, **J**=Jupiter, **S**=Saturn, **U**=Uranus, **N**=Neptune
Uranus and **Neptune** are very faint compared to the other Planets listed in these tables. For **Mercury**, see tables starting on page 193.

Planets at SUNRISE 2028 – 2031

Relative Positions on the 1st of Each Month
FACING SOUTH

2028

Month	EAST ··· CELESTIAL MERIDIAN (divides sky in half) ··· WEST
JAN	J
FEB	J
MAR	J
APR	J
MAY	N
JUN	S N
JUL	M U V S N
AUG	M V U S N
SEP	M V U S N
OCT	V M U S N
NOV	J V M U S
DEC	V J M U

2029

Month	EAST ··· CELESTIAL MERIDIAN (divides sky in half) ··· WEST
JAN	V J M
FEB	J M
MAR	J M
APR	J M
MAY	N J
JUN	S N
JUL	U S N
AUG	U S N
SEP	U S N
OCT	U S N
NOV	U S
DEC	J U

2030

Month	EAST ··· CELESTIAL MERIDIAN (divides sky in half) ··· WEST
JAN	J
FEB	V J
MAR	V J
APR	V J
MAY	N V J
JUN	V N
JUL	U V S N
AUG	M V U S N
SEP	V M U S N
OCT	M U S N
NOV	M U S
DEC	M U S

2031

Month	EAST ··· CELESTIAL MERIDIAN (divides sky in half) ··· WEST
JAN	J M
FEB	J M
MAR	J M
APR	J M
MAY	N J M
JUN	N J
JUL	U S N
AUG	U S N
SEP	V U S N
OCT	V U S N
NOV	V U S
DEC	V U S

See Instructions on Page 155

V=Venus, **M**=Mars, **J**=Jupiter, **S**=Saturn, U=Uranus, N=Neptune
Uranus and *Neptune* are very faint compared to the other Planets listed in these tables.* For **Mercury**, see tables starting on page 193.

Planets at SUNSET 2028 – 2031

Relative Positions on the 1st of Each Month
FACING SOUTH

2028 — EAST ← CELESTIAL MERIDIAN (DIVIDES SKY IN HALF) → WEST

Month	East of Meridian	West of Meridian
JAN	U S N	V M
FEB	U	S N V
MAR	J	U VS N
APR	J	U V S
MAY	J	VU
JUN	J	
JUL		J
AUG		J
SEP		
OCT	N	
NOV	S N	
DEC	U S N	

2029 — EAST ← CELESTIAL MERIDIAN (DIVIDES SKY IN HALF) → WEST

Month	East of Meridian	West of Meridian
JAN	U S N	
FEB	U S N	
MAR	U S N	
APR	J M	U S
MAY	J M	U
JUN	J M	V
JUL		J M V
AUG		MJ V
SEP		M JV
OCT	N	M V
NOV	S N	MV
DEC	U S N	MV

2030 — EAST ← CELESTIAL MERIDIAN (DIVIDES SKY IN HALF) → WEST

Month	East of Meridian	West of Meridian
JAN	U S N	M
FEB	U S N	M
MAR		U S NM
APR		U S
MAY	J	U S
JUN	J	
JUL	J	
AUG		J
SEP		J
OCT	N	J
NOV	N	J
DEC	U S N	

2031 — EAST ← CELESTIAL MERIDIAN (DIVIDES SKY IN HALF) → WEST

Month	East of Meridian	West of Meridian
JAN	U S	N V
FEB	U S	N V
MAR		U S VN
APR		U S V
MAY	M	V US
JUN	J M	V
JUL	J	M V
AUG		J M
SEP		J M
OCT	N	MJ
NOV	N	M J
DEC	U S N	M J

See Instructions on Page 155

V=Venus, **M**=Mars, **J**=Jupiter, **S**=Saturn, U=Uranus, N=Neptune
Uranus and *Neptune* are very faint compared to the other Planets listed in these tables. For **Mercury**, see tables starting on page 193.

175

Planets at SUNRISE 2032 – 2035

Relative Positions on the 1st of Each Month
FACING SOUTH

CELESTIAL MERIDIAN — DIVIDES SKY IN HALF

Positions listed from EAST (left) to WEST (right). The celestial meridian divides the sky in half.

2032

Month	East ← → West
JAN	V
FEB	J V
MAR	V J
APR	J
MAY	N · · · J
JUN	N · · · J
JUL	N · · · J
AUG	S U · · · N
SEP	M · S U · · · N
OCT	M · · · S U · · · N
NOV	M · · · S U
DEC	M · · · S U

2033

Month	East ← → West
JAN	M · · · U S
FEB	M
MAR	M
APR	V J · · · M
MAY	V J · · · M
JUN	V N J · · · M
JUL	V N · · · J · · · M
AUG	S U V · · · N · · · J
SEP	V S U · · · N · · · J
OCT	V · · · S U · · · N
NOV	V · · · S U
DEC	S U

2034

Month	East ← → West
JAN	S U
FEB	
MAR	
APR	
MAY	J
JUN	N J
JUL	N J
AUG	U · · · N J
SEP	S U · · · N J
OCT	M S U · · · N J
NOV	V M · · · S U
DEC	M V · · · S U

2035

Month	East ← → West
JAN	V M · · · S U
FEB	V M · · · S
MAR	V M
APR	V M
MAY	V M
JUN	J N M
JUL	J N M
AUG	U J N M
SEP	S U · · · J N M
OCT	S U · · · J N
NOV	S U · · · J
DEC	S U

See Instructions on Page 155

NOTE
Planet Positions are for 1 hour before Sunrise and 1 hour after Sunset

V=Venus, **M**=Mars, **J**=Jupiter, **S**=Saturn, U=Uranus, N=Neptune
Uranus and *Neptune* are very faint compared to the other Planets listed in these tables. For **Mercury**, see tables starting on page 193.

Planets SunRISE

Planets at SUNSET 2032 – 2035

Relative Positions on the 1st of Each Month
FACING SOUTH

2032 — EAST ← CELESTIAL MERIDIAN (DIVIDES SKY IN HALF) → WEST

Month	East ————————————————— West
JAN	US · · · N · · · M
FEB	· US · · · · N M
MAR	· · US · · · MN
APR	· · · US · M
MAY	· · · · US M
JUN	·
JUL	J
AUG	· J
SEP	· · J · · · · V
OCT	N · · · J · · V
NOV	· N · · · J · V
DEC	· · N · · · J V

2034 — EAST ← CELESTIAL MERIDIAN → WEST

Month	East ————————————————— West
JAN	SU · · N · · M J
FEB	· SU · · · N M · J
MAR	· · SU · · M N V
APR	· · · SU · M V
MAY	· · · · S U MV
JUN	· · · · SVM U
JUL	· · · · · · V M
AUG	· · · · · · V
SEP	· · · · · · V
OCT	NJ
NOV	N J
DEC	· N J

2033 — EAST ← CELESTIAL MERIDIAN → WEST

Month	East ————————————————— West
JAN	SU · · N · · V · J
FEB	· SU · · · N · V
MAR	· · SU · · N V
APR	· · · SU
MAY	· · · · SU
JUN	· · · · · SU
JUL	M
AUG	· M
SEP	J · M
OCT	N · J · M
NOV	· N · J · M
DEC	· · N · JM

2035 — EAST ← CELESTIAL MERIDIAN → WEST

Month	East ————————————————— West
JAN	U · · N · J
FEB	S U · · · N · J
MAR	· S · U · · NJ
APR	· · · S · U
MAY	· · · · S · U
JUN	· · · · · S · U
JUL	· · · · · · · S
AUG	·
SEP	·
OCT	N M
NOV	JN M · · · · · V
DEC	· J N M · · · · V

See Instructions on Page 155

Pages 178 & 179. Images taken by the Voyager spacecraft in 1986/89.
Page 178: Neptune's moon Triton. Page 179: Uranus (top) with Neptune below.

Planets SunSET

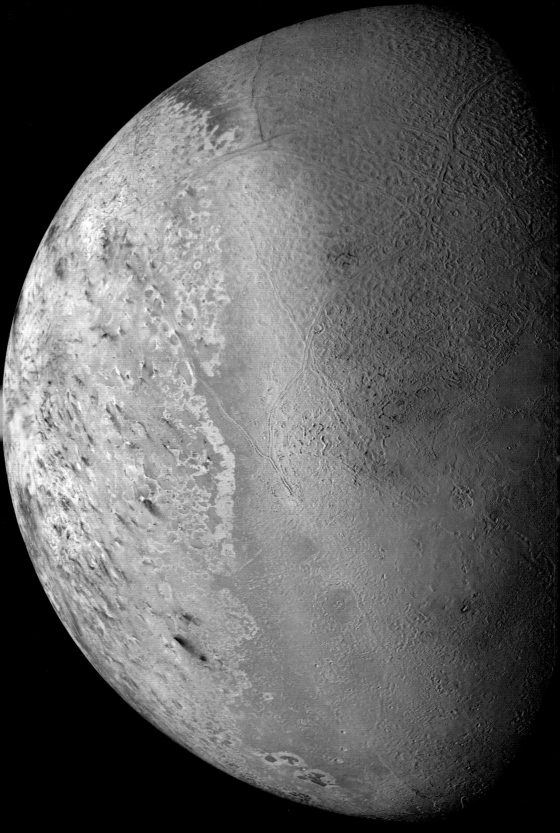

Planets at SUNRISE 2036 – 2039

Relative Positions on the 1st of Each Month
FACING SOUTH

2036 — EAST ← CELESTIAL MERIDIAN (DIVIDES SKY IN HALF) → WEST

Month	Positions (East → West)
JAN	S U
FEB	S
MAR	
APR	
MAY	
JUN	N
JUL	JV N
AUG	U VJ N
SEP	S VU J N
OCT	VS U J N
NOV	MV S U J
DEC	MV S U J

2038 — EAST ← CELESTIAL MERIDIAN (DIVIDES SKY IN HALF) → WEST

Month	Positions (East → West)
JAN	S JU
FEB	V S
MAR	V S
APR	V
MAY	V
JUN	VN
JUL	V N
AUG	UV N
SEP	VJ U N
OCT	S J U N
NOV	S J U N
DEC	S J U

2037 — EAST ← CELESTIAL MERIDIAN (DIVIDES SKY IN HALF) → WEST

Month	Positions (East → West)
JAN	V M S U
FEB	M S
MAR	M S
APR	M
MAY	M
JUN	N M
JUL	N M
AUG	UJ M N
SEP	UJ M N
OCT	S JU M N
NOV	S J U M N
DEC	S JU

2039 — EAST ← CELESTIAL MERIDIAN (DIVIDES SKY IN HALF) → WEST

Month	Positions (East → West)
JAN	M S J U
FEB	M S J U
MAR	M S J
APR	M S
MAY	M
JUN	NM
JUL	MN
AUG	M N
SEP	VU M N
OCT	J V U M N
NOV	S JV U M N
DEC	V S J U M

See Instructions on Page 155

See Instructions on Page 155

NOTE Planet Positions are for 1 hour before Sunrise and 1 hour after Sunset

V=Venus, M=Mars, J=Jupiter, S=Saturn, U=Uranus, N=Neptune
Uranus and *Neptune* are very faint compared to the other Planets listed in these tables. For **Mercury**, see tables starting on page 193.

Planets at SUNSET 2036 – 2039

Relative Positions on the 1st of Each Month
FACING SOUTH

Positions listed East → West. Celestial Meridian divides sky in half.

2036

Month	East → West
JAN	U ... J N M ... V
FEB	S U ... J M N ... V
MAR	S U ... M J V N
APR	S ... U M V J
MAY	S ... U M V J
JUN	S M U
JUL	S M
AUG	
SEP	
OCT	N
NOV	N
DEC	J N

2038

Month	East → West
JAN	J U M N
FEB	J U M N
MAR	S U J M N
APR	S ... J U M ... N
MAY	S J U M
JUN	S M J U
JUL	S M J
AUG	S M
SEP	
OCT	N
NOV	N
DEC	N

See Instructions on Page 155

2037

Month	East → West
JAN	U J N
FEB	U J N
MAR	S U J N
APR	S U J
MAY	S U J
JUN	S U J V
JUL	S V
AUG	V S
SEP	V
OCT	N V
NOV	N V
DEC	M N V

2039

Month	East → West
JAN	N V
FEB	U N V
MAR	J U N V
APR	S J U V N
MAY	S J U V
JUN	S J V U
JUL	S J V
AUG	S J
SEP	S
OCT	
NOV	N
DEC	N

V=Venus, M=Mars, J=Jupiter, S=Saturn, U=Uranus, N=Neptune
Uranus and *Neptune* are very faint compared to the other Planets listed in these tables. For **Mercury**, see tables starting on page 193.

Planets at SUNRISE 2040 – 2043

Relative Positions on the 1st of Each Month
FACING SOUTH

EAST — CELESTIAL MERIDIAN (DIVIDES SKY IN HALF) — WEST

2040

Month	East		Meridian		West
JAN	V		S J		U M
FEB	V			S J	U
MAR	V			S J	
APR				S J	
MAY					
JUN	N				
JUL		N			
AUG			N		
SEP	U			N	
OCT		U			N
NOV	SJ		U		N
DEC		JS		U	

2042

Month	East		Meridian		West
JAN		J S		M	U
FEB		J		S	M U
MAR			J S		
APR				J S	
MAY					J S
JUN	N				J
JUL		N			
AUG			N		
SEP	U			N	
OCT		U			N
NOV	V		U		N
DEC	S V			U	

See Instructions on Page 155

2041

Month	East		Meridian		West
JAN		J S		U	
FEB			J S		U
MAR			J S		
APR	V			J S	
MAY	MV				JS
JUN	NMV				
JUL	VMN				
AUG	V M		N		
SEP	UVM			N	
OCT	V U M				N
NOV	V		UM		N
DEC	J S			M U	

2043

Month	East		Meridian		West
JAN	J	VS		U	
FEB	VJ		S		U
MAR	V		J	S	
APR	V		J		S
MAY	V			J	S
JUN	MN				J
JUL	M N				J
AUG	M		N		
SEP	U M			N	
OCT		U M			N
NOV		MU			N
DEC	S			M U	

V=Venus, **M**=Mars, **J**=Jupiter, **S**=Saturn, U=Uranus, N=Neptune
Uranus *and* ***Neptune*** *are very faint compared to the other Planets listed in these tables.* For **Mercury**, see tables starting on page 193.

NOTE
Planet Positions are for 1 hour before Sunrise and 1 hour after Sunset

Planets SunRISE

Planets at SUNSET 2040 – 2043

Relative Positions on the 1st of Each Month
FACING SOUTH

2040 — EAST ← CELESTIAL MERIDIAN (DIVIDES SKY IN HALF) → WEST

Month	Arrangement (EAST → WEST)
JAN	M N
FEB	U M N
MAR	U M N
APR	S J U M N
MAY	S J MU
JUN	S J M U
JUL	SJM U
AUG	SJM
SEP	SMVJ
OCT	V
NOV	N V
DEC	N V

2042 — EAST ← CELESTIAL MERIDIAN (DIVIDES SKY IN HALF) → WEST

Month	Arrangement (EAST → WEST)
JAN	N
FEB	MU N
MAR	MU N V
APR	MU NV
MAY	S M U V
JUN	J S M U V
JUL	J S M VU
AUG	J S MV
SEP	J SMV
OCT	JMS
NOV	N MJ
DEC	N M

2041 — EAST ← CELESTIAL MERIDIAN (DIVIDES SKY IN HALF) → WEST

Month	Arrangement (EAST → WEST)
JAN	N V
FEB	U N V
MAR	U N V
APR	S U N
MAY	JS U
JUN	JS U
JUL	JS U
AUG	JS
SEP	J S
OCT	J
NOV	N
DEC	N

2043 — EAST ← CELESTIAL MERIDIAN (DIVIDES SKY IN HALF) → WEST

Month	Arrangement (EAST → WEST)
JAN	N
FEB	U N
MAR	U N
APR	U N
MAY	S U
JUN	S U
JUL	J S U
AUG	J S
SEP	J S
OCT	J S
NOV	N J V
DEC	N VJ

See Instructions on Page 155

V=Venus, **M**=Mars, **J**=Jupiter, **S**=Saturn, U=Uranus, N=Neptune
Uranus and *Neptune* are very faint compared to the other Planets listed in these tables. For **Mercury**, see tables starting on page 193.

Planets at SUNRISE 2044 – 2047

Relative Positions on the 1st of Each Month
FACING SOUTH

Column layout for each table: **EAST** → **CELESTIAL MERIDIAN (DIVIDES SKY IN HALF)** → **WEST**

2044

Month	Planets (EAST → WEST)
JAN	S ... M U
FEB	J ... S ... M U
MAR	J ... S ... M U
APR	J ... S ... M
MAY	J ... S
JUN	N ... J ... S
JUL	V N ... J
AUG	V ... N ... J
SEP	U V ... N
OCT	V U ... N
NOV	V ... U ... N
DEC	V ... U

2045

Month	Planets (EAST → WEST)
JAN	V S ... U
FEB	S ... U
MAR	S ... U
APR	J ... S
MAY	J ... S
JUN	N ... J ... S
JUL	M N ... J
AUG	M ... N ... J
SEP	M ... N ... J
OCT	U M ... N
NOV	M U ... N
DEC	M ... U

2046

Month	Planets (EAST → WEST)
JAN	S ... M ... U
FEB	V S ... M ... U
MAR	V S ... M ... U
APR	V ... S ... M
MAY	JV ... S ... M
JUN	NVJ ... S
JUL	V N J
AUG	V ... N ... J
SEP	N ... J
OCT	U ... N ... J
NOV	U ... N
DEC	U

2047

Month	Planets (EAST → WEST)
JAN	U
FEB	S ... U
MAR	S ... U
APR	S
MAY	S
JUN	NJ ... S
JUL	NJ ... S
AUG	JN
SEP	M V ... J N
OCT	U M V ... J N
NOV	M V U ... J N
DEC	V M ... U

NOTE Planet Positions are for 1 hour before Sunrise and 1 hour after Sunset

See Instructions on Page 155

V=Venus, **M**=Mars, **J**=Jupiter, **S**=Saturn, U=Uranus, N=Neptune
Uranus and *Neptune* are very faint compared to the other Planets listed in these tables.* For **Mercury**, see tables starting on page 193.

Planets at SUNSET 2044 – 2047

Relative Positions on the 1st of Each Month
FACING SOUTH

Positions are given relative to the Celestial Meridian (which divides the sky in half), with EAST on the left and WEST on the right.

2044 — EAST | CELESTIAL MERIDIAN | WEST

Month	East of Meridian	West of Meridian
JAN	N	V
FEB	U, N	V
MAR	M, U	N, V
APR	M, U	V, N
MAY	M, U	V
JUN	S	M, U
JUL	S	M, U
AUG	J	S, M
SEP	J	S, M
OCT	J	M, S
NOV	N, J	M, S
DEC	N	J, M

2045 — EAST | CELESTIAL MERIDIAN | WEST

Month	East of Meridian	West of Meridian
JAN	N	J, M
FEB	U, N	M
MAR	U	N, M
APR	U	N
MAY	U	—
JUN	S	U, V
JUL	S	U, V
AUG	S	V
SEP	J, S	V
OCT	J	S, V
NOV	N, J	V, S
DEC	N, J	V

2046 — EAST | CELESTIAL MERIDIAN | WEST

Month	East of Meridian	West of Meridian
JAN	N	J
FEB	—	N, J
MAR	U	N
APR	U	N
MAY	M	U
JUN	S, M	U
JUL	S, M	U
AUG	S	M
SEP	—	S, M
OCT	J	S, M
NOV	N, J	M, S
DEC	N, J	M

2047 — EAST | CELESTIAL MERIDIAN | WEST

Month	East of Meridian	West of Meridian
JAN	N	J, M, V
FEB	—	N, J, M, V
MAR	U	N, J, V, M
APR	U	V, N, M
MAY	U	V, M
JUN	—	U, V
JUL	S	U, V
AUG	S	U
SEP	S	—
OCT	—	S
NOV	J, N	S
DEC	N, J	S

See Instructions on Page 155

V=Venus, **M**=Mars, **J**=Jupiter, **S**=Saturn, U=Uranus, N=Neptune
***Uranus** and **Neptune** are very faint compared to the other Planets listed in these tables.* For **Mercury**, see tables starting on page 193.

Relative Positions on the 1st of Each Month
FACING SOUTH

Legend of positions: EAST — CELESTIAL MERIDIAN (DIVIDES SKY IN HALF) — WEST

2048

Month	Planet positions (East → West)
JAN	V M U
FEB	VS M U
MAR	V S M U
APR	S M
MAY	S M
JUN	S M
JUL	J N S
AUG	J N
SEP	J N
OCT	U J N
NOV	U J N
DEC	U J

2050

Month	Planet positions (East → West)
JAN	M U J
FEB	M U J
MAR	S M U
APR	S M
MAY	S M
JUN	M S
JUL	N M S
AUG	N M S
SEP	J N
OCT	U J N
NOV	V U J N
DEC	V U J

See Instructions on Page 155

2049

Month	Planet positions (East → West)
JAN	U
FEB	S U
MAR	S U
APR	V S
MAY	V S
JUN	V S
JUL	VN S
AUG	JV N
SEP	V J N
OCT	MUV J N
NOV	VM U J N
DEC	M U J

2051

Month	Planet positions (East → West)
JAN	V U J
FEB	V U J
MAR	S V U J
APR	V S
MAY	V S
JUN	S
JUL	N S
AUG	N S
SEP	N
OCT	J N
NOV	M UJ N
DEC	M JU N

V=Venus, M=Mars, J=Jupiter, S=Saturn, U=Uranus, N=Neptune
Uranus and Neptune are very faint compared to the other Planets listed in these tables. For **Mercury**, see tables starting on page 193.

Planets at SUNSET 2048 – 2051

Relative Positions on the 1st of Each Month
FACING SOUTH

Tables read EAST (left) to WEST (right); the CELESTIAL MERIDIAN divides the sky in half (center).

2048

Month	Positions (EAST → WEST)
JAN	NJ (center)
FEB	NJ (center)
MAR	U (east) · JN (center)
APR	U (east) · JN (west of center)
MAY	U (center) · J (west)
JUN	M (east) · U (center)
JUL	S · M (east) · U (west of center)
AUG	S · M (center) · U (west)
SEP	S · M (center) · V (west)
OCT	SM (center) · V (west)
NOV	N (east) · M · S · V (west)
DEC	N (east) · M · V · S (west)

2049

Month	Positions (EAST → WEST)
JAN	J · N (east) · M · V (west)
FEB	J · N (center) · M · V (west)
MAR	U (east) · J · N · M · V (west)
APR	U (east) · J (center) · N M (west)
MAY	U (center) · J · M (west)
JUN	U (center) · J M (west)
JUL	S (east) · U (center)
AUG	S (east) · U (west)
SEP	S (center)
OCT	S (center)
NOV	N (east) · S (center)
DEC	N (east) · S (center)

2050

Month	Positions (EAST → WEST)
JAN	N (center) · S (west)
FEB	J (east) · N (center)
MAR	U (east) · J · N · V (west)
APR	U (east) · J · N · V (west)
MAY	U (center) · J · V (west)
JUN	U · J · V (west)
JUL	U · V · J (west)
AUG	S (east) · V · U (west)
SEP	M S (center) · V (west)
OCT	M · S (center)
NOV	N (east) · M · S
DEC	N (east) · M · S (west)

2051

Month	Positions (EAST → WEST)
JAN	N (center) · M · S (west)
FEB	N (center) · M
MAR	U (east) · J · N · M (west)
APR	U (east) · J · M · N (west)
MAY	U (center) · J · M · N (west)
JUN	U · J · M (west)
JUL	U · J · M (west)
AUG	S (east) · U · J (west)
SEP	S (center)
OCT	S (center)
NOV	S (center) · V (west)
DEC	N (east) · S · V (west)

See Instructions on Page 155

V=Venus, **M**=Mars, **J**=Jupiter, **S**=Saturn, U=Uranus, N=Neptune
Uranus and *Neptune* are very faint compared to the other Planets listed in these tables. For **Mercury**, see tables starting on page 193.

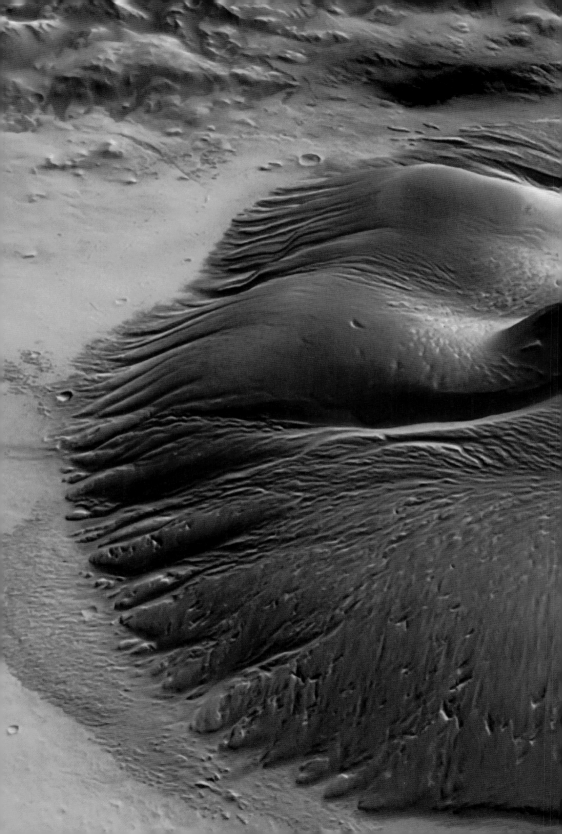

Superior Planet Oppositions 2000 – 2018

Best Viewing of the Superior Planets

The Superior Planets, Mars through Pluto, are at opposition when they are directly opposite the Sun from the Earth. At opposition, a Superior Planet is rising as the Sun is setting, placing it high or overhead at midnight. The Superior Planets are closest to the Earth at opposition. They are also at their brightest magnitude and will appear their largest in a telescope. The best time to observe a Superior Planet is from about one month before to one month after the opposition date, however, do not let this discourage you from observing these planets at other times!

For More Information on Oppositions, See Page 133.

MARS includes (Arc Angle Size, in seconds). See Page 142.

	MARS	JUPITER	SATURN	URANUS	NEPTUNE
2000	—	Nov 27	Nov 19	Aug 10	Jul 27
2001	Jun 13 (20.9")	Dec 31	Dec 3	Aug 15	Jul 30
2002	—	—	Dec 17	Aug 19	Aug 1
2003	Aug 28 (25.2")	Feb 2	Dec 31	Aug 24	Aug 4
2004	—	Mar 3	—	Aug 27	Aug 5
2005	Nov 7 (20.2")	Apr 3	Jan 13	Aug 31	Aug 8
2006	—	Mar 4	Jan 27	Sep 5	Aug 10
2007	Dec 24 (15.8")	Jun 5	Feb 10	Sep 9	Aug 13
2008	—	Jul 9	Feb 24	Sep 12	Aug 14
2009	—	Aug 14	Mar 8	Sep 17	Aug 17
2010	Jan 29 (14.0")	Sep 21	Mar 21	Sep 21	Aug 20
2011	—	Oct 28	Apr 3	Sep 25	Aug 22
2012	Mar 3 (14.0")	Dec 2	Apr 15	Sep 29	Aug 24
2013	—	—	Apr 28	Oct 3	Aug 26
2014	Apr 8 (15.1")	Jan 5	May 10	Oct 7	Aug 29
2015	—	Feb 6	May 22	Oct 11	Aug 31
2016	May 22 (18.7")	Mar 8	Jun 2	Oct 15	Sep 2
2017	—	Apr 7	Jun 15	Oct 19	Sep 4
2018	Jul 26 (24.5")	May 8	Jun 27	Oct 23	Sep 7

Dates are based on Mountain Standard Time

Facing page. *The central peak of Nicholson Crater on Mars shows a considerable amount of wind erosion. Nicholson has a diameter of 62 miles (100 km).* 189

Oppositions

Superior Planet Oppositions 2019 – 2045

Best Viewing Dates

	MARS	JUPITER	SATURN	URANUS	NEPTUNE
2019	—	Jun 10	Jul 9	Oct 28	Sep 9
2020	Oct 13 (22.7")	Jul 14	Jul 20	Oct 31	Sep 11
2021	—	Aug 19	Aug 1	Nov 4	Sep 14
2022	Dec 7 (17.3")	Sep 26	Aug 14	Nov 9	Sep 16
2023	—	Nov 2	Aug 27	Nov 13	Sep 19
2024	—	Dec 7	Sep 7	Nov 16	Sep 20
2025	Jan 15 (14.4")	—	Sep 20	Nov 21	Sep 23
2026	—	Jan 10	Oct 4	Nov 25	Sep 25
2027	Feb 19 (13.7")	Feb 10	Oct 17	Nov 30	Sep 28
2028	—	Mar 12	Oct 30	Dec 3	Sep 29
2029	Mar 25 (14.4")	Apr 11	Nov 13	Dec 8	Oct 2
2030	—	May 13	Nov 27	Dec 12	Oct 4
2031	May 4 (16.9")	Jun 15	Dec 11	Dec 17	Oct 7
2032	—	Jun 18	Dec 24	Dec 20	Oct 8
2033	Jun 27 (22.0")	Aug 24	—	Dec 25	Oct 11
2034	—	Oct 1	Jan 7	Dec 29	Oct 13
2035	Sep 15 (24.5")	Nov 7	Jan 21	—	Oct 16
2036	—	Dec 12	Feb 4	Jan 3	Oct 17
2037	Nov 19 (19.1")	—	Feb 17	Jan 7	Oct 20
2038	—	Jan 14	Mar 3	Jan 12	Oct 22
2039	—	Feb 15	Mar 16	Jan 16	Oct 25
2040	Jan 2 (15.5")	Mar 16	Mar 28	Jan 21	Oct 26
2041	—	Apr 16	Apr 10	Jan 25	Oct 29
2042	Feb 6 (14.0")	May 17	Apr 23	Jan 30	Oct 31
2043	—	Jun 19	May 5	Feb 4	Nov 3
2044	Mar 11 (14.0")	Jul 23	May 16	Feb 9	Nov 4
2045	—	Aug 30	May 29	Feb 12	Nov 7

Dates are based on Mountain Standard Time

Oppositions

Superior Planet Oppositions 2046 – 2051

Best Viewing Dates

	MARS	JUPITER	SATURN	URANUS	NEPTUNE
2046	Apr 17 (15.8")	Oct 6	Jun 10	Feb 17	Nov 9
2047	—	Nov 12	Jun 22	Feb 22	Nov 12
2048	Jun 3 (19.8")	Dec 17	Jul 3	Feb 27	Nov 13
2049	—	—	Jul 15	Mar 3	Nov 16
2050	Aug 14 (24.8")	Jan 19	Jul 28	Mar 8	Nov 18
2051	—	Feb 19	Aug 9	Mar 13	Nov 21

PLUTO. Although Pluto has a yearly opposition date, I have only provided dates every ten years because it is very difficult to observe this Planet with a telescope.

2000 ✦ June 1	2030 ✦ Aug 2
2010 ✦ June 25	2040 ✦ Aug 17
2020 ✦ July 15	2050 ✦ Sep 1

Page 192. *Mariner 10 is the only spacecraft to have visited Mercury. It first flew by Venus in 1974 before encountering Mercury three times from 1974 to 1975. This picture encompasses the north pole area. Although Mariner 10 took over 7,000 pictures of Mercury, only 45% of the surface was imaged.*

Oppositions

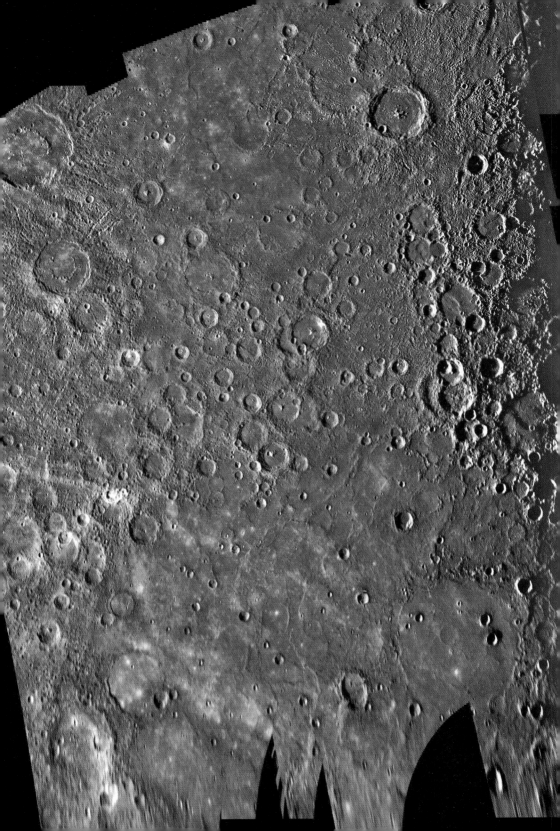

Mercury at Greatest Elong. 2000 – 2003

Mercury when Farthest from the Sun

Mercury can only be observed at or near Greatest Eastern or Western Elongation when it is farthest from the Sun in the sky, thus easiest to see. Not all Greatest Eastern or Western Elongations are favorable for observing Mercury because some factors (see page 138) contribute to placing Mercury closer to the horizon and into the glare of twilight.

TABLE NOTES: Date & Time to Observe. These tables indicate the dates of Greatest Eastern or Western Elongation. Favorable viewing is one week on either side of these dates. **Elongation & *(Degrees Above Horizon)*.** The **E**ast and **W**est numbers indicate Mercury's apparent distance from the Sun. The numbers in parentheses indicate Mercury's distance above the horizon at sunrise or sunset for the *mid-latitude of 39° (Kansas City)* — the larger this number, the easier it will be and the longer you will have to see Mercury after sunset and before sunrise.   LATITUDE CONSIDERATIONS: Mercury's height above the horizon varies depending on your latitude. Mercury is lower in the sky for northern latitudes and higher for southern latitudes. The bolded entries indicate the dates when Mercury is visible for most of the continental US. Those in the south should easily find Mercury but it may be more challenging for those in the north. Mercury does not get very high in the sky for upper Canada and Alaska and will be lost in the glare of twilight most of the time. Dates and times based on Mountain Standard Time.

BOLDED ENTRIES are the Best Dates to View Mercury

	Date & Time to Observe	Elongation & (Degrees Above Horizon)
2000	**Feb 14 Evening**	**18° E** *(16°)*
	Mar 28 Morning	28° W *(10°)*
	Jun 9 Evening	**24° E** *(18°)*
	Jul 27 Morning	20° W *(15°)*
	Oct 6 Evening	26° E *(8°)*
	Nov 14 Morning	**19° W** *(17°)*
2001	**Jan 28 Evening**	**18° E** *(16°)*
	Mar 10 Morning	27° W *(11°)*
	May 21 Evening	**22° E** *(19°)*
	Jul 9 Morning	21° W *(14°)*
	Sep 18 Evening	27° E *(9°)*
	Oct 29 Morning	**19° W** *(17°)*

	Date & Time to Observe	Elongation & (Degrees Above Horizon)
2002	Jan 11 Evening	19° E *(15°)*
	Feb 21 Morning	27° W *(12°)*
	May 3 Evening	**21° E** *(19°)*
	Jun 21 Morning	23° W *(13°)*
	Sep 1 Evening	27° E *(9°)*
	Oct 13 Morning	**18° W** *(17°)*
	Dec 25 Evening	20° E *(13°)*
2003	Feb 3 Morning	25° W *(13°)*
	Apr 16 Evening	**20° E** *(18°)*
	Jun 2 Morning	24° W *(11°)*
	Aug 14 Evening	27° E *(11°)*
	Sep 26 Morning	**18° W** *(17°)*
	Dec 8 Evening	21° E *(11°)*

For More Information on Observing
Mercury, See Page 138

Mercury Elong

Mercury at Greatest Elong. 2004 – 2011

Mercury when Farthest from the Sun

BOLDED ENTRIES are Best Dates to View Mercury

	Date & Time to Observe	Elongation & *(Degrees Above Horizon)*		Date & Time to Observe	Elongation & *(Degrees Above Horizon)*
2004	Jan 17 Morning	24° W *(14°)*	**2008**	Jan 21 Evening	19° E *(15°)*
	Mar 29 Evening	**19° E** ***(18°)***		Mar 3 Morning	27° W *(11°)*
	May 14 Morning	26° W *(10°)*		**May 13 Evening**	**22° E** ***(19°)***
	Jul 26 Evening	27° E *(13°)*		Jul 1 Morning	22° W *(13°)*
	Sep 9 Morning	**18° W** ***(16°)***		Sep 10 Evening	27° E *(9°)*
	Nov 20 Evening	22° E *(9°)*		**Oct 22 Morning**	**18° W** ***(17°)***
	Dec 29 Morning	**22° W** ***(16°)***	**2009**	Jan 4 Evening	19° E *(14°)*
2005	**Mar 12 Evening**	**18° E** ***(17°)***		Feb 13 Morning	26° W *(12°)*
	Apr 26 Morning	27° W *(10°)*		**Apr 26 Evening**	**20° E** ***(19°)***
	Jul 8 Evening	26° E *(15°)*		Jun 13 Morning	23° W *(12°)*
	Aug 23 Morning	**18° W** ***(16°)***		Aug 24 Evening	27° E *(10°)*
	Nov 3 Evening	24° E *(8°)*		**Oct 5 Morning**	**18° W** ***(17°)***
	Dec 12 Morning	**21° W** ***(17°)***		Dec 18 Evening	20° E *(12°)*
2006	**Feb 23 Evening**	**18° E** ***(17°)***	**2010**	Jan 26 Morning	25° W *(14°)*
	Apr 8 Morning	28° W *(10°)*		**Apr 8 Evening**	**19° E** ***(18°)***
	Jun 20 Evening	**25° E** ***(17°)***		May 25 Morning	25° W *(11°)*
	Aug 6 Morning	**19° W** ***(16°)***		Aug 6 Evening	27° E *(12°)*
	Oct 16 Evening	25° E *(8°)*		**Sep 19 Morning**	**18° W** ***(17°)***
	Nov 25 Morning	**20° W** ***(17°)***		Dec 1 Evening	21° E *(11°)*
2007	**Feb 7 Evening**	**18° E** ***(16°)***	**2011**	Jan 9 Morning	23° W *(15°)*
	Mar 21 Morning	28° W *(11°)*		**Mar 22 Evening**	**19° E** ***(18°)***
	Jun 2 Evening	**23° E** ***(19°)***		May 7 Morning	27° W *(10°)*
	Jul 20 Morning	20° W *(15°)*		Jul 19 Evening	27° E *(14°)*
	Sep 29 Evening	26° E *(8°)*		**Sep 2 Morning**	**18° W** ***(16°)***
	Nov 8 Morning	**19° W** ***(17°)***		Nov 14 Evening	23° E *(9°)*
				Dec 22 Morning	**22° W** ***(16°)***

For More Information on Observing Mercury, See Page 138

Mercury Elong

Mercury at Greatest Elong. 2012 – 2019

Mercury when Farthest from the Sun

BOLDED ENTRIES are Best Dates to View Mercury

	Date & Time to Observe		Elongation & (Degrees Above Horizon)			Date & Time to Observe		Elongation & (Degrees Above Horizon)	
2012	**Mar 5**	**Evening**	**18° E**	**(17°)**	**2016**	Feb 6	Morning	26° W	(13°)
	Apr 18	Morning	28° W	(10°)		**Apr 18**	**Evening**	**20° E**	**(19°)**
	Jun 30	**Evening**	**26° E**	**(16°)**		Jun 5	Morning	24° W	(12°)
	Aug 16	**Morning**	**19° W**	**(16°)**		Aug 16	Evening	27° E	(11°)
	Oct 26	Evening	24° E	(8°)		**Sep 28**	**Morning**	**18° W**	**(17°)**
	Dec 4	**Morning**	**21° W**	**(17°)**		Dec 10	Evening	21° E	(12°)
2013	**Feb 16**	**Evening**	**18° E**	**(17°)**	**2017**	Jan 19	Morning	24° W	(14°)
	Mar 31	Morning	28° W	(10°)		**Apr 1**	**Evening**	**19° E**	**(18°)**
	Jun 12	**Evening**	**24° E**	**(18°)**		May 17	Morning	26° W	(10°)
	Jul 30	**Morning**	**20° W**	**(16°)**		Jul 29	Evening	27° E	(13°)
	Oct 9	Evening	25° E	(8°)		**Sep 12**	**Morning**	**18° W**	**(16°)**
	Nov 17	**Morning**	**19° W**	**(17°)**		Nov 23	Evening	22° E	(10°)
2014	**Jan 31**	**Evening**	**18° E**	**(16°)**	**2018**	**Jan 1**	**Morning**	**23° W**	**(16°)**
	Mar 13	Morning	28° W	(11°)		**Mar 15**	**Evening**	**18° E**	**(17°)**
	May 25	**Evening**	**23° E**	**(19°)**		Apr 29	Morning	27° W	(10°)
	Jul 12	Morning	21° W	(14°)		Jul 11	Evening	26° E	(15°)
	Sep 21	Evening	26° E	(9°)		**Aug 26**	**Morning**	**18° W**	**(16°)**
	Nov 1	**Morning**	**19° W**	**(17°)**		Nov 6	Evening	23° E	(9°)
2015	Jan 14	Evening	19° E	(15°)		**Dec 15**	**Morning**	**21° W**	**(17°)**
	Feb 24	Morning	27° W	(12°)	**2019**	**Feb 26**	**Evening**	**18° E**	**(17°)**
	May 6	**Evening**	**21° E**	**(19°)**		Apr 11	Morning	28° W	(10°)
	Jun 24	Morning	23° W	(13°)		**Jun 23**	**Evening**	**25° E**	**(17°)**
	Sep 4	Evening	27° E	(9°)		**Aug 9**	**Morning**	**19° W**	**(16°)**
	Oct 15	**Morning**	**18° W**	**(17°)**		Oct 19	Evening	25° E	(8°)
	Dec 28	Evening	20° E	(13°)		**Nov 28**	**Morning**	**20° W**	**(17°)**

For More Information on Observing Mercury, See Page 138

Mercury Elong

Mercury at Greatest Elong. 2020 – 2027

Mercury when Farthest from the Sun

BOLDED ENTRIES are Best Dates to View Mercury

For More Information on Observing Mercury, See Page 138

	Date & Time to Observe		Elongation & (Degrees Above Horizon)			Date & Time to Observe		Elongation & (Degrees Above Horizon)
2020	**Feb 10**	**Evening**	**18° E**	**(16°)**	**2024**	Jan 12	Morning	24° W (15°)
	Mar 23	Morning	28° W (11°)			**Mar 24**	**Evening**	**19° E** **(18°)**
	Jun 4	**Evening**	**24° E**	**(19°)**		May 9	Morning	26° W (10°)
	Jul 22	Morning	20° W (15°)			Jul 22	Evening	27° E (13°)
	Oct 1	Evening	26° E	(8°)		**Sep 4**	**Morning**	**18° W**	**(16°)**
	Nov 10	**Morning**	**19° W**	**(17°)**		Nov 16	Evening	23° E (10°)
2021	Jan 23	Evening	19° E (15°)		**Dec 24**	**Morning**	**22° W**	**(16°)**
	Mar 6	Morning	27° W (11°)	**2025**	**Mar 7**	**Evening**	**18° E**	**(17°)**
	May 16	**Evening**	**22° E**	**(19°)**		Apr 21	Morning	27° W (10°)
	Jul 4	Morning	22° W (14°)		**Jul 3**	**Evening**	**26° E**	**(16°)**
	Sep 13	Evening	27° E	(9°)		**Aug 19**	**Morning**	**19° W**	**(16°)**
	Oct 24	**Morning**	**18° W**	**(17°)**		Oct 29	Evening	24° E (9°)
2022	Jan 7	Evening	19° E (14°)		**Dec 7**	**Morning**	**21° W**	**(17°)**
	Feb 16	Morning	26° W (12°)	**2026**	**Feb 19**	**Evening**	**18° E**	**(17°)**
	Apr 29	**Evening**	**21° E**	**(19°)**		Apr 3	Morning	28° W (10°)
	Jun 16	Morning	23° W (12°)		**Jun 15**	**Evening**	**25° E**	**(18°)**
	Aug 27	Evening	27° E (10°)		**Aug 2**	**Morning**	**19° W**	**(16°)**
	Oct 8	**Morning**	**18° W**	**(17°)**		Oct 12	Evening	25° E (8°)
	Dec 21	Evening	20° E (13°)		**Nov 20**	**Morning**	**20° W**	**(17°)**
2023	Jan 29	Morning	25° W (13°)	**2027**	**Feb 2**	**Evening**	**18° E**	**(16°)**
	Apr 11	**Evening**	**19° E**	**(18°)**		Mar 16	Morning	28° W (11°)
	May 28	Morning	25° W (11°)		**May 28**	**Evening**	**23° E**	**(19°)**
	Aug 9	Evening	27° E (12°)		Jul 15	Morning	21° W (15°)
	Sep 22	**Morning**	**18° W**	**(17°)**		Sep 24	Evening	26° E (8°)
	Dec 4	Evening	21° E (11°)		**Nov 4**	**Morning**	**19° W**	**(17°)**

Mercury Elong

Mercury at Greatest Elong. 2028 – 2035

Mercury when Farthest from the Sun

BOLDED ENTRIES are Best Dates to View Mercury

	Date & Time to Observe	Elongation & (Degrees Above Horizon)
2028	Jan 17 Evening	19° E (15°)
	Feb 27 Morning	27° W (12°)
	May 9 Evening	**21° E (19°)**
	Jun 26 Morning	22° W (13°)
	Sep 6 Evening	27° E (9°)
	Oct 17 Morning	**18° W (17°)**
	Dec 30 Evening	20° E (14°)
2029	Feb 8 Morning	26° W (13°)
	Apr 21 Evening	**20° E (19°)**
	Jun 8 Morning	24° W (12°)
	Aug 19 Evening	27° E (10°)
	Oct 1 Morning	**18° W (17°)**
	Dec 13 Evening	21° E (12°)
2030	Jan 22 Morning	24° W (14°)
	Apr 4 Evening	**19° E (18°)**
	May 20 Morning	26° W (11°)
	Aug 1 Evening	27° E (12°)
	Sep 15 Morning	**18° W (17°)**
	Nov 26 Evening	22° E (10°)
2031	Jan 4 Morning	23° W (15°)
	Mar 18 Evening	**18° E (17°)**
	May 2 Morning	27° W (10°)
	Jul 15 Evening	27° E (14°)
	Aug 29 Morning	**18° W (16°)**
	Nov 9 Evening	23° E (9°)
	Dec 18 Morning	**21° W (17°)**

For More Information on Observing Mercury, See Page 138

	Date & Time to Observe	Elongation & (Degrees Above Horizon)
2032	**Feb 29 Evening**	**18° E (17°)**
	Apr 13 Morning	28° W (10°)
	Jun 25 Evening	**25° E (17°)**
	Aug 11 Morning	**19° W (16°)**
	Oct 21 Evening	24° E (8°)
	Nov 30 Morning	**20° W (17°)**
2033	**Feb 12 Evening**	**18° E (16°)**
	Mar 26 Morning	28° W (11°)
	Jun 7 Evening	**24° E (19°)**
	Jul 25 Morning	20° W (15°)
	Oct 4 Evening	26° E (8°)
	Nov 13 Morning	**19° W (17°)**
2034	**Jan 26 Evening**	**18° E (16°)**
	Mar 9 Morning	27° W (11°)
	May 20 Evening	**22° E (19°)**
	Jul 7 Morning	21° W (14°)
	Sep 16 Evening	27° E (9°)
	Oct 27 Morning	**18° W (17°)**
2035	Jan 10 Evening	19° E (15°)
	Feb 19 Morning	26° W (12°)
	May 2 Evening	**21° E (19°)**
	Jun 19 Morning	23° W (13°)
	Aug 30 Evening	27° E (10°)
	Oct 11 Morning	**18° W (17°)**
	Dec 24 Evening	20° E (13°)

Mercury at Greatest Elong. 2036 – 2043

Mercury when Farthest from the Sun

BOLDED ENTRIES are Best Dates to View Mercury

Mercury Elong

Year	Date & Time to Observe		Elongation & (Degrees Above Horizon)	
2036	Feb 1	Morning	25° W	(13°)
	Apr 13	**Evening**	**20° E**	**(18°)**
	May 31	Morning	25° W	(11°)
	Aug 11	Evening	27° E	(11°)
	Sep 24	**Morning**	**18° W**	**(17°)**
	Dec 6	Evening	21° E	(11°)
2037	Jan 14	Morning	24° W	(15°)
	Mar 27	**Evening**	**19° E**	**(18°)**
	May 12	Morning	26° W	(10°)
	Jul 25	Evening	27° E	(13°)
	Sep 7	**Morning**	**18° W**	**(16°)**
	Nov 19	Evening	22° E	(10°)
	Dec 28	**Morning**	**22° W**	**(16°)**
2038	**Mar 10**	**Evening**	**18° E**	**(17°)**
	Apr 24	Morning	27° W	(10°)
	Jul 6	**Evening**	**26° E**	**(16°)**
	Aug 22	**Morning**	**19° W**	**(16°)**
	Nov 1	Evening	24° E	(9°)
	Dec 10	**Morning**	**21° W**	**(17°)**
2039	**Feb 22**	**Evening**	**18° E**	**(17°)**
	Apr 6	Morning	28° W	(10°)
	Jun 18	**Evening**	**25° E**	**(18°)**
	Aug 5	**Morning**	**19° W**	**(16°)**
	Oct 15	Evening	25° E	(8°)
	Nov 23	**Morning**	**20° W**	**(17°)**

Year	Date & Time to Observe		Elongation & (Degrees Above Horizon)	
2040	**Feb 5**	**Evening**	**18° E**	**(16°)**
	Mar 19	Morning	28° W	(11°)
	May 30	**Evening**	**23° E**	**(19°)**
	Jul 17	Morning	20° W	(15°)
	Sep 26	Evening	26° E	(8°)
	Nov 5	**Morning**	**19° W**	**(17°)**
2041	Jan 19	Evening	19° E	(15°)
	Mar 1	Morning	27° W	(11°)
	May 12	**Evening**	**22° E**	**(19°)**
	Jun 29	Morning	22° W	(13°)
	Sep 9	Evening	27° E	(9°)
	Oct 20	**Morning**	**18° W**	**(17°)**
2042	Jan 2	Evening	19° E	(14°)
	Feb 11	Morning	26° W	(13°)
	Apr 24	**Evening**	**20° E**	**(19°)**
	Jun 11	Morning	24° W	(12°)
	Aug 22	Evening	27° E	(10°)
	Oct 4	**Morning**	**18° W**	**(17°)**
	Dec 16	Evening	20° E	(12°)
2043	Jan 25	Morning	25° W	(14°)
	Apr 6	**Evening**	**19° E**	**(18°)**
	May 23	Morning	25° W	(11°)
	Aug 5	Evening	27° E	(12°)
	Sep 17	**Morning**	**18° W**	**(16°)**
	Nov 29	Evening	22° E	(10°)

For More Information on Observing Mercury, See Page 138

Mercury at Greatest Elong. 2044 – 2051

Mercury when Farthest from the Sun

BOLDED ENTRIES are Best Dates to View Mercury

	Date & Time to Observe	Elongation & (Degrees Above Horizon)
2044	Jan 7 Morning	23° W (15°)
	Mar 20 Evening	**19° E (18°)**
	May 4 Morning	27° W (10°)
	Jul 17 Evening	27° E (14°)
	Aug 31 Morning	**18° W (16°)**
	Nov 11 Evening	23° E (9°)
	Dec 20 Morning	**22° W (16°)**
2045	**Mar 3 Evening**	**18° E (17°)**
	Apr 16 Morning	28° W (10°)
	Jun 28 Evening	**26° E (17°)**
	Aug 14 Morning	**19° W (16°)**
	Oct 24 Evening	24° E (8°)
	Dec 2 Morning	**20° W (17°)**
2046	**Feb 14 Evening**	**18° E (16°)**
	Mar 29 Morning	28° W (10°)
	Jun 10 Evening	**24° E (18°)**
	Jul 28 Morning	20° W (15°)
	Oct 7 Evening	25° E (8°)
	Nov 16 Morning	**19° W (17°)**
2047	**Jan 29 Evening**	**18° E (16°)**
	Mar 12 Morning	28° W (11°)
	May 23 Evening	**22° E (19°)**
	Jul 10 Morning	21° W (14°)
	Sep 19 Evening	27° E (9°)
	Oct 30 Morning	**19° W (17°)**

For More Information on Observing Mercury, See Page 138

	Date & Time to Observe	Elongation & (Degrees Above Horizon)
2048	Jan 12 Evening	19° E (15°)
	Feb 22 Morning	27° W (12°)
	May 4 Evening	**21° E (19°)**
	Jun 21 Morning	23° W (13°)
	Sep 1 Evening	27° E (9°)
	Oct 13 Morning	**18° W (17°)**
	Dec 26 Evening	20° E (13°)
2049	Feb 4 Morning	25° W (13°)
	Apr 16 Evening	**20° E (19°)**
	Jun 3 Morning	24° W (11°)
	Aug 14 Evening	27° E (11°)
	Sep 26 Morning	**18° W (17°)**
	Dec 9 Evening	21° E (12°)
2050	Jan 17 Morning	24° W (14°)
	Mar 30 Evening	**19° E (18°)**
	May 15 Morning	26° W (10°)
	Jul 28 Evening	27° E (13°)
	Sep 10 Morning	**18° W (16°)**
	Nov 22 Evening	22° E (10°)
	Dec 30 Morning	**23° W (16°)**
2051	**Mar 13 Evening**	**18° E (17°)**
	Apr 27 Morning	27° W (10°)
	Jul 10 Evening	26° E (15°)
	Aug 25 Morning	**18° W (16°)**
	Nov 4 Evening	23° E (9°)
	Dec 13 Morning	**21° W (17°)**

Mercury Elong

Venus at Greatest Elongation 2000 – 2021

Venus when Farthest from the Sun

These tables provide the dates when Venus is at Greatest Eastern or Western Elongation — when it appears farthest from the Sun in the sky. At these times, Venus is near half phase. About a month after Greatest Eastern Elongation and a month before Greatest Western Elongation, Venus is at its brightest, around magnitude −4.5 and appears as a large crescent, visible with binoculars. Dates and times based on Mountain Standard Time.

For More Information on Observing Venus, See Page 139

Year	Date & Time to Observe		Elongation (Degrees from Sun)	Year	Date & Time to Observe		Elongation (Degrees from Sun)
2000	No Greatest Elongations			2011	Jan 8	Morning	47° W
2001	Jan 17	Evening	47° E	2012	Mar 27	Evening	46° E
	Jun 7	Morning	46° W		Aug 15	Morning	46° W
2002	Aug 22	Evening	46° E	2013	Nov 1	Evening	47° E
2003	Jan 10	Morning	47° W	2014	Mar 22	Morning	47° W
2004	Mar 29	Evening	46° E	2015	Jun 6	Evening	45° E
	Aug 17	Morning	46° W		Oct 26	Morning	46° W
2005	Nov 3	Evening	47° E	2016	No Greatest Elongations		
2006	Mar 25	Morning	47° W	2017	Jan 12	Evening	47° E
2007	Jun 8	Evening	45° E		Jun 3	Morning	46° W
	Oct 28	Morning	47° W	2018	Aug 17	Evening	46° E
2008	No Greatest Elongations			2019	Jan 5	Morning	47° W
2009	Jan 14	Evening	47° E	2020	Mar 24	Evening	46° E
	Jun 5	Morning	46° W		Aug 12	Morning	46° W
2010	Aug 19	Evening	46° E	2021	Oct 29	Evening	47° E

Venus Elong

Facing page. *The top image was taken in 1990 by the Galileo spacecraft on its way to Jupiter (arrived at Jupiter in December 1995). Venus is normally white to the eyes, but this picture, taken in ultraviolet-light was colorized to bring out details in the clouds. The bottom image is a composite of many images taken by the Magellan spacecraft that orbited Venus from 1990 to 1994. Since Venus is covered in thick sulfuric-acid clouds, radar was used to penetrate the clouds and provide this mapping.*

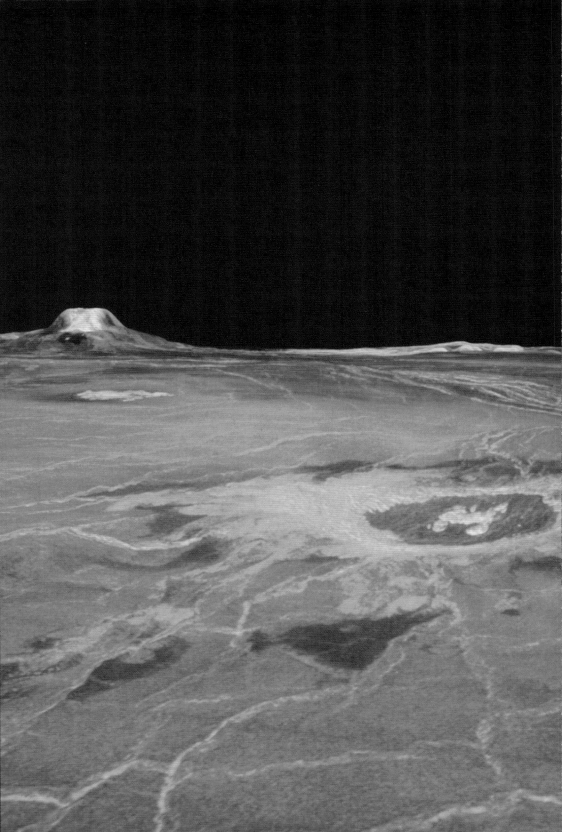

Venus at Greatest Elongation 2022 – 2051

Venus when Farthest from the Sun

Year	Date & Time to Observe	Elongation (Degrees fron Sun)	Year	Date & Time to Observe	Elongation (Degrees fron Sun)
2022	Mar 20 Morning	47° W	2038	Mar 15 Morning	47° W
2023	Jun 4 Evening	45° E	2039	May 30 Evening	45° E
	Oct 23 Morning	46° W		Oct 18 Morning	46° W
2024	No Greatest Elongations		2040	No Greatest Elongations	
2025	Jan 9 Evening	47° E	2041	Jan 5 Evening	47° E
	May 31 Morning	46° W		May 27 Morning	46° W
2026	Aug 14 Evening	46° E	2042	Aug 10 Evening	46° E
2027	Jan 3 Morning	47° W		Dec 29 Morning	47° W
2028	Mar 22 Evening	46° E	2043	No Greatest Elongations	
	Aug 10 Morning	46° W	2044	Mar 17 Evening	46° E
2029	Oct 27 Evening	47° E		Aug 5 Morning	46° W
2030	Mar 17 Morning	47° W	2045	Oct 22 Evening	47° E
2031	Jun 1 Evening	45° E	2046	Mar 12 Morning	47° W
	Oct 21 Morning	46° W	2047	May 28 Evening	45° E
2032	No Greatest Elongations			Oct 16 Morning	46° W
2033	Jan 7 Evening	47° E	2048	No Greatest Elongations	
	May 29 Morning	46° W	2049	Jan 2 Evening	47° E
2034	Aug 12 Evening	46° E		May 24 Morning	46° W
2035	Jan 1 Morning	47° W	2050	Aug 7 Evening	46° E
2036	Mar 19 Evening	46° E		Dec 27 Morning	47° W
	Aug 8 Morning	46° W	2051	No Greatest Elongations	
2037	Oct 24 Evening	47° E			

For More Information
on Observing Venus,
See Page 139

Venus Elong

Facing page. A computer-generated picture of the surface of Venus from data collected by the Magellan spacecraft that orbited Venus from 1990 to 1994. *Page 204.* The moon Dione of Saturn (see table on page 149) as imaged by the Cassini Orbiter in 2005.

Conjunctions 2000 – 2025

Planets and Moon Close Together in the Sky

When the Planets or Moon appear close to one another in the sky, they are said to be in conjunction. How close is close? For these tables, I have chosen the closest approaches, of a Moon diameter or less. Conjunctions do not hold any special astronomical significance because they represent the random alignment of the Planets and Moon as they circle the Sun or Earth. However, conjunctions are pretty. It is very striking to see two bright celestial bodies close to one another in the sky. And, all you need to enjoy the sight is your naked eyes.

SPECIAL NOTE: For many of the conjunctions listed that involve the Moon, the Planet will be occulted, that is, the Moon will pass in front of the Planet for a short period of time. Please consult the popular monthly astronomy magazines for more information about these events for your specific location.

Date & Time to Observe		Celestial Bodies and Degrees of Separation (Moon's diameter is 0.5°)	
Aug 10	Early Morning	**Mercury & Mars**	0.07°
Sep 10	Early Morning	**Moon & Saturn**	0.02°
Nov 30	Early Evening	**Moon & Saturn**	0.21°
Dec 28	Early A.M.	**Moon & Saturn**	0.04°
Jul 2	Early Morning	**Mercury & Saturn**	0.21°
Jul 17	Early A.M.	**Moon & Mars**	0.48°
Jul 26	After Sunset	**Mercury & Jupiter**	0.35°
Dec 23	Early Evening	**Moon & Mars**	0.48°
Feb 21	Early Evening	**Venus & Mars**	0.40°
Jun 30	Early Evening	**Venus & Jupiter**	0.33°
Feb 18	Early Morning	**Moon & Mars**	0.15°
May 28	After Sunset	**Mercury & Venus**	0.39°
Aug 18	After Sunset	**Mercury & Mars**	0.07°
Dec 7	Early Evening	**Moon & Mars**	0.12°
Jan 30	Late Night	**Moon & Mars**	0.17°
May 17	Early Morning	**Moon & Jupiter**	0.08°
Sep 17	Early Morning	**Moon & Saturn**	0.15°
Jan 13	Evening	**Moon & Mars**	0.00°

Conjunctions 2029 – 2045

Planets and Moon Close Together in the Sky

Conjunctions

Date & Time to Observe		Celestial Bodies and Degrees of Separation (Moon's diameter is 0.5°)	
Oct 10	Early Evening	Moon & Venus	0.18°
Aug 13	Early Morning	Venus & Saturn	0.34°
May 11	Early Evening	Venus & Mars	0.44°
Sep 28	Early Morning	Moon & Jupiter	0.04°
Nov 10	Late Night	Moon & Mars	0.47°
Jul 19	After Sunset	Mars & Saturn	0.11°
Oct 15	Early Morning	Moon & Saturn	0.09°
Jan 5	Early Morning	Moon & Saturn	0.17°
Feb 28	Early Evening	Moon & Saturn	0.01°
Nov 27	Early Morning	Moon & Jupiter	0.38°
Dec 24	Early Morning	Moon & Jupiter	0.09°
Mar 15	Late Night	Moon & Jupiter	0.43°
May 9	Early Evening	Moon & Jupiter	0.29°
Jun 6	Late Night	Moon & Mars	0.15°
Nov 2	Early Morning	Venus & Jupiter	0.21°
Dec 3	Late Night	Moon & Mars	0.39°
Sep 12	After Sunset	Venus & Mars	0.21°
Oct 8	Early Evening	Moon & Venus	0.35°
Nov 30	Early Morning	Moon & Saturn	0.40°
Feb 20	Late Night	Moon & Jupiter	0.21°
Jul 6	Late Night	Moon & Jupiter	0.23°
Feb 4	Evening	Moon & Mars	0.11°
Jun 21	Early Evening	Mercury & Venus	0.42°
Sep 8	Early Morning	Moon & Mars	0.18°

Conjunctions 2047 – 2051

Planets and Moon Close Together in the Sky

	Date & Time to Observe		Celestial Bodies and Degrees of Separation (Moon's diameter is 0.5°)	
2047	Feb 24	Early Evening	**Venus & Mars**	0.29°
	Nov 7	Early Morning	**Venus & Mars**	0.11°
2048	Jan 30	Early Morning	**Venus & Saturn**	0.07°
	May 28	Early A.M.	**Moon & Mars**	0.03°
	May 29	Late Night	**Moon & Saturn**	0.17°
	Aug 19	Evening	**Moon & Saturn**	0.02°
	Sep 29	Early Morning	**Moon & Jupiter**	0.41°
2049	Feb 11	Evening	**Moon & Jupiter**	0.31°

Dates & Time are based on Mountain Standard Time

There are no "major" conjunctions in 2050 or 2051.

Conjunctions

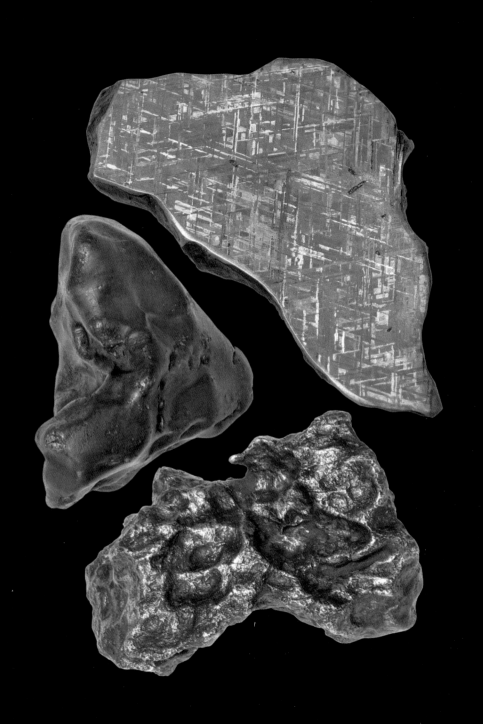

Meteors & Showers

On a typical clear night, while looking at the sky, you stand a good change of seeing a meteor, commonly called a shooting star. In fact, normally, about seven meteors per hour can be seen. But at specific times of the year, there are meteor showers which may allow you to see 15 to 100 meteors per hour. On very rare occasions, and if you are very fortunate, you may witness a storm with thousands of meteors falling per hour.

Meteoroid, Meteor and Meteorite

These terms are often confused. A meteoroid is a small rock in space. When a meteoroid enters the Earth's atmosphere, we view it as a white luminous streak called a meteor. If the meteoroid survives its journey through the atmosphere to reach the Earth's surface as a "rock," it is then called a meteorite.

Meteoroid	Small rock in space (or grain of sand)
Meteor	White luminous streak seen in sky
Meteorite	"Space rock" on ground

Size, Speed & Height

Most meteors are caused by meteoroids the size of a grain of sand. Atmospheric speeds reach up to 45 miles per second or 162,000 miles per hour (72 km/sec or 257,500 km/hr), and trail heights range from 30 to 60 miles (48 to 96 km) above the Earth's surface.

The Bright Ones

A very bright meteor, about the brightness of Jupiter (magnitude −3) or brighter is called either a fireball or bolide, although, if it explodes in the air or is accompanied by sound, it is usually referred to as a bolide. The trail of bright meteors can show some color.

*Facing page. Three iron meteorites whose composition is mostly iron and nickel. At the top is a slice that has been polished and etched with nitric acid to bring out the crisscrossing Widmanstatten pattern, a pattern unique to metal rocks that formed in space. The cone-shaped meteorite in the middle was so shaped by its steady passage through the atmosphere. The bottom meteorite is covered with dimples that are informally called thumbprints, formed by tumbling through the atmosphere with the passing air blowing "bowls" into the molten surface. These meteorites originated from the asteroid belt and would have been seen as fireballs in the sky. **Top.** A rare meteorite from Mars.*

Meteor Showers

Meteor Showers

Meteor showers are generated by sand-size silicate particles left behind by comets. A dozen meteor showers occur every year as the Earth passes through semi-permanent fields of cometary debris that also orbit the Sun.

Earth intersects the debris fields at specific points along its path about the Sun. Hence, meteors associated with showers radiate from particular spots in the sky. In fact, if you photographed the meteors from a shower and extended their streaks, they would all intersect at the same point in the sky. Showers are named after the constellation from which the meteors appear to originate.

New showers will be established when future cometary debris crosses Earth's orbit. Existing showers will eventually fade away as debris dissipates. The Perseids have been around for a thousand years, while there is no indication of the Quadrantids further back than 200 years.

Meteor Storms

The last storm was associated with the Leonids in 1966. For a period of about an hour, hundreds of thousands of meteors pierced the sky. To say the least, watching meteors rain down, filling the entire sky would be awesome!

The Draconids and Leonids are currently the only known showers capable of storms. Storms result when the Earth hits pockets of concentrated silicate particles. At this time, scientists cannot accurately predict the occurence of storms. Debris from new comets in the future may also produce such displays.

Woodcut depicting the November 12, 1799 Leonids storm.

OBSERVING METEORS & SHOWERS

Meteors are observed best with the naked eye. It is not practical to view them with binoculars or a telescope because they last just a fraction of a second and extend arcs greater than what can be viewed through these instruments. Additionally, their appearance and paths in the sky cannot be predicted.

Annual Showers

Annual Meteor Showers

Shower[1] (Constellation)	Date[2]		Hourly Rate[3]
	Peak	(Active Period)	
QUADRANTIDS (Bootes)[4]	**January 3**	(Jan 1 – Jan 5)	60 – 200
LYRIDS (Lyra)	**April 22**	(Apr 16 – Apr 25)	15 – 20+
Eta (η) AQUARIDS (Aquarius)[5]	**May 5**	(Apr 19 – May 28)	60
Southern Delta (δ) AQUARIDS[5]	**July 29**	(Jul 12 – Aug 19)	20
PERSEIDS (Perseus)	**August 12**	(Jul 17 – Aug 24)	120 – 160
DRACONIDS (Draco)	**October 8**	(Oct 6 – Oct 10)	5[6]
ORIONIDS (Orion)	**October 21**	(Oct 2 – Nov 7)	20
Southern TAURIDS (Taurus)	**November 5**	(Oct 1 – Nov 25)	5
Northern TAURIDS	**November 13**	(Oct 1 – Nov 25)	5
LEONIDS (Leo)	**November 17**	(Nov 14 – Nov 21)	10[6]
GEMINIDS (Gemini)	**December 14**	(Dec 7 – Dec 17)	120
URSIDS (Ursa Minor)	**December 22**	(Dec 17 – Dec 26)	10+

[1]Showers have traditionally been named after the constellation they appear to radiate from. [2]Peak date is approximate and may vary by a day from year to year. [3]Hourly rate is frequency or number of meteors per hour around the Peak date. [4]The Quadrantids was named after an obsolete constellation recognized in the 1800s. Today, this shower is sometimes referred to as the Bootids, after the constellation Bootes. [5]The constellation Aquarius has two associated showers which are distinguished by the Greek letter designation of the stars closest to the radiant points. [6]These showers have the potential to become meteor storms, with spectacular displays of thousands of meteors per hour.

Meteors not associated with showers are called sporadic meteors. Both sporadic meteors and shower meteors can appear *anywhere* in the sky. Although the meteors from showers originate from "spots" in the sky, this will not be immediately apparent when you watch showers. So, it is not necessary to face the constellation associated with the shower. I have found that lying on a lawn chair and looking up is not only comfortable, it also allows one to see the most meteors possible during such events.

Although the most favorable time to observe meteors or showers is from around midnight to early morning when the night side of the Earth is moving toward the meteoroids, don't let this dissuade you from watching during the more convenient early evening. And, the viewing is best when the Moon is not out.

Oh, those beautiful Comets!

Comets are spectacular to behold. They span the sky in a splendor unequaled by any other celestial object. But what I really like about comets is that they bring astronomy to continents of people — in a grand display that unites us in the awe of the Universe.

In earlier times, comets were harbingers of the future. Something as impressive as the unexpected appearance of a comet in the sky had to be significant! Depending on the culture, a comet represented either a good or bad omen.

Today, we can enjoy comets as neither good nor bad but as the spectacular objects they are. It is good fortune when we get the opportunity to view one of these marvelous treasures.

Bright comets are like unexpected gifts — we remember them with a special fondness.

Famous Comets to Grace our Skies
The really great comets appear less often than we might like. Here are the best since 1682.

1682. Comet Halley. Named after the English astronomer Edmond Halley (1656–1742) who concluded that this was the same comet that appeared in 1531 and 1607. Comet Halley returns about every 76 years. Its regularity along with its brightness have made it the most familiar comet in the Solar System. During its 1986 appearance, six research spacecraft were sent out to learn more about it.

1744. Comet Chéseaux. Spectacular six-tailed comet.

1769. Comet Messier. The brightest comet discovered by the "Comet Ferret" and the year Napoleon was born.

1843. Great March Comet. Longest recorded tail.

1882. Great September Comet. Visible during the daytime.

1910. Comet Halley. Spectacular return display. Not all returns of Halley's comet are spectacular.

1976. Comet West. Really nice but never got much publicity.

Facing page. Comet Hale-Bopp with its two tails. The blue tail is the ion tail and the whitish the dust tail. *Above.* The impactor that was purposely crashed into Comet Tempel 1 in 2005 in order to study its composition.

Comets

Origin of Comets

1993. Comet Shoemaker-Levy 9. Discovered the night of March 23, 1993, by Gene and Carolyn Shoemaker and David Levy from photographs taken at the Palomar Observatory complex in California. On July 16, 1994, this comet, which had broken into 21 fragments, rained down on Jupiter for a week. The impacts disrupted Jupiter's clouds for almost a year, and the initial scars were visible in small telescopes. This collision was the most spectacular astronomical event of the twentieth century.

1995. Comet Hale-Bopp. A very beautiful comet.

1996. Comet Hyakutake. This comet took astronomers by surprise because they were in the midst of observing and investigating Hale-Bopp.

Origin and Orbits of Comets
Comets are leftover aggregate from the formation of our Solar System. They represent matter that did not condense into the Sun, Planets or moons. They circle the Sun in very elongated, elliptical orbits with revolution periods ranging from just a few years to tens of thousands of years. Some of their orbits reach halfway to our nearest star, Proxima Centauri, four light years away.

Orbit of Halley's Comet

JUPITER's Orbit

PLUTO's Orbit

Halley's Orbit. Revolution about 76 years. Closest approach to Sun is a little farther than Mercury.

There are three major groupings of comets. Based on their orbits, they are named the Jupiter family, the Kuiper belt and the Oort cloud.

The Jupiter family contains a small number of comets with orbits that reach a little farther than Jupiter's and revolve around the Sun in as little as 3½ years (Comet Encke is the most well known). Jupiter's strong gravity has created this family by "roping in" longer period comets.

The Kuiper belt comets reside in a region that extends from beyond Neptune to about 1,000 astronomical units. These shorter period comets have revolution periods of around 200 years.

Composition of Comets

Most comets have long orbital periods in the thousands of years. Their orbits take them to the outer reaches of our Solar System, into the Oort cloud. They can reach distances of 20,000 to 100,000 astronomical units (1.6 light years) from the Sun. The Oort cloud is a roughly spherical area that surrounds the Sun and contains the bulk of the comets, estimated at a few trillion.

The Size and and Composition of Comets

The nuclei of comets, that is, their solid bodies, vary in size. Diameters range from just a few to perhaps 150 miles (3 to 240 km). Comet Halley's nucleus is the only one ever imaged. It resembles a potato in shape and measures approximately 9.5 by 6 miles (15.3 by 9.6 km). Comet Hale-Bopp's nucleus is estimated to be 37 miles (60 km) in diameter, which is considered a large comet.

Comet Attributes

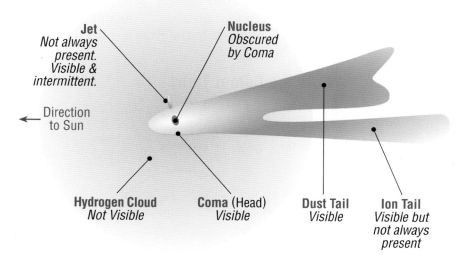

Jet
Not always present. Visible & intermittent.

Nucleus
Obscured by Coma

← **Direction to Sun**

Hydrogen Cloud
Not Visible

Coma (Head)
Visible

Dust Tail
Visible

Ion Tail
Visible but not always present

Comets

The often used phrase "dirty snowball" aptly describes a comet's composition. Comets are a mixture of various ices, called ice volatiles (frozen water, ammonia, methane and other chemicals) and dust (sand-size silicate particles — the basic mineral of rocks).

Composition of Comets

As a comet approaches the Sun and heats up, the ice volatiles in the nucleus sublime, that is, they change directly from solids to gases, to become the coma and tail. A new comet would be considered an asteroid until it develops a coma or tail.

The coma can have a diameter of 125,000 to 1.2 million miles (200,000 to 2 million km) and always obscures the small nucleus. Comas start to develop at a distance around three astronomical units (between Mars and Jupiter), the tails a little farther out. In 1970, it was discovered that an invisible, tenuous hydrogen cloud extends from the coma, with a diameter in the range of millions of miles.

Comet tails can stretch for millions of miles; the longest being around 1½ astronomical units. The solar wind and pressure from sunlight push the tail away from the Sun. Often, comets develop two tails: a yellowish-white dust tail and a blue ion tail (blue from fluorescing ions). Either one or both tails may be present.

A comet may exhibit a jet or jets, which are spurious eruptions that shoot out from the nucleus. They develop when pockets of ice volatiles are exposed. A jet can turn on and off, depending on the rotation of the nucleus and exposure to the Sun.

As the Comet Turns

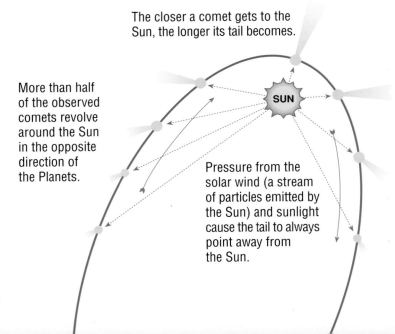

The closer a comet gets to the Sun, the longer its tail becomes.

More than half of the observed comets revolve around the Sun in the opposite direction of the Planets.

SUN

Pressure from the solar wind (a stream of particles emitted by the Sun) and sunlight cause the tail to always point away from the Sun.

Observing Comets

A Comet's Legacy: Meteor Showers

The annual meteor showers are compliments of comets. Showers occur when the Earth passes through the wakes of comets, containing sand-size silicate particles (see page 211).

When will the next comet appear?

Astronomers cannot predict when bright, visible comets will appear. Most comets come from the outer regions of our Solar System and do not become noticeable until they get close to the Sun. They wait for individuals like David Levy to gaze up and discover them so they can be announced to the world.

Unexpected gifts are often remembered the most, and so it is with comets. These unexpected and marvelous guests leave us with the fondest memories.

OBSERVING COMETS

When a bright comet is in the sky, everyone starts looking up. Whether you are out in a parking lot or in your backyard, you will see eyes gazing upward to glimpse the splendor in the heavens.

The naked eye, binoculars and telescopes at low magnifications can be used to observe the large visible comets. Binoculars mounted on a tripod are a good observing combination. Binoculars will enable you to see most or all of a comet in the same field of view while the tripod will help steady the binoculars and allow easy extended viewing.

Although the bright and highly visible comets are what we long for, unfortunately, they appear too infrequently. However, every year, a few new comets are usually discovered but they are too faint to be seen with the naked eye. They can only be viewed with telescopes. Their paths and magnitudes are often posted on the internet.

Comets

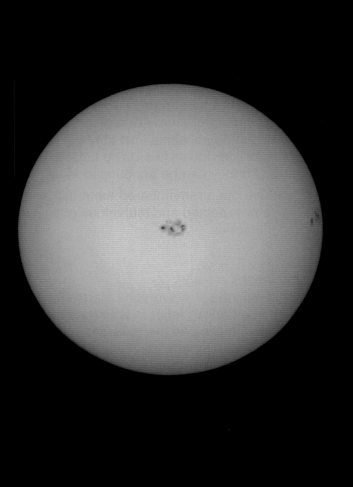

Our Sun

How often do we stop and think of the Sun when we think of the day? I think we take our days and nights for granted because they are natural, automatic cycles, like breathing. And, more importantly, how often do we think of the Sun when we think of life on Earth? The energy from the Sun is the reason that life developed and is sustained on Earth.

Although the Sun is special to us, it *is* like all the other stars in the sky. Stars are created in a simple and natural process. They are the most common celestial object in the Universe. And, galaxies represent their abodes, where these fiery balls are congregated, where they are born, live and die.

Nuclear Fusion and the Sun's Life

Our Sun is a typical or average star. Like all stars, its energy comes from nuclear fusion. Four hydrogen atoms are fused (forced) together to create one helium atom in the core of the Sun. The mass of the resulting helium atom is 1% less than the total mass of the four hydrogen atoms. The 1% difference in mass produces the energy that we see as the blazing Sun. About five million tons (4½ million metric tons) of matter are converted into energy every second in the core of the Sun. Fusion in the Sun is triggered by the tremendous pressure at the core, brought about by the sheer mass of the Sun. The Sun does not collapse upon itself because of the outward expansive pressure of the generated energy.

Our Sun's energy is produced from the conversion of matter into energy as expressed by Einstein's equation $E = mc^2$.

The Sun is about 4.6 billon years old and will last for another 5.5 billion years. Toward the end of its life, it will become a red giant with an outer atmosphere extending to about the orbit of Mercury. During its final days, the Sun will shed its outer layers in one final heave. Outwardly, this heave will produce a planetary nebula (see page 242) while the core shrinks inward to become a white dwarf, an

Facing page. The Sun as it appears through a small telescope using a "regular" white-light solar filter. Sunspots are easily visible with this type of filter. The orange color in this photo is intense because the exposure was longer than normal in order to bring out detail in the very large sunspot. ***Above.*** A looping solar prominence that requires a special hydrogen-alpha filter to see.

Structure of the Sun

object no bigger than the Earth but with significantly more mass and a high surface temperature.

Structure of the Sun

Interior. Nuclear fusion occurs in the interior core where the temperature reaches 27,000,000° F (15,000,000° C). Outside the core is a radiative zone where a process of energy absorption and re-emission takes place. This zone transfers energy from the core to the convection zone that lies below the visible surface. The convection zone has huge circulating currents that transfer the energy from the radiative zone to the surface. It takes about 200,000 years for light to make its way from the core to the surface.

Surface. The visible surface, called the photosphere, is composed of a lattice of cells, each about the size of Texas, called granules. Granules are the tops of the convection currents that bring the energy from the convection zone to the surface.

Sunspots are visible on the photosphere and are associated with strong magnetic fields that restrict the convection currents, creating cooler areas that appear darker against the brighter photosphere. Sunspots are about 6,300° F (3,500° C) compared to an average surface temperature of 10,000° F (5,500° C).

Immediately above the photosphere is a thin layer of gases about 2,000 miles (3,220 km) thick called the chromosphere. The temperature there ranges from just 7,600° F (4,200° C) near the photosphere to 14,800° F (8,200° C) at its outer edge.

Beyond the chromosphere is the corona, the most tenuous part of the Sun's atmosphere. This rarified hydrogen gas reaches temperatures of up to 1,800,000° F (1,000,000° C) and extends for millions of miles from the surface. The corona is visible during total solar eclipses as the irregular halo surrounding the Moon.

Prominences (as pictured on pages 135 & 219) are massive protrusions of ionized gas carried from the surface of the Sun into the corona. They usually protrude outward but sometimes loop back to the surface. Large prominences easily extend 10 to 30 Earth diameters from the photosphere.

Sun

Solar Surface & Atmosphere

Sun Parts

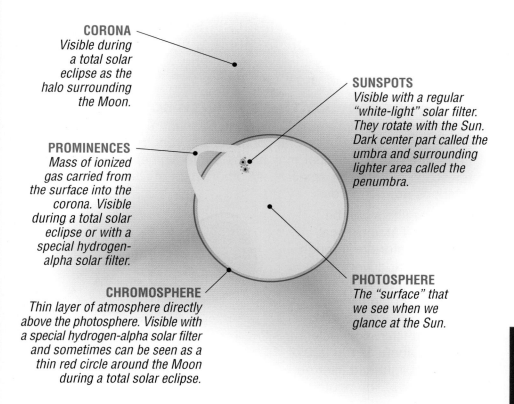

CORONA
Visible during a total solar eclipse as the halo surrounding the Moon.

PROMINENCES
Mass of ionized gas carried from the surface into the corona. Visible during a total solar eclipse or with a special hydrogen-alpha solar filter.

CHROMOSPHERE
Thin layer of atmosphere directly above the photosphere. Visible with a special hydrogen-alpha solar filter and sometimes can be seen as a thin red circle around the Moon during a total solar eclipse.

SUNSPOTS
Visible with a regular "white-light" solar filter. They rotate with the Sun. Dark center part called the umbra and surrounding lighter area called the penumbra.

PHOTOSPHERE
The "surface" that we see when we glance at the Sun.

A flare is like a prominence but releases enormous amounts of energy and energetic particles into the Solar System, causing the aurorae on Earth as well as radio and communication disruptions.

The Sun produces a solar wind made of highly ionized gas that permeates the Solar System. This gas can reach speeds up to 435 miles per second (700 km/sec) with a density varying from 160 to 1,600 particles per cubic inch (10 to 100 particles per cubic centimeter). Additionally, sunlight itself exerts a small amount of pressure. Both the solar wind and radiating sunlight are responsible for pushing a comet's tail away from the Sun.

Safely Observing the Sun/Solar Filters

SAFELY OBSERVING THE SUN WITH SOLAR FILTERS

There is only one safe way to view the Sun with a telescope, and that is to use a solar filter that completely covers the front of the telescope (the actual filter may be the same diameter as your telescope or could be smaller). *All* other types of filters or methods are dangerous!

Solar filters can be purchased at your local telescope store or through retailers that advertise in the popular monthly astronomy magazines. DO NOT attempt to make your own filter. Solar filters transmit about 1/100,000 of the Sun's light and filter out harmful rays. The photo to the right shows a telescope fitted with a solar filter for safely viewing the Sun.

Use ONLY solar filters that completely cover the front of the telescope. All other filters or methods to view the Sun are dangerous! Note that the reflex-sight finder is also covered.

Once the filter is fastened securely to the front of the telescope, use the telescope in a normal fashion.

IMPORTANT: Remember to cover up your finderscope or reflex-sight finder — better yet, remove it! These also present viewing hazards and/or can be damaged by the Sun if they are not covered. To point the telescope at the Sun, let the telescope's shadow be your guide. Move the telescope until the shadow of its tube is smallest. The Sun should then be in or near your eyepiece field of view if you are using a low magnification around 50x.

Observing the Sun

OBSERVING THE SUN

The Sun emits so much energy that many of its features are overpowered by its brilliance. With a regular, white-light solar filter, only the photosphere and sunspots are visible. A special hydrogen-alpha filter is required to view prominences.

Sunspots. Sunspots are plainly visible with a regular, white-light solar filter. They form, grow and dissipate, rotating with the Sun, changing their appearance daily. The inner and darkest part of a sunspot is called the umbra, while the surrounding lighter area is called the penumbra. Sunspots often appear in groups composed of many larger and smaller spots.

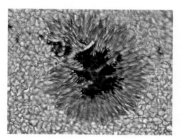

Sunspot closeup. The darkest part is called the umbra and the surrounding lighter part, which looks similar to embroidery, is the penumbra.

There is an 11-year waxing and waning cycle of sunspot activity, however, the length of this cycle can vary by a few years.

Prominences. In order to view prominences, telescopes must be fitted with a special hydrogen-alpha filter. Unfortunately, these filters are expensive, therefore they are not common (they start at around $2,000 as of this book's printing).

Hydrogen-alpha filters transmit only a very narrow range of light on the red end of the spectrum where prominences are visible. Prominences cannot be seen with regular light-white solar filters because they get "washed out" among all the other colors that these filters transmit. Without a hydrogen-alpha filter, prominences can sometimes be seen around the edge of the Moon during a total solar eclipse.

The hydrogen-alpha filter provides incredible views of the Sun. Not only will you see prominences, but you will also see the Sun's mottled surface as well as the chromosphere. Changes in prominences occur hourly. I highly recommend making inquires at your local planetarium, club or telescope store about the possibility of observing the Sun through a hydrogen-alpha filter.

Sun

Solar & Lunar Eclipses

A total solar eclipse is one of the most spectacular natural events to behold. Those who witness total solar eclipses consider themselves fortunate. They carry an indelible impression that is as much visual as it is emotional. It is disheartening that most people never experience one of the greatest astronomical and sensory events on our Planet.

It is an incredible coincidence that the Sun and Moon appear the same size in the sky. It is even more amazing that our Moon gets the chance to perfectly eclipse the Sun. The odds of this coincidence are brought to light when we consider that our Moon is the only moon in our Solar System that perfectly eclipses the Sun. All the other moons of the Planets are either too large or too small in their orbits to eclipse the Sun in precisely the same manner as ours.

Our Moon is the only moon in our Solar System that perfectly eclipses the Sun.

Although I have emphasized the glorious nature of the total solar eclipse, I don't want to undermine the beauty of a total lunar eclipse. But they are two different kinds of events. Total lunar eclipses are great "casual" events that allow one to comfortably sit and watch the coloration of the Moon gradually change as it moves through the Earth's shadow.

Overview of Solar and Lunar Eclipses

Both solar and lunar eclipses involve an alignment of the Earth, Moon and Sun. A solar eclipse is the blocking of the Sun by the Moon, either partially or totally. A lunar eclipse is the blocking of the Moon's light (from the Sun) by Earth's shadow.

Solar eclipses can occur only at the time of New Moon; lunar eclipses only at the time of Full Moon.

In order to see a total or annular solar eclipse, one must be on a narrow path that can stretch for a thousand miles or so on the Earth. Only those on the path will see the total or annular eclipse — those near it will see only a partial eclipse. On the other hand, lunar eclipses can be seen by almost everyone on the night side of the world.

*Facing page. The bright "flare" at the top of this total solar eclipse picture is known as a "diamond-ring effect" and is produced by a minute vestige of the Sun's surface that pokes through the edge of the Moon. **Above**. Everyone gets to experience at least a few partial solar eclipses during their life.*

Solar & Lunar Eclipses

Umbra and Penumbra Shadows

These are the names of the shadows responsible for all eclipses. The umbra is the innermost and darkest shadow. The penumbra is a secondary shadow around the umbra. You will see a solar eclipse if you are in the Moon's umbra or penumbra shadow. Lunar eclipses occur when the Moon passes into Earth's umbra or penumbra shadow.

This exaggerated illustration depicts the formation of the umbra at (a) and the surrounding penumbra at (b). The geometry of these shadows is a result of the Sun's diameter.

Umbra and penumbra shadows are visible whenever it is sunny. If you look at the edge of an object's shadow, you will notice that it is fuzzy. This fuzzy edge is the penumbra and the main body of the shadow is the umbra.

Solar Eclipses

There are three types of solar eclipses: total, annular and partial. They are illustrated and explained below.

Total Solar Eclipse
Moon completely blocks Sun. The irregularly shaped halo around the Moon is the Sun's corona.

Annular Solar Eclipse
Moon moves completely in front of the Sun but does not cover the Sun.

Partial Solar Eclipse
Moon only partially blocks Sun. Those outside the path of a total or annular eclipse only see a partial eclipse.

Why do annular eclipses occur? The Moon's orbit, like those of all orbiting bodies, is an ellipse; so the distance from the Moon to the Earth varies (see page 102). Annular eclipses occur when the Moon is farther away in its orbit than usual, making the apparent size of the Moon slightly smaller than the apparent size of the Sun. In these instances, the Moon is simply too small to totally block the Sun.

Solar & Lunar Eclipses

Total Solar Eclipses

1 **UMBRA.** The darkest part of the shadow where a total eclipse can *only* be seen. On Earth, the umbra can reach 170 miles (270 km) wide and travel one-third of the way around the world in a few hours.

2 **PENUMBRA.** The secondary shadow where only a partial eclipse of the Sun will be seen. The penumbra is thousands of miles wide and straddles the path of the umbra on the Earth's surface.

3 Observers outside of the penumbra will not see the Sun eclipsed.

*The **umbra path** for the total solar eclipse of August 21, 2017. The penumbra stretches for thousands of miles on both sides of the umbra.*

Lunar Eclipses

1 **TOTAL LUNAR ECLIPSES** occur when the Moon enters the Earth's umbra shadow. The Moon does not turn completely dark during a total lunar eclipse, instead, it turns a pretty red-orange color. A lunar eclipse is visible to almost half of the world.

2 **PARTIAL LUNAR ECLIPSES** occur when only part of the Moon enters the Earth's umbra shadow. Partial lunar eclipses will show one edge of the Moon turning a slight orange color.

3 **PENUMBRAL LUNAR ECLIPSES** occur when the Moon only enters the Earth's penumbra shadow. Penumbral lunar eclipses may not be noticeable.

Eclipses

Solar & Lunar Eclipses

Lunar Eclipses

Lunar eclipses can be total, partial or penumbral, however, they do not share the characteristics of solar eclipses. Total lunar eclipses turn the Moon into a dark red-orange color instead of turning it completely black. The red-orange color is caused by sunlight refracted through the Earth's atmosphere. You see the same coloring at sunrise and sunset. Partial lunar eclipses may not be noticeable with the exception that an edge of the Moon may turn a little orange. Penumbral eclipses are usually not noticeable to the average observer.

Why Eclipses Do Not Happen Every Month

Solar and lunar eclipses do not happen every month because the Moon's orbit is tilted 5.1° to Earth's orbit, placing the Moon above or below the Sun or Earth's shadow at New Moon and Full Moon most of the time. The Moon must be positioned exactly at the point where its orbit crosses the Earth's orbit for an eclipse to occur. The Earth, Moon and Sun get perfectly aligned every 173 days, producing an eclipse somewhere on Earth.

Eclipses

Missed Eclipses

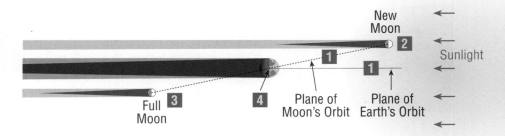

1. **The Moon's orbit is tilted 5.1° to the Earth's orbit.** This slight tilt is enough to place the shadows necessary for eclipses out of reach of the Earth or Moon.

2. The shadow of most **New Moons** falls either above or below the Earth.

3. At **Full Moon**, the Moon is usually above or below the Earth's shadow.

4. **Eclipses occur** when the Moon is either New or Full *and* the Moon crosses the plane of the Earth's orbit. This intersection happens every 173 days and this time interval is known as an eclipse season.

Observing Solar Eclipses

Frequency of Eclipses: The Saros

Up to two eclipses can occur during a 173-day eclipse season: one lunar and one solar. Anywhere from two to seven lunar and solar eclipses can therefore occur in a year. Eclipses also repeat themselves in 18 year cycles called Saros (actually 18 years, 11 days, 8 hours). So, all of the eclipses that happen in the year 2000 will repeat 18 years later in 2018. However, the 2018 eclipses will advance by 11 days and 8 hours, placing them one-third farther around the world than their previous locations. There are 42 Saros series running concurrently, providing us with an ongoing cycle of eclipses. The intensity of eclipses in a Saros (the ones that repeat every 18 years) waxes and wanes over time.

WARNING

Instant blindness or serious eye injury will result from looking at or near the Sun through telescopes, binoculars or cameras that are not properly equipped with solar filters.

OBSERVING SOLAR ECLIPSES

Safely Viewing an Eclipse. Safety of the eyes is of the utmost importance when viewing solar eclipses. Do not stare or even look directly at the Sun. Not only is this harmful to the eyes, but you cannot see the partially eclipsed Sun this way! I highly recommend using a solar or eclipse viewer/filter (like that pictured below). These inexpensive viewers are available at telescope shops, planetarium gift shops and from telescope dealers listed in the popular monthly astronomy magazines.

Eclipse viewers/filters like this are necessary for safely viewing the Sun during all solar eclipses. They can also be used to see large sunspots.

THOUSAND OAKS OPTICAL   SOLAR ECLIPSE VIEWER
Solar ECLIPSES 2000 to 2050

Eclipses

Observing Solar Eclipses

During a solar eclipse, the Moon's progress can be viewed with a telescope that is properly fitted with a solar filter. Please see page 222 on safely observing the Sun for more information.

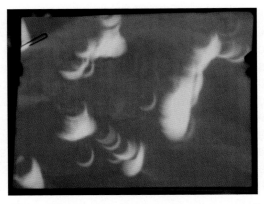

The multitude of crescents in this picture are the eclipsed Sun, projected through pinholes formed from the interweaving of leaves on a tree.

There are novel ways to view the progress of solar eclipses. My favorite is using trees. If you look at a tree's shadow (the tree must have leaves) during a solar eclipse, you will notice that mixed in with the shadow are hundreds of crescent Suns. A tree with leaves creates a multitude of pinholes (like a pinhole camera) that project the outline of the Sun. Some trees work better than others.

Partial and Annular Eclipses. Partial eclipses can last for several hours. They are not noticeable unless a substantial portion of the Sun is covered by the Moon. Even with half of the Sun eclipsed, you may not notice any appreciable difference in sunlight.

To observe an annular solar eclipse, consult the local media, internet or popular monthly astronomy magazines for the location of the eclipse path. You cannot see the annular eclipse if you are not in its path. It will not get dark during an annular eclipse and the Moon will only be completely in front of the Sun for several minutes.

A solar or eclipse viewer/filter is needed to view the Sun during the entire partial and annular eclipse.

Total Solar Eclipse & Totality. Remember, to see a total solar eclipse, you must be on the eclipse path. Consult the local media, internet or popular monthly astronomy magazines for details and locations of the path.

A total solar eclipse will last for several hours and is treated as a partial eclipse until the time of totality, that is, when the Moon completely blocks the Sun's light. During the one to five

Observing Lunar Eclipses

minutes of totality, no solar filter is required. Everyone stands and stares in wonder. Many things happen during totality. The sky darkens a little (it does not get completely dark), and almost immediately, the white shimmering corona is seen surrounding the Moon. Around the Moon's edge, the thin red ring of the chromosphere may be visible along with prominences and flares protruding outward. If you look at the sky around the Moon, you will probably see a few stars and Planets (usually Venus and Mercury) and if you scan the whole sky, you will see the umbra shadow circling the sky and extending almost to the horizon. The sky near the horizon is still light but may have a red coloring like that at sunset. The entire scene is incredible. There is nothing like it! No camera can capture the experience of totality, and everyone is touched differently. People clap, cheer, cry and pray. I recommend that everyone experience a total solar eclipse!

OBSERVING LUNAR ECLIPSES

No special equipment or caution is necessary to view lunar eclipses but binoculars and telescopes can be used to enhance the event. Lunar eclipses are especially enjoyable when you can sit outside, talk with others and casually watch the event unfold.

For the most part, the Moon will turn a dark red-orange when it is completely in Earth's umbra shadow. Various hues of red and orange will slowly dance across the Moon's surface as it enters, passes through and exits the umbra. Since the umbra is considerably larger than the Moon, total lunar eclipses can last up to 3½ hours. If the Moon crosses the umbra dead center, it takes about an hour to completely enter the umbra. It will stay in the umbra for 1½ hours and finish as it started, taking an hour to leave.

2000–2050 Solar and Lunar Eclipse Tables for North America on Pages 230–234

The solar and lunar eclipse tables on the following pages summarize the location and time of these events. Since the intensity of the event and the exact time vary considerably depending on your viewing location, please consult your local media, the internet or the popular monthly astronomy magazines for details. Enjoy.

Eclipses

231

SOLAR Eclipses 2000 – 2031

Solar Eclipses in North America

Date of Solar Eclipse	Type of Solar Eclipse	Time of Day to View[1]	Locations[2]
July 30, 2000	Partial	Around Sunset	*Alaska*, Western Canada, Northwest
December 25, 2000	Partial	Around Noon	*Midwest*, Continental US, Southern Canada
December 14, 2001	Partial	Early to Late Afternoon	*Hawaii*, Continental US
June 10, 2002	Partial	Late Afternoon	*West*, Midwest, Hawaii, Alaska, West Canada
May 30, 2003	Partial	Around Sunset	*Alaska*
April 8, 2005	Partial	Late Afternoon	*Florida*, South, Southwest
July 21, 2009	Partial	Around Sunset	*Hawaii*
May 20, 2012	**Annular**	**Around Sunset**	***West***, Hawaii, Alaska, Western Canada
May 9, 2013	Partial	Late Afternoon	*Hawaii*
October 23, 2014	Partial	Mid Afternoon	*West*, Midwest, Alaska, Western Canada
March 8, 2016	Partial	Around Sunset	*Hawaii*, Alaska
August 21, 2017	**Total**	**Around Noon**	***Across the US!*** Hawaii, Canada & Alaska
June 10, 2021	Partial	Early Morning	*Northeast*, East
October 14, 2023	**Annular**	**Late Morning**	***West*,** Continental US, Canada
April 8, 2024	**Total**	**Around Noon**	***Midwest*,** Continental US, Canada, Hawaii
October 2, 2024	Partial	Early Morning	*Hawaii*
August 12, 2026	Partial	Early to Late Morning	*Alaska* to Northeast
January 26, 2028	Partial	Late Morning	*Florida*, South, East, Midwest
January 14, 2029	Partial	Around Noon	*Canada*, Continental US
June 11, 2029	Partial	Around Sunset	*Alaska*, Canada, Northwest
November 14, 2031	Partial	Mid Afternoon	*Hawaii*, Southwest, South, Florida

[1]Check media sources for specific times for your location.
[2]First listed area is most favorable viewing location.

SOLAR Eclipses 2033 – 2051

Solar Eclipses in North America

Date of Solar Eclipse	Type of Solar Eclipse	Time of Day to View[1]	Locations[2]
March 30, 2033	**Total**	**Morning**	***Alaska***, Canada, Hawaii, West, Midwest
September 1, 2035	Partial	Around Sunset	*Hawaii*
August 21, 2036	Partial	Morning	*Alaska*
January 5, 2038	Partial	Early Morning	*East*, Florida
July 2, 2038	Partial	Early Morning	*Florida*, Southeast, East
June 21, 2039	**Annular**	**Early Morning**	***Alaska***, Canada, Hawaii, West, Midwest
November 4, 2040	Partial	Around Noon	*East*, Continental US, Canada
October 24, 2041	Partial	Late Afternoon	*Hawaii*
April 19, 2042	Partial	Around Sunset	*Alaska*, Northwest Canada, Hawaii
April 9, 2043	Partial	Around Noon	*Alaska*, Western Canada, Hawaii, Northwest
August 22, 2044	**Total**	**Around Sunset**	***Northwest***, Alaska, Canada, Hawaii, West
February 16, 2045	Partial	Late Afternoon	*Hawaii*
August 12, 2045	**Total**	**Around Noon**	***South to West***, Hawaii, Canada, Alaska
February 5, 2046	**Annular**	**Mid Afternoon**	**Hawaii**, Alaska, West
June 11, 2048	**Annular**	**Early Morning**	***Northern Midwest/ Canada***, East, South, Florida
May 31, 2049	Partial	Morning	*Florida*
November 14, 2050	Partial	Early Morning	*East Canada*, Northeast
April 10, 2051	Partial	Around Sunset	*Alaska*, Northwest Canada

[1]Check media sources for specific times for your location.
[2]First listed area is most favorable viewing location.

LUNAR Eclipses 2000 – 2021

Lunar Eclipses in North America

Date of Lunar Eclipse	Type of Lunar Eclipse	Time of Day to View[1]	Locations
January 20, 2000	Total	Around Midnight	Hawaii, Alaska, Continental US, Canada
July 16, 2000	Total	Before Sunrise	Hawaii, West Coast
July 5, 2001	Partial	Before Sunrise	Hawaii
May 15, 2003	Total	Before Midnight	Continental US, Canada
November 8, 2003	Total	Early Evening	Continental US, Canada
October 27, 2004	Total	Evening	Continental US, Canada
October 17, 2005	Penumbra	Before Sunrise	Hawaii, Alaska, West
March 14, 2006	Penumbra	Early Evening	East Coast
March 3, 2007	Total	Early Evening	East Coast
August 28, 2007	Total	Before Sunrise	Continental US, Canada
February 20, 2008	Total	Around Midnight	Continental US, Canada
June 26, 2010	Partial	Before Sunrise	Hawaii, West
December 21, 2010	Total	After Midnight	Hawaii, Alaska, Continental US, Canada
December 10, 2011	Total	Before Sunrise	Hawaii, Alaska, West
June 4, 2012	Partial	Before Sunrise	Hawaii, West
November 28, 2012	Penumbra	Before Sunrise	Hawaii, Alaska
April 14, 2014	Total	Around Midnight	Hawaii, Alaska, Continental US, Canada
October 8, 2014	Total	Before Sunrise	Hawaii, Alaska, Continental US, Canada
April 4, 2015	Total	Before Sunrise	Hawaii, Alaska, West
September 27, 2015	Total	Evening	Continental US, Canada
February 10, 2017	Penumbra	Evening	Continental US, Canada
January 31, 2018	Total	Early Morning	Hawaii, Alaska, West
January 20, 2019	Total	Around Midnight	Hawaii, Alaska, Continental US, Canada
May 26, 2021	Partial	Before Sunrise	Hawaii, Alaska, West
November 19, 2021	Almost Total	Before Sunrise	Hawaii, Alaska, Continental US, Canada

[1]Check media sources for specific times for your location.

LUNAR Eclipses 2022 – 2043

Lunar Eclipses in North America

Date of Lunar Eclipse	Type of Lunar Eclipse	Time of Day to View[1]	Locations
May 15, 2022	Total	Around Midnight	Continental US, Canada
November 8, 2022	Total	Before Sunrise	Hawaii, Alaska, Continental US, Canada
March 24, 2024	Penumbra	Around Midnight	Hawaii, Alaska, Continental US, Canada
March 13, 2025	Total	Around Midnight	Hawaii, Alaska, Continental US, Canada
March 3, 2026	Total	Before Sunrise	Hawaii, Alaska, West, Midwest, Canada
August 27, 2026	Partial	Around Midnight	Continental US, Canada
January 11, 2028	Penumbra	Around Midnight	Hawaii, Alaska, Continental US, Canada
December 31, 2028	Total	Early Evening	Hawaii, Alaska
June 25, 2029	Total	Before Midnight	Continental US, Canada
December 9, 2030	Penumbra	Early Evening	East
April 25, 2032	Total	Before Sunrise	Hawaii
October 8, 2033	Total	Before Sunrise	Hawaii, Alaska, Continental US, Canada
August 18, 2035	Penumbra	Early Evening	Midwest, East
August 6, 2036	Total	Evening	Continental US except West Coast
January 31, 2037	Total	Before Sunrise	Hawaii, Alaska, West
July 26, 2037	Partial	Evening	Continental US, Canada
November 30, 2039	Partial	Early Evening	Alaska
May 26, 2040	Total	Before Sunrise	Hawaii, Alaska, West Coast
May 15, 2041	Penumbra	Early Evening	East Coast
November 7, 2041	Penumbra	Around Midnight	Hawaii, Alaska, Continental US, Canada
April 5, 2042	Penumbra	Before Sunrise	Hawaii, Alaska
March 25, 2043	Total	Before Sunrise	Hawaii, Alaska
September 18, 2043	Total	Early Evening	Midwest, East

[1]Check media sources for specific times for your location.

LUNAR Eclipses 2044 – 2051

Lunar Eclipses in North America

Date of Lunar Eclipse	Type of Lunar Eclipse	Time of Day to View[1]	Locations
September 7, 2044	Total	Before Sunrise	Hawaii, Alaska, West
July 17, 2046	Partial	Early Evening	East Coast
January 11, 2047	Total	Early Evening	Continental US, Canada, Alaska
July 7, 2047	Total	Before Sunrise	Hawaii, Alaska, West
December 31, 2047	Total	Around Midnight	Hawaii, Alaska, Continental US, Canada
June 25, 2048	Partial	Around Midnight	Midwest, East
December 19, 2048	Penumbra	Around Midnight	Hawaii, Alaska, Continental US, Canada
October 29, 2050	Total	Evening	Continental US, Canada, Alaska
April 25, 2051	Total	Early Evening	Continental US, Canada

[1]Check media sources for specific times for your location.

Eclipse Tables

Facing page. Beautiful shades of orange and brown dance across the Moon during total lunar eclipses.

Deep Sky Objects

What's does one view after observing the Moon, Planets and Sun? Most move on to the brightest Deep Sky Objects (DSOs) which includes star clusters, nebulae, and galaxies, that is, distant objects beyond our Solar System. Everyone is familiar with these objects for the biggest and brightest are frequently pictured in the media and have names like the Pleiades, the Orion Nebula and the Andromeda Galaxy.

Traditionally, double and variable stars are not considered deep sky objects, but I have included them in this section, starting on page 254, to "round out" the kinds of objects that are observed after one's initial foray into astronomy.

The first catalogue of Deep Sky Objects was published in 1772 by the Frenchman Charles Messier and contained 45 entries.

STAR CLUSTERS

A star cluster is a group of stars born out of the same nebulae (see page 241). Most star clusters are easy to recognize because their stars are close together or bunched up, often forming a distinct pattern or shape, so they stand out from their surroundings. The term "star cluster" is a general term referring to an **open cluster**, **galactic cluster** or **globular cluster**.

Open Cluster. A star cluster containing several dozen to a thousand or so members. A few open clusters are visible to the naked eye but most require a telescope to see. The best examples of open clusters are the Pleiades (page 273), the Praesepe (page 279), M6 and M7 (page 293).

Galactic Cluster. Specific term for an open cluster that lies within an arm of a spiral galaxy. Galactic clusters are composed of young stars born from the nebulae located in the arms of spiral galaxies.

DSOs

Facing page. *A barred-spiral galaxy located in the direction of the constellation Eridanus. It lies about 69 million light years away and has a length that extends for 130,000 light years, which makes it much bigger than our Milky Way Galaxy. Barred-spiral galaxies are a variation of "normal" spirals, and are characterized by curved arms connected to a "bar" of stars that contains the nucleus.*
Top of page. *A planetary nebula 7,000 light years away in the constellation Hercules.*

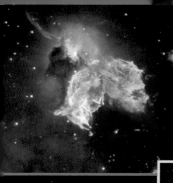

Left. **Supernova Remnant** located in the Large Magellanic Cloud (LMC), a companion galaxy to our Galaxy that is visible from the southern hemisphere.

Above. This **Galaxy**, desig NGC 4622 is 111 million li years away in the direction the constellation Centaurus

Below.
The layers of this **Planetary Nebula** suggest that they formed from a series of cycles.

Below. An **Open Cluster** o in Crux dubbed the "Jewel because of its colored star

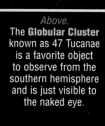

Above.
The **Globular Cluster** known as 47 Tucanae is a favorite object to observe from the southern hemisphere and is just visible to the naked eye.

Below.
Galactic Nebula out of which stars will be born to create an Open Cluster.

Nebulae

Globular Cluster. Distinctly different from open or galactic clusters, a globular cluster represents a collection of old stars, anywhere from thousands to a million compacted into the shape of a ball. In a small telescope, globular clusters look like faint, fuzzy cotton balls. In larger telescopes, they are fantastic sights because thousands of the fainter stars that produce the fuzziness in smaller telescopes are resolved into individual pinpoints of light. Our Galaxy has about 200 globular clusters positioned above and below its plane, arranged somewhat in the shape of a sphere, in fact, a "spherical halo."

*Left, the open cluster designated M34 in Perseus and **right**, the globular cluster designated M3 in Canes Venatici.*

NEBULAE

The word nebulae is a general term that refers to gaseous clouds composed mostly of hydrogen gas. They reside in galaxies. There are several types of nebulae: galactic nebula, planetary nebulae and supernova remnants.

Galactic Nebula. Emission, reflective and dark nebulae represent three types of galactic nebulae. These nebulae reside mainly in the arms of spiral galaxies. They span 100 light years or so in size and serve as cauldrons for the birth of stars. Galactic cloud nebulae represent the original-type matter of galaxies.

An **Emission Nebula**, like the Great Orion Nebula, emits its own light, stimulated by the ultraviolet radiation from nearby stars. **Reflection Nebulae** are the same type of gas clouds as emission nebulae but are visible because they only reflect light from nearby stars. **Dark Nebulae** have no nearby stars to light them up. They are indirectly visible as silhouettes or dark patches against a background of stars or bright nebulae.

Nebulae

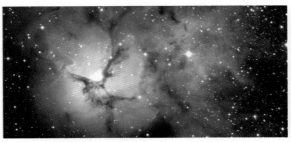 

Left. *M20, the Trifid Nebula is an example of an emission and reflective nebula. The pinkish part is giving off its own light while the bluish part is reflecting light from nearby stars.* *Right.* *The Horsehead Nebula is a favorite example of a dark nebula and is located below the left belt star in Orion. It takes about a 20-inch diameter telescope to see this silhouette.*

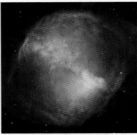

Top. The M27 planetary nebulae is known as the Dumbbell. The opposing lobes are created from the spin and magnetic field characteristics of its central white dwarf star. Bottom. M1, the Crab Nebula, is the only supernova explosion in Messier's catalogue.

Planetary Nebulae are different from the humongous galactic cloud nebulae in several ways. First, they are small and span just a few light years. Secondly, their shapes are spherical, ringed or having diametrically opposed lobes. Finally, these nebulae represent the blown-off atmospheres of giant stars before they collapse down to become white dwarf stars (which are about the size of Earth). Like emission nebulae, ultraviolet radiation from the white dwarfs stimulates the gas of planetary nebulae to emit their own light. Our Sun will most likely generate a planetary nebula at the end of its life.

Obviously, planetary nebulae have nothing to do with the Planets. The term was coined before astronomers understood their true nature because many planetary nebulae are small and round in appearance, hence the name.

Supernova Remnants are nebulae created from the explosions of stars that are much larger or more massive than those that create planetary nebulae. The stars that created these explosions become either neutron stars or black holes. The last supernova explosion that occurred in our Galaxy was seen as a very bright star in 1604. Supernova remnants are rare compared to other nebulae.

GALAXIES

All galaxies lie outside our Milky Way Galaxy at distances in the millions of light years. Galaxies represent the largest groupings of stars in the Universe, each containing anywhere from tens of millions to billions of stars. There are no stars between galaxies. Galaxies tend to be spherical or circular in shape.

The most visually distinctive galaxies are called **spirals**, which have bright curved arms radiating from a bulged center or nucleus. There is a variation of the spiral called the barred-spiral which has a central bar, off of which the spiral arms radiate, (see picture on page 238). Spirals account for less than 5% of all the galaxies in the Universe

The most prevalent galaxy shape, representing the very smallest and largest galaxies, and accounting for over 90% of all the galaxies in the Universe is the **elliptical**. These take on the shape of spheres or elongated balls. They have bright nuclei, no arms and little internal structure. Elliptical galaxies may be the result of spiral galaxies that have collided and merged.

Irregular galaxies are irregular in shape, lack arms and have mottled interiors with no obvious nuclei. Like spiral galaxies, they account for less than 5% of all galaxies. Irregulars most likely represent a galaxy in transition — either from galaxies colliding and merging or one that is receiving gravitational pulls and tugs from another nearby, larger galaxy.

Left. The elliptical galaxy, M87. *Middle.* The spiral galaxy, M74. *Right.* Extreme closeup view of the irregular galaxy, M82.

  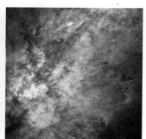

DSOs

Messier & NGC Catalogues

CELESTIAL CATALOGUES

Over the past few centuries, astronomers have compiled numerous catalogues of celestial objects, some very specialized and others more general. The specialized catalogues are most often used by professional astronomers whereas the general catalogues are used by amateurs and professionals alike. Below are descriptions of the two most popular catalogues.

"M" Objects of Charles Messier

The most well-known catalogue of celestial objects, which is also the first such catalogue, was compiled by Frenchman Charles Messier (1730–1817) in the latter half of the 1700s. This catalogue is still widely used today because its 112 deep sky objects represent the biggest and brightest visible from the northern hemisphere. In astronomy circles, whenever you hear someone say the letter "M," followed by a number from 1 to 112, it refers to an object from this catalogue. Included are the Great Orion Nebula (M42), the Pleiades (M45), the Great Hercules Cluster (M13), the Ring Nebula (M57) and many more. It just so happens that at least one of every type of deep sky object is represented in this catalogue.

All of the Messier objects can be seen with a small telescope, as little as 3 inches in diameter. About 80 of these objects are visible with binoculars (they just appear smaller and fainter than in a telescope) and a few can be seen with the naked eye. Once a year, around the New Moon in March, it is possible to see all of the Messier objects in a single night, an event that is called a **Messier Marathon** (read a bit more about this on page 74).

New General Catalogue (NGC) and IC addendum

It became apparent in the 1800s that a thorough catalogue of deep sky objects would be invaluable to astronomers worldwide in their study of the celestial sphere. In 1888, J. L. E. Dreyer published a comprehensive compilation entitled, *New General Catalogue of Nebulae and Clusters of Stars* (NGC), listing 7,840 deep sky objects in the northern and southern hemispheres. By 1908, he added another 5,386 objects to what is called the *Index Catalogue* (IC). These catalogues represent the last major compilations of star clusters, nebulae, and galaxies. With the advent of astrophotography, the number of objects, mostly galaxies, that can be imaged have become too numerous to sensibly catalogue. Professional astronomers looking deep into the cosmos for the faintest objects use photographic atlases instead of traditional star charts.

A larger telescope, 12 inches in diameter or greater, and dark skies are required to observe all the NGC and IC objects. This is because most of the objects are very faint. I generally observe with a 4-inch refractor and have found that I can see many, but not all, of the open, galactic and globular clusters listed in the NGC/IC catalogues, but most of the listed galaxies are well beyond its grasp.

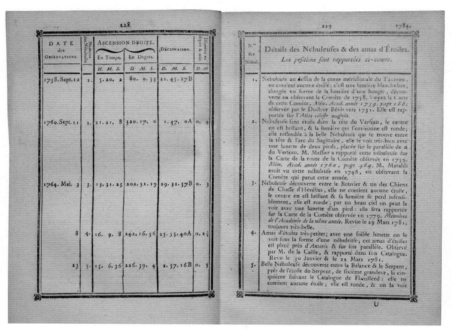

Charles Messier was the first astronomer to compile a catalogue of deep sky objects. He published three catalogues, each growing in size, with the final 1784 edition listing 103 objects. His first catalogue was published in the 1772 annual reports of the French Royal Academy of Sciences. The final two editions were published in Connaissance des Temps (Knowledge of the Times). Above are the first two pages of the last catalogue edition in the 1784 Connaissance des Temps. Although Messier numbered his objects, it is a modern-day practice that adds a "M" in front to provide a catalogue reference.

Catalogues

Charles Messier (1730–1817)

Charles Messier (pronounced Mess-ee-ay) was born in the foothills town of Badonviller, located 200 miles due east of Paris. Messier's father held a mayoral-type position in this town that served as the regional administrative center for the Princes of Salms, the family that held territorial control of the area.

Messier's father died when he was 11 so his oldest brother Hyacinthe took him under his wing, training him as an administrator's assistant until Charles was 21 in 1751. At this time, territorial control of the area was being reorganized and jobs became scarce but Hyacinthe was able to find Charles employment in Paris as an assistant to an astronomer.

Messier's official portrait painted upon his appointment as Astronomer of the Navy in 1771. The red medal is a tribute as a French Royal Academy of Sciences member.

In Paris, Messier lived and worked at the Royal College of France for the aristocrat-astronomer Joseph Delisle. For his first two years, he helped draw maps and worked on several projects.

Messier's "probation" was over in 1753 when Delisle noted, firsthand, Messier's enthusiastic and skillful assistance helping astronomers during a transit of Mercury (when Mercury crosses in front of the Sun), a viewing event hosted by Delisle. Thereafter, Delisle encouraged and helped Messier to study astronomy.

It was from 1754 to 1760 that Messier's astronomical knowledge and observing skills were honed. In 1758, he discovered his first comet and noted what would become his first deep sky object (M1). A year later, he discovered the comet predicted to return

First DSO Cataloguer

by Edmond Halley, and which now bears Halley's name. Then in 1760, Messier discovered two more comets and kept on going.

Messier had a deep passion for searching and finding comets and is credited with discovering 20 during his lifetime. At one point, he was even dubbed "The Comet Ferret" by Louis XV. However, despite this penchant, *he can best be described as the leading observational astronomer of his time.* During his career, he published over 100 articles in major journals on his astronomical observations and only 30% were related to comets.

In 1770, Messier married Marie Vermanchampt after 15 years of courtship. Unfortunately, in 1772, both Marie and their first child died a week after the birth.

A 1700s Dollond refractor made in London and of a type used by Messier.

Also in 1770, Messier was made a member of the French Royal Academy of Sciences. During his life, Messier was inducted into 17 science academies throughout Europe.

In 1754, Delisle's income from the Royal College of France may have become tenuous because he negotiated with the Navy, the salaried and titled position,"Astronomer of the Navy." In 1771 Messier assumed this title with an increase in salary that allowed him to afford lodging at Hotel Cluny.

Messier published three deep sky object catalogues, each growing in size. The first was in 1771 with the second and third following in 1783 and 1784. The purpose of these catalogues, from the start, was to provide a detailed list of "nebular stars," a reference work that was lacking in the field of astronomy. The final 1784 catalogue had 103 entries.

As a boy who grew up in the country, Messier never would have dreamed that he would become the leading observational astronomer of his time, develop a passion for comets, and create a legacy for compiling a small catalogue of celestial objects. Messier passed away at Hotel Cluny in 1817.

Far left. *Hotel Cluny, where Messier worked, eventually lived and died, is now the National Museum of the Middle Ages and Thermal Baths of Cluny. The smaller drawing is one of the few depictions of the observatory atop the tower which was built and equipped around 1747 by Messier's boss, Joseph Delisle.*

Messier Catalogue & Chart

#	Const.	Object	Mag.	Arc Size	Name
M1*	Tau	Supernova Remnant	8	6' x 4'	Crab Nebula
M2*	Aqr	Globular Cluster	6.5	13'	
M3*	CVn	Globular Cluster	6.2	16'	
M4*	Sco	Globular Cluster	5.9	26'	Cat's Eye
M5*	Ser	Globular Cluster	5.7	17'	
M6*	Sco	Open Cluster	4.2	15'	Butterfly Cluster
M7*	Sco	Open Cluster	3.3	80'	
M8*	Sgr	Nebula	6	90' x 40'	Lagoon Nebula
M9	Oph	Globular Cluster	7.7	9'	
M10*	Oph	Globular Cluster	6.6	15'	
M11*	Sct	Open Cluster	5.8	14'	Wild Duck Cluster
M12*	Oph	Globular Cluster	6.7	15'	
M13*	Her	Globular Cluster	5.8	17'	Great Hercules Cluster
M14*	Oph	Globular Cluster	7.6	12'	
M15*	Peg	Globular Cluster	6.2	12'	Great Pegasus Cluster
M16*	Ser	Nebula/Open Cluster	6	7'	Eagle Nebula

Entries with a **red star** are described on the Monthly Star Charts A–I.

Charts Indicating the Location of All the Messier Objects

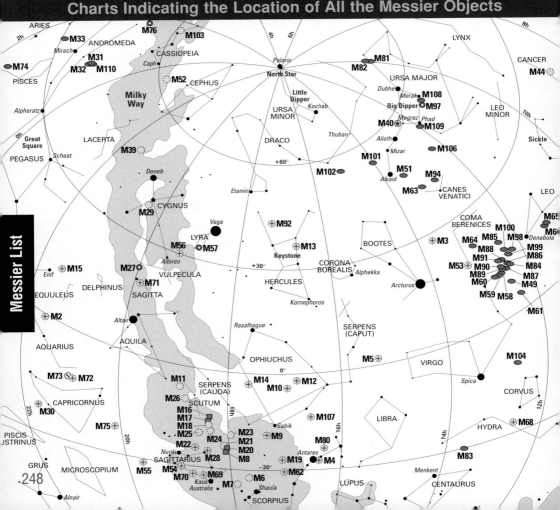

Messier Catalogue & Chart

#	Const.	Object	Mag.	Arc Size	Name
M17*	Sgr	Nebula/Open Cluster	7	46' x 37'	Omega Nebula
M18	Sgr	Open Cluster	6.9	9'	Black Swan
M19	Oph	Globular Cluster	6.8	14'	
M20	Sgr	Nebula/Open Cluster	8	28' x 28'	Trifid Nebula
M21	Sgr	Open Cluster	5.9	13'	
M22*	Sgr	Globular Cluster	5.1	24'	Great Sagittarius Cluster
M23	Sgr	Open Cluster	5.5	27'	
M24	Sgr	Thick Milky Way Patch	4	90' x 60'	
M25	Sgr	Open Cluster	4.6	32'	
M26	Sct	Open Cluster	8.0	15'	
M27*	Vul	Planetary Nebula	8	8' x 4'	Dumbbell Nebula
M28	Sgr	Globular Cluster	6.8	11'	
M29	Cyg	Open Cluster	6.6	7'	
M30*	Cap	Globular Cluster	7.2	11'	
M31*	And	Spiral Galaxy	3.5	178' x 63'	Andromeda Galaxy
M32*	And	Elliptical Galaxy	8.2	8' x 6'	

Entries with a **red star** are described on the Monthly Star Charts A–I.

Charts Indicating the Location of All the Messier Objects

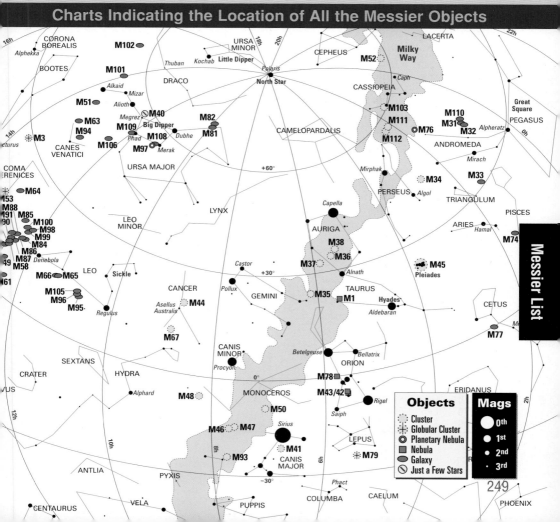

Objects
- Cluster
- Globular Cluster
- Planetary Nebula
- Nebula
- Galaxy
- Just a Few Stars

Mags
- 0th
- 1st
- 2nd
- 3rd

Messier List

249

Messier Catalogue & Chart

#	Const.	Object	Mag.	Arc Size	Name
M33*	Tri	Spiral Galaxy	5.7	62' x 39'	Pinwheel Galaxy
M34*	Per	Open Cluster	5.2	35'	
M35*	Gem	Open Cluster	5.1	28'	
M36*	Aur	Open Cluster	6.0	12'	
M37*	Aur	Open Cluster	5.6	24'	
M38*	Aur	Open Cluster	6.4	21'	
M39	Cyg	Open Cluster	4.6	32'	
M40	UMa	Double Star	10.1	1'	
M41*	CMa	Open Cluster	4.5	38'	Little Beehive
M42*	Ori	Nebula	4	66' x 60'	The Great Orion Nebula
M43	Ori	Nebula	9	20' x 15'	
M44*	Cnc	Open Cluster	3.1	95'	Praesepe
M45*	Tau	Open Cluster	1.2	110'	Pleiades
M46*	Pup	Open Cluster	6.1	27'	
M47*	Pup	Open Cluster	4.4	30'	
M48	Hya	Open Cluster	5.8	54'	
M49	Vir	Elliptical Galaxy	8.4	9' x 7'	
M50	Mon	Open Cluster	5.9	16'	
M51*	CVn	Spiral Galaxy	8.1	11' x 8'	Whirlpool Galaxy
M52	Cas	Open Cluster	6.9	13'	The Scorpion
M53*	Com	Globular Cluster	7.6	13'	
M54*	Sgr	Globular Cluster	7.6	9'	
M55*	Sgr	Globular Cluster	7.0	19'	The Spectre
M56	Lyr	Globular Cluster	8.3	7'	
M57*	Lyr	Planetary Nebula	9	1.3'	Ring Nebula
M58	Vir	Spiral Galaxy	9.8	5' x 4'	
M59	Vir	Elliptical Galaxy	9.8	5' x 3'	
M60	Vir	Elliptical Galaxy	8.8	7' x 6'	
M61*	Vir	Spiral Galaxy	9.7	6' x 5'	Swelling Spiral
M62	Oph	Globular Cluster	6.5	14'	Flickering Globular
M63	CVn	Spiral Galaxy	8.6	12' x 8'	Sunflower Galaxy
M64	Com	Spiral Galaxy	8.5	9' x 5'	Black Eye Galaxy
M65*	Leo	Spiral Galaxy	9.3	10' x 3'	
M66*	Leo	Spiral Galaxy	9.0	9' x 4'	
M67	Cnc	Open Cluster	6.9	30'	King Cobra
M68*	Hya	Globular Cluster	8.2	12'	
M69	Sgr	Globular Cluster	7.6	7'	
M70*	Sgr	Globular Cluster	8.1	8'	
M71	Sge	Globular Cluster	8.2	7'	
M72*	Aqr	Globular Cluster	9.3	6'	
M73	Aqr	4-Star Asterism	10.5 (Brightest)	1'	
M74*	Psc	Spiral Galaxy	9.2	10' x 9'	The Phantom
M75	Sgr	Globular Cluster	8.5	6'	
M76	Per	Planetary Nebula	11	2' x 1'	Little Dumbbell
M77*	Cet	Spiral Galaxy	8.8	7' x 6'	
M78*	Ori	Nebula	8	8' x 6'	
M79*	Lep	Globular Cluster	7.7	9'	
M80	Sco	Globular Cluster	7.3	9'	

Messier Catalogue & Chart

#	Const.	Object	Mag.	Arc Size	Name
M81*	UMa	Spiral Galaxy	6.8	26' x 14'	
M82*	UMa	Irregular Galaxy	8.4	11' x 5'	Cigar Galaxy
M83	Hya	Spiral Galaxy	8	11' x 10'	
M84	Vir	Elliptical Galaxy	9.3	5' x 4'	
M85	Com	Elliptical Galaxy	9.2	7' x 5'	
M86	Vir	Elliptical Galaxy	9.2	7' x 5'	
M87	Vir	Elliptical Galaxy	8.6	7'	Virgo A
M88	Com	Spiral Galaxy	9.5	7' x 4'	
M89	Vir	Elliptical Galaxy	9.8	4'	
M90	Vir	Spiral Galaxy	9.5	10' x 5'	
M91	Com	Spiral Galaxy	10.2	5' x 4'	
M92*	Her	Globular Cluster	6.4	11'	
M93*	Pup	Open Cluster	6	22'	
M94	CVn	Spiral Galaxy	8.1	11' x 9'	Croc's Eye
M95*	Leo	Spiral Galaxy	9.7	7' x 5'	
M96*	Leo	Spiral Galaxy	9.2	7' x 5'	
M97*	UMa	Planetary Nebula	11	3'	Owl Nebula
M98	Com	Spiral Galaxy	10.1	10' x 3'	
M99	Com	Spiral Galaxy	9.8	5'	
M100	Com	Spiral Galaxy	9.4	7' x 6'	The Mirror
M101	UMa	Spiral Galaxy	7.7	27' x 26'	Pinwheel Galaxy
M102	Dra	Elliptical Galaxy	9.9	6' x 3'	Méchain's Lost Galaxy
M103	Cas	Open Cluster	7	6'	
M104	Vir	Spiral Galaxy	8.3	9' x 4'	Sombrero Galaxy
M105*	Leo	Elliptical Galaxy	9.3	5' x 4'	
M106	CVn	Spiral Galaxy	8.3	18' x 8'	
M107	Oph	Globular Cluster	8.1	10'	
M108	UMa	Spiral Galaxy	10.0	8' x 2'	
M109	UMa	Spiral Galaxy	9.8	8' x 5'	
M110*	And	Elliptical Galaxy	8.0	17' x 10'	
M111*	Per	Open Cluster	4.5	30'	West Part of Double Cluster
M112*	Per	Open Cluster	4.5	30'	East Part of Double Cluster

Entries with a red star are described on the Monthly Star Charts A–I.

Discussion

1. Messier's last catalogue listed 103 entries but this has since been expanded to 112. Objects 104 to 110 were discovered by Messier, but never added to the catalogue for various reasons. M111 and M112, the Double Cluster (see page 265) are honorary entries because it is believed that Messier knew of these clusters but made an amazing oversight by not including them.

2. Messier's friend and colleague Pierre Méchain helped with the catalogue starting with object number M63.

3. It is believed by some that M102 is a duplicate entry of M101, that is, Messier & Méchain made a mistake. In this table, the galaxy listed for M102 is not a duplicate of M101 but what others think may in fact be the "lost" galaxy.

4. There were several short lists of deep sky objects that Messier drew from. M40 is a "double star" and is a report of a negative "find" of a deep sky object from one of these lists. M73 is not a deep sky object, but four stars shaped in the form of a triangle, which is Messier's only misidentification in the entire catalogue.

5. For size comparison, the Moon extends an arc angle distance of 30' (30 minutes). Many of the Messier objects are around this size.

OBSERVING Deep Sky Objects

OBSERVING DEEP SKY OBJECTS (DSOs)

Deep sky objects are markedly fainter than the Planets, Moon or Sun, so they are observed differently. Below are some suggestions to helping you see these object better.

1 Since DSOs are faint, it is best to observe them when the Moon is not because its light whitewashes these objects along with the sky. The fainter deep sky objects cannot be seen when the Moon is out, especially near or during Full Moon. As you can imagine, the Moon is a bane for those studying deep sky objects.

2 DSOs can only be observed when the sky is at its darkest, generally around or after astronomical twilight in the evening, which usually starts about 90 minutes after sunset.

3 Situate or position your telescope away from bright or glaring lights. If this is impossible, at least keep your back to these lights.

4 Once outside at your observing site, let your eyes "dark-adapt" for a good 5 to 15 minutes before observing fainter deep sky objects (see page 54). Eat up this time by looking at some of your favorite brighter objects.

5 To preserve your dark-adapted eyes, use only a red-light flashlight to look at your reference material or for writing notes. Using a white-light flashlight will interfere with your night vision.

6 If you have never found a DSO, begin with easier objects — like those spotlighted on the following pages. Some of the objects indicated on the monthly star charts are fairly easy to find and see, while others require more diligence or dark skies. Once you get a feel for what DSOs look like in general, it will become easier to spot them.

7 If you continue having difficulty finding DSOs, enlist the help of others. If this is not practical, search for these objects in many short sessions over several days, weeks or months, instead of long, drawn-out sessions. You may find that failing to see these objects is not your fault, but simply due to your sky, especially if you must contend with light pollution.

8 If light pollution is a problem, try observing DSOs when they are higher in the sky, near the zenith. Or, when they move into a

OBSERVING Deep Sky Objects

darker part of your sky. More often than not, you may simply have to observe away from your area. I live on the immediate outskirts of Tucson, so half of my sky is immersed in the city's glow, but the other half is okay, however, I still have to travel about 30 miles (with all my equipment) to get to reasonably dark skies for serious deep sky exploration.

Larger Telescopes. More DSOs and detail can be seen with larger diameter telescopes than smaller ones because they collect more light. Larger scopes make fainter DSOs brighter. This is one reason why some amateurs purchase telescopes in the 20-inch to 30-inch diameter range. I can see about twice as many DSOs with my 6-inch telescope as I can with my 4-inch, and, the DSOs are brighter in my 6-inch than in the 4-inch.

Using Averted Vision to Help See Fainter Objects. Using averted vision means viewing a faint object using peripheral vision instead of looking directly at it. Why do this? Objects that are faint, at the threshold of what our eyes can see disappear if you stare or look at them directly. This is because our eyes have a reduced number of light receptacles in the center of the retina which makes this area literally "blind" (called the blind spot) to objects with very low brightness. In observational astronomy, a "trick" to seeing fainter objects (including fainter stars) is to use peripheral vision. The downside of using averted vision is a degraded view and it does strain the eye.

Color of DSOs. Except for some planetary nebulae and colored stars in open clusters, all of the deep sky objects appear whitish. The beautiful colors and detail that you see in pictures are not possible to see with your eyes because the eyes interpret low levels of colored light as white light. I have looked through a 60-inch diameter telescope — galaxies and galactic nebulae look as colorless through it as through any 4-inch telescope.

Other Resources. The book, *The Next Step: Finding and View Messier Objects* is an excellent resource for helping the beginner "step" into the "world" of finding DSOs. Also, a more detailed star chart, like the *Sky Atlas 2000* (there are several versions) can be helpful to locate stars and other celestial objects.

Observing DSOs

Double Stars

DOUBLE STARS

A double star is two stars that look like one, but when viewed with binoculars or with significant magnification using a telescope, the "single" star separates or "resolves" into two stars. Sometimes, a "double" star may be a multiple star having three or more stars close to one another. There are two categories of double stars: optical and binaries.

Optical double stars appear to be stars close to each other simply because they are in the same line of sight. In reality, they are separated by quite some distance.

About 85% of all the stars in the sky are **binary** or **multiple** stars. A binary is a pair of stars orbiting each other, while multiple stars represent a system of three or more stars revolving around each other. Revolution periods of binary stars range in years to thousands of years.

Mizar, a star in the handle of the Big Dipper is a highly illustrative example of a "double star." To start, Mizar has a naked-eye optical double called Alcor (see pages 60 and 261). But there is more here than meets the naked eye. Using a small telescope at about 50x, Mizar can be separated into two stars, known as Mizar A (the actual Mizar that we see with the naked eye) and a fainter Mizar B. However, each of these stars has another star revolving about it, making this a multiple star

Mizar with Mizar B is located in the upper left corner. Alcor is in the upper right corner. The star at the bottom is known as Sidus Ludoviciana.

system having a total of four stars. The two stars that make up Mizar (Mizar A) revolve around each other in 20.5 days while the two stars that make up Mizar B revolve around each other in 175.6 days. Neither of these close companions to Mizar A and B can be seen in a telescope. Now, it is estimated that Mizar A and B take thousands of years to revolve around each other.

The star Capella is actually two binary stars that are so close together, no ordinary telescope can separate them.

Why can't we see the fainter companions of Mizar A & B and the companions of all the other stars? Simply because most binary stars orbit so close to one another, they

Observing Double Stars

Two favorites. **Left.** *The Double-Double or ε (epsilon) Lyrae in Lyra.* **Right.** *The star Albireo in Cygnus is an easy split of a pretty amber and blue colored star.* **Both of these images look much more striking through an eyepiece!**

cannot be resolved into separate stars by ordinary telescopes. For example, Capella in Auriga (picture shown on the previous page), the sixth brightest star in the night sky, is actually a pair of stars that are 100 times closer together than the closest double star listed in the table starting on the next page. Our turbulent atmosphere prevents us from seeing or resolving stars this close together.

OBSERVING DOUBLE STARS

I and most amateurs enjoy looking at double stars. Their range of magnitudes, colors and separations make them fun as well as very pretty sights. And as a "bonus," the Moon and light pollution do not readily interfere with viewing them.

A list of favorite double stars starts on the next page. They are also indicated on the monthly star charts A–J. All of these doubles can be resolved with a small telescope using magnifications of 30x to 200x. Doubles with smaller separation numbers are closer together and require higher magnifications to resolve or separate.

When observing doubles, start with a low-powered eyepiece to find the star. Then increase your magnification until the "star" splits into two stars. For "close" doubles, the split may be very little, even at higher magnifications. If the stars have color, this shows up better at higher magnifications. On some nights, when the atmosphere is turbulent, it may be difficult or impossible to resolve the closer doubles.

Larger diameter telescopes do resolve closer doubles better (see Dawes' Limit on page 358), but our turbulent atmosphere limits resolutions to about one-half an arc second (½"). A 10-inch diameter telescope provides about the highest resolution possible of any Earth-based telescope.

Double Stars

Double Stars

Favorite Small-Telescope Double Stars

Constellation	Designation or Name[2]	Mags	Separation in Arc Seconds[3]	Comments
Andromeda	γ	2.3/5.5	9.8"	Blue & yellow
Aquarius	ζ	4.3/4.5	1.8"	Tight & white
Auriga	θ	2.6/7.1	3.6"	Tight, contrasty
Bootes	δ	3.5/8.7	105"	Easy & contrasty
	ε	2.5/4.9	2.8"	Tight yellow & orange
	κ	4.6/6.6	13.6"	Easy blue & yellow
	ξ	4.8/6.8	6.9"	Blue & orange
	π	4.9/5.8	5.6"	Good example
Cancer	ι	4.2/6.6	30"	Like Albireo
Canis Major	ε	1.5/7.4	7.5"	High contrast
	145	5.0/5.8	26.8"	Winter Albireo
Canes Venatici	α	2.9/5.5	19.4"	Easy
Capricornus	α	3.6/4.2	378"	Golden duo plus more
	Dabih	3.4/6.2	206"	Bino double
Cassiopeia	η	3.4/7.5	12"	Yellow & orange
Cepheus	β	3.2/7.9	13.3"	Fainter is bluish
	δ	3.9/6.3	41"	Easy blue & yellow
	ξ	4.4/6.5	7.7"	Tight blue & yellow
Cetus	γ	3.5/7.3	2.8"	Tight, contrasty
Corvus	Algorab	3.0/9.2	24.2"	Easy
Cygnus	Albireo	3.1/5.1	34.4"	Famous blue & gold
	μ	4.8/6.1	1.9"	Very tight
	o	3.8/4.8/4.0	107"/338"	Bino triplet
Delphinus	γ	4.5/5.5	9.6"	Easy blue & red
Draco	16–17	5.4/5.5/6.4	3.4"/90.3"	Easy to tight
	ν	4.9/4.9	62"	Can split with binos
Eridanus	θ	3.2/4.4	8.3"	Easy example
Gemini	Castor	1.9/2.9	3.9"	A Classic
	δ	3.5/8.2	6.8"	Contrasty
Hercules	α	3.5/5.4	4.7"	Blue & orange
	δ	3.1/8.2	8.9"	Contrasty
	ρ	4.6/5.6	4.1"	Good example
Leo	γ	2.2/3.5	4.4"	Golden pair
	54	4.5/6.3	6.5"	Blue & yellow
Lepus	γ	3.7/6.3	96"	Bino double

Greek Alphabet

α alpha
β beta
γ gamma
δ delta
ε epsilon
ζ zeta
η eta
θ theta
ι iota
κ kappa
λ lambda
μ mu
ν nu
ξ xi
o omicron
π pi
ρ rho
σ sigma
τ tau
υ upsilon
φ phi
χ chi
ψ psi
ω omega

Double Stars

Double Stars

Favorite Small-Telescope Double Stars

Constellation	Designation or Name[2]	Mags	Separation in Arc Seconds[3]	Comments
Libra	α	2.8/5.2	231"	Bino double
Lynx	38	3.9/6.6	2.7"	Tight, contrasty
Lyra	β	3.4/8.6	46"	Easy
	ε	5.0/6.1/5.2/5.5	208"/2.6"/2.3"	THE "Double-Double"
	ζ	4.3/5.9	44"	Easy
Monoceros	β	4.6/5.4/5.6	2.8"/7.4"	Easy to tight
	ε	4.4/6.7	12.9"	Easy blue & yellow
Ophiuchus	70	4.2/6.0	4.6"	Yellow & orange
Orion	Rigel	0.1/6.8	9.5"	High contrast
	β	2.2/6.3	52.6"	Very easy
	ζ	1.9/4.0/9.9	2.4"/58"	Need high power
	ι	2.8/6.9	11.3"	Contrasty magnitudes
	λ	3.6/5.5	4.4"	White & pale blue
	σ	4.0/7.5/6.5	12.9"/43"	Nice! 4 stars
Pegasus	Enif	2.4/8.4	142"	Bino double
Perseus	η	3.8/8.5	28.3"	Easy. Blue & yellow
Pisces	α	4.2/5.1	1.7"	Need high power
	ζ	5.6/6.5	23"	Blue & gold
	ψ	5.6/5.8	30"	Easy twins
Puppis	κ	4.5/4.7	9.9"	Easy twins
Scorpius	Antares	1.0/6.5	3"	Tight "green" & red
	Graffias	2.6/4.9	13.6"	Easy example
	ξ	4.8/7.3	7.6"	Double & a double
Serpens	δ	4.2/5.2	3.9"	Both yellow
	θ	4.5/5.4	22.3"	Easy twins
Taurus	Aldebaran	1.0/11.6	31.4"	Easy
Ursa Major	Mizar	2.3/4.0/4.0	14.4"/709"	See page 254
Ursa Minor	Polaris	2.0/9.0	18.4"	Easy & contrasty
Virgo	Porrima	3.5/3.5	3.6"	Tight twins

Greek Alphabet

α	alpha
β	beta
γ	gamma
δ	delta
ε	epsilon
ζ	zeta
η	eta
θ	theta
ι	iota
κ	kappa
λ	lambda
μ	mu
ν	nu
ξ	xi
ο	omicron
π	pi
ρ	rho
σ	sigma
τ	tau
υ	upsilon
φ	phi
χ	chi
ψ	psi
ω	omega

[1]There are many more wonderful double stars, but this is a good list to start from. [2]The names and designations correspond to those on the monthly star charts A–J that begin on page 61. [3]See page 137 for more about arc angles compared to the sizes of the Planets. The Moon spans about 30 arc minutes (30'), which is equivalent to 1,800 arc seconds (1,800"). One-half of an arc second is about the best resolution that a telescope on Earth can achieve, a limit that is caused by our turbulent atmosphere.

Double Stars

Variable Stars

Any star that changes in actual brightness over a period of hours to days or years is considered a variable star. Traditionally, variable stars are not considered deep sky objects, but I have included them in this section to round out the types of objects amateurs observe.

For the record, **twinkling stars are not variable stars**. Twinkling is caused by atmospheric turbulence and is most noticeable when stars are near the horizon.

Greek Alphabet

α alpha
β beta
γ gamma
δ delta
ε epsilon
ζ zeta
η eta
θ theta
ι iota
κ kappa
λ lambda
μ mu
ν nu
ξ xi
ο omicron
π pi
ρ rho
σ sigma
τ tau
υ upsilon
φ phi
χ chi
ψ psi
ω omega

Most Noticable Variable Stars

Constellation	*Designation* or Name of Star[1]	Magnitude Range	Period
AQUILA	*η Aquilae*	3.5–4.4	7.177 days
CARINA	*L Carinae*	3.3–4.2	35.52 days
	R Carinae	4.6–9.6	308.71 days
CASSIOPEIA	**Navi**	1.6–3.0	203.59 days
CEPHEUS	*δ Cephei*	3.5–4.4	5.366 days
	μ Cephei	3.4–5.1	about 730 days
CETUS	**Mira**	2.0–10.1	331.96 days
CYGNUS	*χ Cygni*	5.2–13.4	406.93 days
DORADO	*β Doradus*	3.5–4.1	9.942 days
GEMINI	*ζ Geminorum*	3.6–4.2	10.2 days
	η Geminorum	3.2–3.9	234–235 days
HERCULES	*α Herculis*	2.7–4.0	about 128 days
HOROLOGIUM	*R Horologii*	6.0–13.0	407.6 days
LYRA	*β Lyrae*	3.3–4.4	12.936 days
ORION	**Betelgeuse**	0.0–1.3	about 2,070 days
PAVO	*κ Pavonis*	3.9–4.8	9.09 days
PEGASUS	**Scheat**	2.3–2.7	irregular
PERSEUS	**Algol**[2]	2.1–3.4	2.867 days
	ρ Persei	3.3–4.0	about 50 days
PUPPIS	*L2 Puppis*	2.6–6.2	141 days
TAURUS	*λ Tauri*	3.4–3.9	3.953 days

[1]These stars are identified on the monthly charts A–J starting on page 61. [2]The popular monthly astronomy magazines report the date and times of Algol's "dip" in magnitude, which are called "Minima of Algol." Be prepared to convert UT time to your local time.

Variable Stars

Observing Variable Stars

Stars change in brightness for two reasons. Most variable stars change in brightness due to **intrinsic** physical changes that occur within the star's structure. The Cepheid variables are the best known type. On the other hand, Algol in Perseus is an example of a **extrinsic** variable star that is an eclipsing binary. Algol is orbited by a significantly fainter star that passes between Algol and Earth, blocking and lowering Algol's light and magnitude for a period of several hours.

Cepheid Variable Yardstick Stars

Cepheid variables are a famous category of stars. Historically, these stars gave astronomers the "yardstick" tool for measuring the distances to many objects within our Galaxy and even nearby galaxies (but not to the distant ones).

Cepheid variables are named after the first-known of its kind, δ (delta) Cephei in the constellation Cepheus, next to Cassiopeia. This type of variable is either a giant or supergiant star near the end of its life. They slowly change in brightness over a period of a few days to months by expanding and contracting in size — their diameters changing anywhere from 5 to 10 percent. Polaris, the North Star, is a Cepheid variable, but its brightness changes very little.

In 1912, Henrietta Leavitt discovered that the true brightness (like knowing the actual wattage) of a Cepheid variable solely depends on its pulsation period. If the true brightness of a star is known, then it is easy (for astronomers) to calculate its distance. For a down-to-Earth example, if we took a 60 watt light bulb (a known brightness) and moved it to any distance, that distance could be determined simply by measuring its new apparent brightness (the brightness of light falls off by a factor of exactly four when its distance is doubled). So, astronomers have used this discovery to measure the distances of Cepheid variables in star clusters, nebulae and even nearby galaxies.

OBSERVING VARIABLE STARS

All of the variable stars listed in the table can be monitored with the naked eye. The most challenging part will be finding the stars and taking the time to observe them. To notice change, compare the variable stars to the brightness of the stars around them.

Mizar, a Double Star in the Big Dipper

NAMES: Mizar or Zeta (ζ) Ursae Majoris

CATALOGUE DESIGNATIONS: Double stars are not Deep Sky Objects so they are not listed in the Messier or NGC catalogues.

DESCRIPTION: Mizar is a well-known binary star with an optical counterpart, Alcor. When I was growing up, my next door neighbor said that a measure of good eyesight was being able to see Mizar and Alcor as two stars. Back then, it was easy for me to separate them; today, I need my glasses. See more about Mizar as a multiple star system on page 254.

Visual magnitudes: +2.3 for Mizar A, +3.95 for Mizar's companion, Mizar B and +4.0 for Alcor

Distances from our Sun: 78 light years to Mizar A & Mizar B; 81 light years to Alcor

Distance between Mizar A and Mizar B: over 10 times the distance from our Sun to Neptune

Arc degree separations in sky: Between Mizar A and B: 14" (arc *seconds*). There are 12' (arc *minutes*) of separation between Mizar and Alcor. The Moon spans about 30 arc minutes or 1,800 arc seconds.

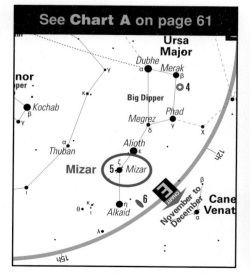

See **Chart A** on page 61

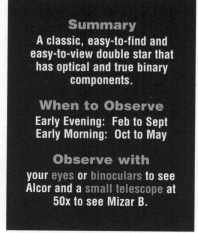

Summary
A classic, easy-to-find and easy-to-view double star that has optical and true binary components.

When to Observe
Early Evening: Feb to Sept
Early Morning: Oct to May

Observe with
your eyes or binoculars to see Alcor and a small telescope at 50x to see Mizar B.

Favorite DSOs

Facing page. *The Big Dipper one early morning.*

Favorite **Deep Sky Objects**

Pair of Galaxies in Ursa Major

CATALOGUE DESIGNATIONS: **M81** (NGC 3031); **M82** (NGC 3034). *See page 244 about catalogue designations.*

NAMES: Bode's Galaxies. By itself, M82 is often referred to as the Cigar Galaxy.

DESCRIPTIONS: Two very bright galaxies that are not far from the bowl of the Big Dipper. Both galaxies can be seen in the same eyepiece view at low powers and are visible in many light polluted areas. M81 is a spiral galaxy that appears ovalish. M82 is cigar shaped and is considered an irregular galaxy because its insides are mixed up. These galaxies are more difficult to locate than most objects in this section because they are not near any conspicuously bright stars.

Visual magnitudes: 6.8 for M81 and 8.4 for M82

Distances: 9.5 million light years away for both

Physical sizes: 72,000 light years in diameter for M81and 30,000 light years for M82

Arc degree lengths in sky: 26' for M81 and 11' for M82 (the Moon spans 30', that is, 30 arc minutes)

➤*Check out the DSO observing tips on page 252.*

Realistic Telescope View

See **Chart A** on page 61

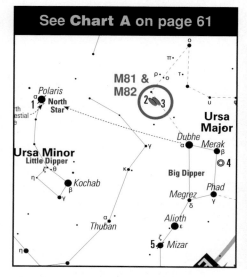

Summary
Bright galaxies, near one another, that are easy to see even in light-polluted skies.

When to Observe
Early Evening: Jan to July
Early Morning: Sept to April

Observe with
a small telescope at 50x to 100x. Both can be seen in the same eyepiece view at lower magnifications.

Favorite DSOs

Facing page. M81 and M82 (inset).

263

Double Cluster in Perseus

CATALOGUE DESIGNATIONS: NGC 869 has the Honorary designation of **M111**; NGC 884 is the Honorary **M112**

NAMES: Known as the "Double Cluster." Before the telescope was invented (1609), it was referred to as "The nebulous mass on the right hand of Perseus."

DESCRIPTIONS: Absolutely beautiful sight! A must-see object. Although you can spot these clusters with your eyes and see them through binoculars, you need a telescope at low power to view their glory. M111 is the cluster that has a higher concentration of brighter stars near its center. M111 consists of about 200 stars with the brightest shining at magnitude 6.6 and M112 has about 115 stars with the brightest shining at magnitude 8.1. Can you see the faint red star halfway between the clusters?

Visual magnitudes: about 4 for M111 and 5 for M112

Distances: 7,100 light years to NGC 869 and 7,500 light years to NGC 884

Physical sizes: each spans a little over 60 light years

Arc degree sizes in sky: each spans about 30' and together they extend about 1° in the sky (2 Moon diameters)

➤*Check out the DSO observing tips on page 252.*

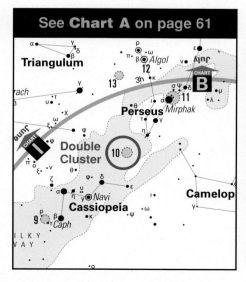

See **Chart A** on page 61

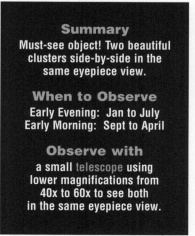

Summary
Must-see object! Two beautiful clusters side-by-side in the same eyepiece view.

When to Observe
Early Evening: Jan to July
Early Morning: Sept to April

Observe with
a small telescope using lower magnifications from 40x to 60x to see both in the same eyepiece view.

Favorite DSOs

Facing page. *M111 above and M112 below.*

Algol, Variable Star in Perseus

NAMES: Algol, Beta (β) Persei and in ancient times, it was known as the Demon Star.

CATALOGUE DESIGNATIONS: Variable stars are not Deep Sky Objects so they are not listed in the Messier or NGC catalogues.

DESCRIPTION: Most visible, dramatic, predictable and "accessible" variable star in the northern sky. Its magnitude drops by 1.3 (a change in brightness of 3.3 times) for about two hours every three days when a much fainter star passes in front of it. It takes several hours for Algol to fade and then brighten again. You will need to consult one of the popular monthly astronomy magazines to find exact times when its magnitude dips. These dips are referred to as the "Minima of Algol." Also, see the time calculation example on page 303. In Greek mythology, Algol represents the turn-to-stone, snake-hair head of Medusa that Perseus had cut off for a wedding gift.

Visual magnitudes: normally +2.1 but dips to +3.4 for a few hours

Distance: 93 light years

Type of variable: eclipsing binary with a period of 68 hours, 48.5 minutes or 2 days, 20 hours, 48.5 minutes

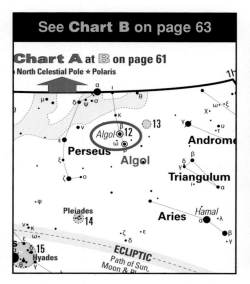

See Chart B on page 63

Chart A at **B** on page 61

North Celestial Pole ★ Polaris

Perseus

Algol

Androme

Triangulum

Pleiades

Aries

Hamal

Hyades

ECLIPTIC

Path of Sun, Moon & Pl

Summary
Most visible, dramatic and easy-to-find variable star in the northern hemisphere. Changes magnitude for a few hours every 2.9 days.

When to Observe
Early Evening: Jan to July
Early Morning: Sept to April

Observing with
the naked eye is adequate. Compare the brightness change to the surrounding stars.

Favorite DSOs

Facing page. *The constellation Perseus with Algol near the center.*

267

Three Open Clusters in Auriga

CATALOGUE DESIGNATIONS: **M36** (NGC 1960); **M37** (NGC 2099); **M38** (NGC 1912). *See page 244 about catalogue designations.*

NAMES: No common names

DESCRIPTIONS: Three beautiful clusters in Auriga. All three are visible as fuzzy patches in binoculars on moonless nights. M37 is a favorite because it has a pretty red star amidst a sprinkle of many fainter stars. M36 consists of 60 stars with the brightest shining at magnitude 8.9. M37 has 150 stars with the brightest shining at magnitude 9.2 while M38 has 100 stars with the brightest shining at magnitude 9.5.

Visual magnitudes: 6 for M36, 5.6 for M37 and 6.4 for M38

Distances: 3,700 light years to M36, 4,200 light years to M37 and 2,800 light years to M38

Physical sizes: M36 spans 13 light years, M37 spans 29 light years and M38 spans 17 light years

Arc degree sizes in sky: 12' for M36, 24' for M37 and 21' for M38 (the Moon spans 30' or 30 arc minutes)

➤ *Check out the DSO observing tips on page 252.*

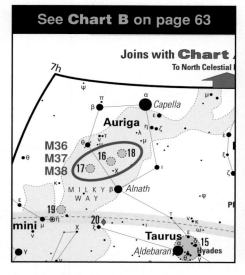

See **Chart B** on page 63

Joins with **Chart**
To North Celestial

7h

ψ
π
β
Capella
Auriga
η
λ
μ
M36
M37
16
18
M38
17
θ
x
M I L K Y β Alnath
W A Y
φ
19
mini μ η
20
Taurus
15
Aldebaran Hyades
γ

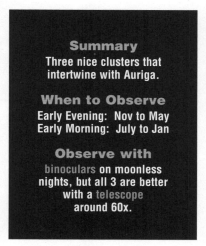

Summary
Three nice clusters that intertwine with Auriga.

When to Observe
Early Evening: Nov to May
Early Morning: July to Jan

Observe with
binoculars on moonless nights, but all 3 are better with a telescope around 60x.

Favorite **DSOs**

Facing page. *Background, M36. M37 left inset. M38 right inset.*   269

Favorite **Deep Sky Objects**

Open Cluster in Gemini

CATALOGUE DESIGNATION: M35 (NGC 2168);
See page 244 about catalogue designations.

NAME: No common name

DESCRIPTION: This favorite cluster is easy to find and remember because it is at the foot of Gemini. M35 is large, very open, and has many bright members. If you look carefully, you may see a smaller, fainter cluster (NGC 2158) about a Moon's diameter from its center (in the photo on the facing page, NGC 2158 appears in the upper right corner and looks more like a globular cluster than an open cluster). M35 contains about 200 stars with the brightest shining at magnitude 8.2. Its stars were born, out of the same nebula, about 110 million years ago. Auriga is next to Gemini, so take some time to compare the size and brightness of M36, M37 and M38 with M35.

Visual magnitude: 5.1

Distance: 2,800 light years

Physical size: stretches across 23 light years

Arc degree size in sky: 28' (Moon is 30')

➤*Check out the DSO observing tips on page 252.*

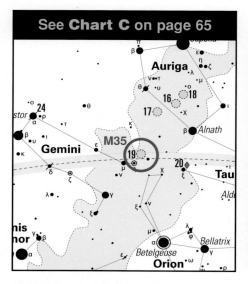

See **Chart C** on page 65

Summary
Large, pretty, easy-to-find open cluster with many bright stars.

When to Observe
Early Evening: Nov to May
Early Morning: Aug to Jan

Observe with
binoculars as a faint fuzzy patch. Better with a telescope from 50x to 100x.

Favorite DSOs

Facing page. M35 fills the bottom half with NGC 2158 in the upper right corner. 271

Favorite **Deep Sky Objects**

Pleiades in Taurus

CATALOGUE DESIGNATION: **M45**. No NGC designation because is is plainly visible to the naked eye.

NAMES: Pleiades, the Seven Sisters

DESCRIPTION: Most prominent naked eye star open cluster in the sky. I frequently hear people refer to this cluster as a little dipper. While its shape is similar, it is not The Little Dipper. The seven sisters are the daughters of Atlas and Pleione. They were changed into doves and sent into the heavens as stars to avoid the amorous clutches of Orion. Thus, the Pleiades always rise before Orion, forever escaping him. The Pleiades are also the half-sisters of the Hyades (see pages 62–63) which make up the 14 Atlantides. This cluster consists of about 100 stars, with the brightest, Alcyone, shining at magnitude 2.9. The blue Merope Nebula surrounding these stars is not the nebula out of which these stars formed, but simply another one they are passing through.

Visual magnitude: 1.2

Distance: 395 light years

Physical size: spans 13 light years

Arc degree size in sky: 1.8° which is about 4 Moon diameters across

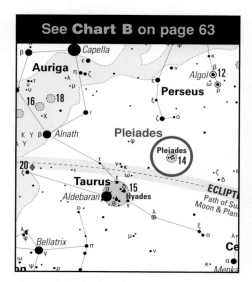

Summary
Bright, pretty, and easy to see with the naked eye. Looks like a little dipper but it is *not* "The Little Dipper."

When to Observe
Early Evening: Oct to April
Early Morning: June to Dec

Best Observed with
binoculars because you can see the entire cluster in the view. Not that great in telescopes because you can only see a portion of it.

Favorite DSOs

Facing page. *The Pleiades' nebulosity is visually difficult to see.*

273

Favorite Deep Sky Objects

The Great Nebula in Orion

CATALOGUE DESIGNATIONS: M42 (NGC 1976).
See page 244 about catalogue designations.

NAMES: Orion Nebula, the Great Orion Nebula, the Great Nebula in Orion. The four stars known as the Trapezium are designated with the Greek Bayer letter θ (theta).

DESCRIPTION: Most prominent and spectacular emission nebula in the northern hemisphere. Visible in light-polluted areas. Even small telescopes will reveal subtle details and wisps. Most of its luminosity is fueled by the stimulation of its gas from four central stars known as the Trapezium, which are about a million years old. New stars are being formed in this nebula. The Orion Nebula is part of Orion's sword.

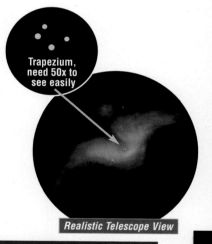

Trapezium, need 50x to see easily

Visual magnitude: 4

Distance: 1,500 light years

Physical size: 29 x 26 light years

Arc degree size in sky: 66' at its widest which is about 2 Moon diameters

➤ *Check out the DSO observing tips on page 252.*

Realistic Telescope View

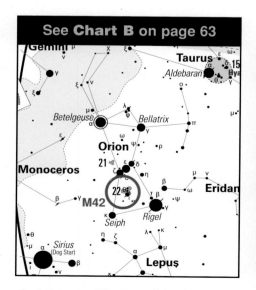

See **Chart B** on page 63

Summary
Bright, very large, easy to find. Best nebula in the northern hemisphere.

When to Observe
Early Evening: Dec to April
Early Morning: Aug to Dec

Observe with
a telescope at 40x to 100x. Need at least 50x to see the Trapezium.

Favorite DSOs

Facing page. The Great Orion Nebula with the harder to see NGC 1977 above it. 275

Favorite **Deep Sky Objects**

Andromeda Galaxy & Companions

CATALOGUE DESIGNATIONS: **M31** (NGC 224), **M32** (NGC 221), **M110** (NGC 205). *See page 244 about catalogue designations.*

NAME: Andromeda Galaxy (for **M31**)

DESCRIPTIONS: The Andromeda Galaxy spans over six Moon diameters in the sky. However, the visible central portion, which is the part that is actually seen, spans about two Moon diameters. The softly glowing central oval is visible to the naked eye in some light-polluted areas. M32 and M110 are smaller elliptical companion galaxies, gravitationally bound to the Andromeda Galaxy. These three galaxies and our Milky Way Galaxy are part of a group of about 30 galaxies called the Local Group. The Andromeda Galaxy contains about 300 billion stars. Research suggests that it will collide with ours in about 3 billion years and that it may have a diameter as great as 220,000 light years.

Visual magnitudes: 3½/M31, 8/M32, 9/M110

Distances: 2,500,000 ly away for all three

Diameters: 120,000 ly or greater for M31, 5,600 ly for M32, 12,000 for M110

Arc degree sizes in sky: 3° x 1° (6 by 2 Moon diameters) for M31, 8'x6' for M32, 17'x10' for M110 (our Moon is 30')

Realistic Telescope View

See **Chart I** on page 77

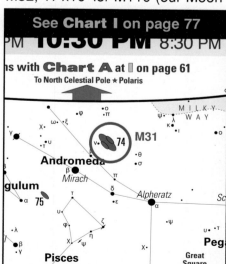

ns with **Chart A** at ▌ on page 61

To North Celestial Pole ★ Polaris

MILKY WAY

M31

Andromeda

Mirach

Alpheratz

gulum

Pisces

Peg.

Great Square

Summary
Andromeda is the largest appearing galaxy in the northern hemisphere sky!

When to Observe
Early Evening: Aug to March
Early Morning: April to Nov

Observing
Andromeda is visible to the naked eye but best in binoculars. Use telescope at low powers, 20x to 50x. Need telescope at 50x for two companion galaxies

Favorite DSOs

Facing page. *M31 with M32 on the galaxy's edge and M110 at the top right.*

Beehive Cluster in Cancer

CATALOGUE DESIGNATIONS: M44 (NGC 2632).
See page 244 about catalogue designations.

NAMES: Beehive Cluster, Praesepe

DESCRIPTION: Although this cluster is similar in size to the Pleiades, its stars are much fainter, so it appears as a fuzzy patch in the sky. As such, it has been known since ancient times. Like most open clusters, the Beehive looks better through binoculars than in photographs. Even though the Beehive is located in an area of the sky sparse with bright stars, it "pops out" when panning with binoculars halfway between the stars Regulus in Leo and Pollux in Gemini. The Beehive contains about 50 stars with the brightest shining at magnitude 6.3. The word Praesepe is a Latin word meaning enclosure, crib, manger, stall, a haunt or hive. This open cluster is most often associated with a beehive but some mythology attributes it to the donkey ears of King Midas, given to him as punishment for his greed.

Visual magnitude: 3.1

Distance: 580 light years

Physical size: spans 16 light years

Arc degree size in sky: 1.6° which is a little over 3 Moon diameters

➤ *Check out the DSO observing tips on page 252.*

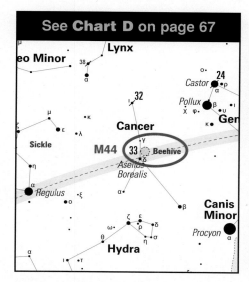

See **Chart D** on page 67

Summary
Easy-to-find fuzzy patch
in the sky that opens up
with binoculars.

When to Observe
Early Evening: Jan to June
Early Morning: Sept to Feb

Observing
Visible to the naked eye
as a fuzzy patch.
Best with binoculars.
Use low powers with telescope,
20x to 50x.

Favorite DSOs

Facing page. *M44 looks much prettier through binoculars than in photographs.* 279

Globular Clusters in Hercules

CATALOGUE DESIGNATIONS: M13 (NGC 6205); **M92** (NGC 6341)

NAMES: Great Hercules Cluster (for M13). No common name for M92.

DESCRIPTIONS: The globular cluster M13 is the largest and brightest northern globular cluster, hence a favorite to amateur astronomers. It is easy to find because it straddles one side of Hercules' Keystone. M92 always takes a back seat to M13, however, it is a spectacular globular cluster with a bright center. M13 contains about 500,000 stars.

Visual magnitudes: 5.8 for M13 and 6.4 for M92

Distances: 21,000 light years to M13 and 26,000 light years to M92

Physical sizes: M13 spans 104 light years and M92 spans 85 light years

Arc degree sizes in sky: 17' for M13, 11' for M92 (Moon is 30')

➤ *Check out the DSO observing tips on page 252.*

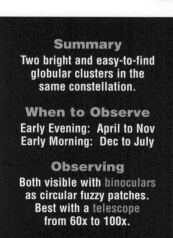
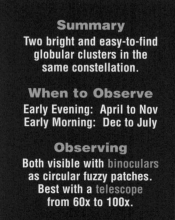

M92

Realistic Telescope Views

M13

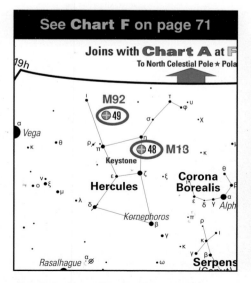

See **Chart F** on page 71

Joins with **Chart A** at F

To North Celestial Pole ★ Pola

19h

M92
49

α
Vega
κ   θ   ρ   π   σ   X
Keystone   48 M13   κ

ε   ζ   ξ
v   ξ   θ
o   ξ   **Hercules**   **Corona Borealis**
μ   ε   δ   γ   Alph
λ   δ
Kornephoros   ρ
β   γ

Rasalhague   ω   **Serpens**

Summary
Two bright and easy-to-find globular clusters in the same constellation.

When to Observe
Early Evening: April to Nov
Early Morning: Dec to July

Observing
Both visible with binoculars as circular fuzzy patches. Best with a telescope from 60x to 100x.

Favorite **DSOs**

Facing page. *M13 and M92 in the inset.*

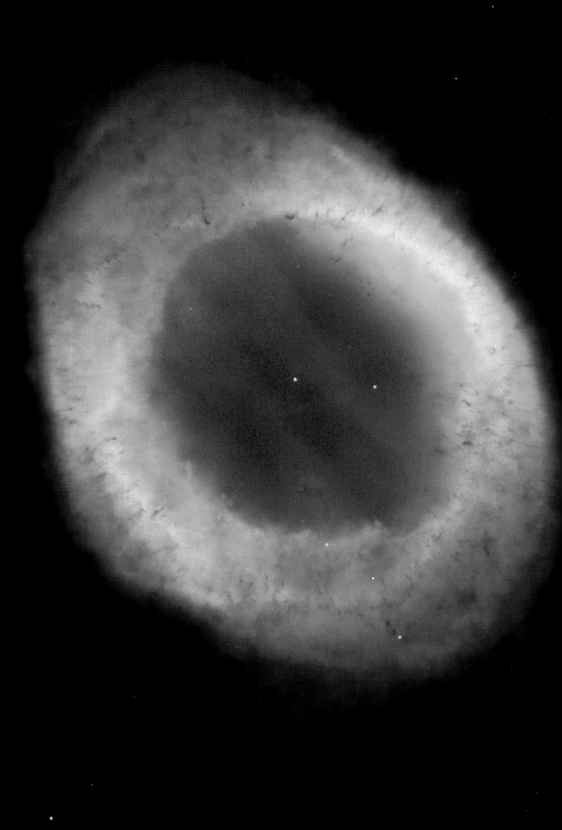

Ring Nebula in Lyra

CATALOGUE DESIGNATIONS: M57 (NGC 6720).
See page 244 about catalogue designations.

NAMES: Ring Nebula, Smoke Ring Nebula, Donut Nebula

DESCRIPTION: This great planetary nebula represents the remnants of a dying star, now a white dwarf, at its center, having a magnitude of 15.2. Astronomers disagree on the actual shape of the "ring," for some say it may be a cylinder or shell. M57 is one of the few Messier nebulae that appears to have a sharply defined edge. Although this little wonder is fairly faint and small, it is easy to locate because it lies between the two end stars in Lyra.

Visual magnitude: 9

Distance: Estimates range from 1,400 to 5,000 light years

Physical size: 0.5 to 1.9 light years across depending on its actual distance

Arc degree size in sky: 76" which is about twice the size that Jupiter normally appears in a telescope, although M57 will seem smaller than Jupiter because of its low luminosity.

Realistic Telescope View

➤*Check out the DSO observing tips on page 252.*

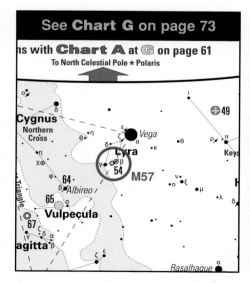

See **Chart G** on page 73

ns with **Chart A** at Ⓖ on page 61

To North Celestial Pole ★ Polaris

Cygnus
Northern Cross
Vega
Lyra
54 M57
64
Albireo
65
Vulpecula
67
agitta
Triangle
Keys
Rasalhague

Summary
Small, faint smoke ring that is easy to find and can be seen in some light-polluted skies.

When to Observe
Early Evening: June to Dec
Early Morning: Feb to Aug

Observe with
a telescope at 50x to 100x. It will appear smaller than you think.

Favorite **DSOs**

Facing page. *Popular Hubble Space Telescope picture of M57.*

Favorite **Deep Sky Objects**

Albireo, a Double Star in Cygnus

NAMES: Albireo or Beta (β) Cygni

CATALOGUE DESIGNATION: Double stars are not Deep Sky Objects so they are not listed in the Messier or NGC catalogues.

DESCRIPTION: A well-known double star because it is pretty and easy to locate. With the naked eye and through binoculars, this beautiful pair of golden-yellow and blue stars looks like a single star, so a telescope at low power is needed to separate and appreciate their colors. The brighter yellow-colored star has a diameter 50 times greater, and its blue companion about 1½ times greater than our Sun. Astronomers believe that these two stars move around each other with a revolution that takes tens of thousands of years. See page 255 for a picture of Albireo.

Visual magnitudes: Albireo shines at magnitude 3.4. Separately, the yellow star has a magnitude of +3.1 and the blue star has a magnitude of +5.1

Distance from our Sun: 385 light years for both

Distance between the two stars: 10 times the distance from the Sun to Pluto

Arc degree separation in sky: 34" (34 arc seconds)

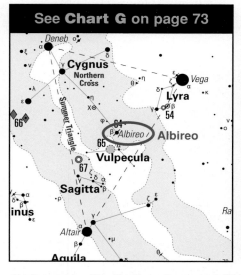

See **Chart G** on page 73

Summary
Prettiest pair of stars because of their colors, gold and blue

When to Observe
Early Evening: June to Dec
Early Morning: Feb to Aug

Observing
Telescope needed.
Stars can be separated at 20x, but best around 80x.

Favorite **DSOs**

Facing page. *The Northern Cross and Albireo, swathed in the Milky Way.*

285

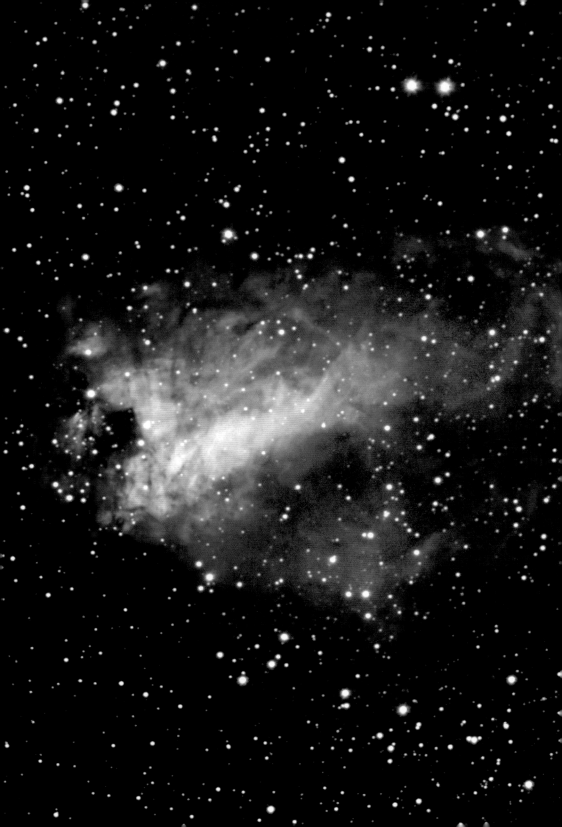

Favorite **Deep Sky Objects**

Omega Nebula in Sagittarius

CATALOGUE DESIGNATIONS: M17 (NGC 6618).
See page 244 about catalogue designations.

NAMES: Omega Nebula, Swan Nebula, Horseshoe Nebula

DESCRIPTION: A bright, long patch of nebulosity with a hook on one end. This galactic emission nebula is more striking and noticeable than its southern neighbor M8. Unfortunately, M17 is more difficult to find because there are no conspicuous celestial markers. This area is saturated with Messier objects and you will probably encounter several in your search for the Omega Nebula.

Visual magnitude: 7

Distance: 3,000 light years

Physical size: spans 40 light years

Arc degree sizes in sky: length stretches for 47' compared to the Moon's 30' diameter

➤*Check out the DSO observing tips on page 252.*

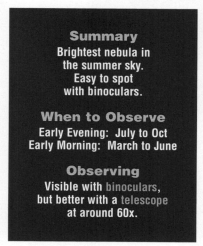

Realistic Telescope View

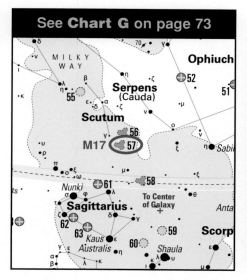

See **Chart G** on page 73

Favorite DSOs

Summary
Brightest nebula in
the summer sky.
Easy to spot
with binoculars.

When to Observe
Early Evening: July to Oct
Early Morning: March to June

Observing
Visible with binoculars,
but better with a telescope
at around 60x.

Facing page. *M17, the second brightest nebula in northern skies.*

287

Favorite **Deep Sky Objects**

Lagoon Nebula in Sagittarius

CATALOGUE DESIGNATIONS: M8 (NGC 6523).
See page 244 about catalogue designations.

NAME: Lagoon Nebula

DESCRIPTION: A very large and fairly bright galactic emission nebula in a thick part of the Milky Way. With binoculars, the Lagoon Nebula looks like a large, bright patch. In fact, it appears brighter in binoculars than through a telescope. M8 is visually striking because it is nested in a cluster of stars. Take some time to study this nebula. You will see an abundance of faint nebulosity along with some dark lanes.

Visual magnitude: 6

Distance: 4,800 light years

Physical size: 126 x 56 light years

Arc degree size in sky: 90' x 40' which is 3 Moon diameters on its longest side

➤ *Check out the DSO observing tips on page 252.*

Realistic Telescope View

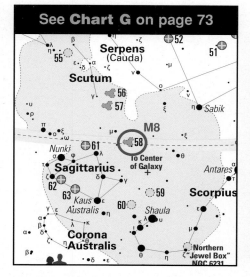

See **Chart G** on page 73

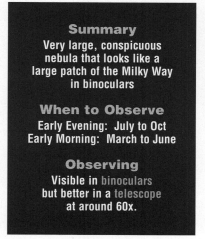

Favorite DSOs

Summary
Very large, conspicuous nebula that looks like a large patch of the Milky Way in binoculars

When to Observe
**Early Evening: July to Oct
Early Morning: March to June**

Observing
Visible in binoculars but better in a telescope at around 60x.

Facing page. The Lagoon Nebula has an embedded open cluster.

289

Favorite **Deep Sky Objects**

Globular Cluster in Sagittarius

CATALOGUE DESIGNATIONS: M22 (NGC 6656).
See page 244 about catalogue designations.

NAMES: Great Sagittarius Cluster, Crackerjack Cluster

DESCRIPTION: This is my favorite northern hemisphere globular cluster. It hangs low in the sky with a beautiful glow unlike any of the others, even in a small telescope, because you can see a multitude of its stars speckled against a background haze of unresolvable fainter stars. A beautiful sight! It is estimated that this globular contains about 70,000 stars. There are many globular clusters around Sagittarius, but none compare to M22.

Visual magnitude: 5.1

Distance: 10,000 light years

Physical size: 70 light years in diameter

Arc degree size in sky: 24' so it is almost the same size as the Moon at 30'

➤*Check out the DSO observing tips on page 252.*

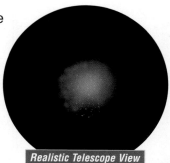
Realistic Telescope View

See **Chart G** on page 73

Summary
Large, bright, spectacular globular that is easy to find.

When to Observe
Early Evening: July to Oct
Early Morning: March to June

Observing
Visible with binoculars. Best with a telescope at 70x to 100x. Can see many individual stars

Favorite DSOs

Facing page. Most northerners like M22 better than M13 in Hercules.

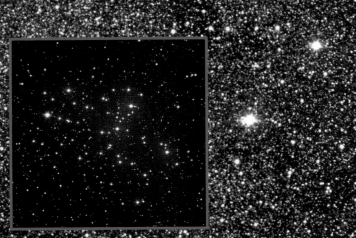

Favorite **Deep Sky Objects**

Two large Open Clusters in Scorpius

CATALOGUE DESIGNATIONS: **M6** (NGC 6405);
M7 (NGC 6475). *See page 244 about catalogue designations.*

NAMES: M6 is known as the Butterfly Cluster but M7 has no common name.

DESCRIPTIONS: Two beautiful and very large clusters that are easy to spot with binoculars. Each fills the whole eyepiece field-of-view in a telescope. See if you can spot them at a dark location with your eyes. M6 contains about 330 stars ranging in magnitude from 6.2 to 14. M7 totals about 80 stars with the brightest shining at magnitude 5.6.

Visual magnitudes: 4.2 for M6 and 3.3 for M7

Distances: M6 is 1,500 light years away and M7 is 800 light years away

Physical sizes: M6 spans 6.6 light years while M7 spans across 20 light years

Arc degree sizes in sky: M6 extends 15' (arc minutes) and M7 extends to 80'. Remember, the Moon's diameter is 30'.

►*Check out the DSO observing tips on page 252.*

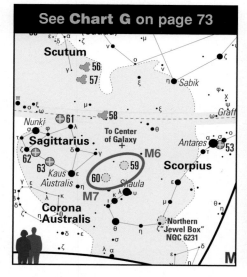

See **Chart G** on page 73

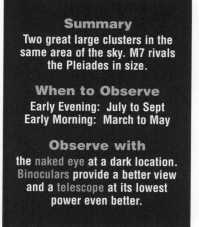

Summary
Two great large clusters in the same area of the sky. M7 rivals the Pleiades in size.

When to Observe
Early Evening: July to Sept
Early Morning: March to May

Observe with
the naked eye at a dark location. Binoculars provide a better view and a telescope at its lowest power even better.

Favorite DSOs

Facing page. M7 with M6 in the inset.

Favorite **Deep Sky Objects**

Omega Centauri Globular Cluster

CATALOGUE DESIGNATIONS: NGC 5139. This object is not in the Messier catalogue because it was too far south for Messier to observe from Paris.

NAME: Omega (ω) Centauri

DESCRIPTION: The largest globular cluster in our skies. Omega Centauri often goes unnoticed because it can only be seen easily south of latitude 35° N (about the bottom of Tennessee) and then for only a few months around Spring. Use binoculars to scan for Omega Centauri, due south and just above the horizon during May and June after it gets dark. It will look like a faint round disk. In Miami, it reaches 15° above the southern horizon. It is estimated that it contains over a million stars. This object was catalogued as a faint star until 1677 when Edmond Halley discovered that it was nonstellar.

Visual magnitude: Looks like a 4th to 5th magnitude star.

Distance: 18,000 light years

Physical size: 350 light years in diameter

Arc degree size in sky: 53' which makes it almost 2 Moon diameters across.

Realistic Telescope View

See **Chart E** on page 69

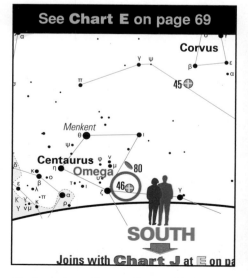

SOUTH

Joins with **Chart J** at **E** on p.

Summary
Awesome. Largest globular cluster in the sky. Can only be observed in the US from southern states.

When to Observe
Early Evening: May & June
Early Morning: Jan & Feb

Observing
Visible to the naked eye. To find, scan the southern horizon with binoculars. Incredible in a telescope at 50x to 100x.

Favorite DSOs

Facing page. Omega Centauri is best viewed from the Southern Hemisphere. 295

PRIME
MERIDIAN
OF THE
WORLD

Time & Practices

Our concept of time is rooted in the day, created from the rotation of the Earth on its axis. However, it is the "movement" of the Sun through the sky and the cycles of day and night that provide us with the sense of passing time.

I think one of humankind's most ingenious ideas was the division of the day into 24 hours, the hours into 60 minutes and the minutes into 60 seconds (seconds are further divided into tenths). With these divisions, the day can be divided into half, thirds and quarters, and the hours and minutes further divided into fifths and tenths. All of this adds up to incredible flexibility in dividing our time into convenient intervals. Although I applaud the metric system for its simplicity, it would be awkward to base our system of time on divisions of ten because decimal numbers would have to be used for most of our current divisions.

Dividing the day into 24 hours and the hours and minutes into 60 parts was pure genius.

The measurement of time has become very sophisticated. Today, the highest accuracy obtained is a one second error in 20 million years. And, as with most technological advances, this will be further refined in the years to come.

TIME, DIVISIONS & PRACTICES

Apparent Solar Time. This is the time that is indicated on a sundial. It would be impractical to use Apparent Solar Time because cities or towns just a short distance apart would have slightly different times.

Standard Time Zones. The Earth is divided into 24 time zones, each 15° wide in longitude. Everyone in a time zone sets their clocks to the same time. The time difference between adjacent time zones is one hour. In the middle of the oceans, the time zone boundaries are straight vertical lines, however, over populated land, they are often redefined to take into account political, economical and social considerations. The continental United States is spanned by four standard time zones.

Facing page. *Where time begins. The prime meridian or 0° longitude at the Old Royal Observatory in Greenwich, England, just outside of London.*
Above. *The astrolabe was a device to help tell time before the clock was invented.*

Time

Universal Time

Standard Time or Local Standard Time. The time on our clocks which is based on the 24 standard time zones as defined above.

Daylight-Saving Time (DST). The practice of advancing the clocks from Standard Time by one hour from the first Sunday in April to the last Saturday in October (in the US). DST is sometimes referred to as Summer Time. Most, but not all of the world changes its clocks to Daylight-Saving Time. This practice of changing the clocks has been a societal decision (At the writing of this edition, there is talk in Washington to change the beginning and ending dates of Daylight-Saving Time). The following locations in North America DO NOT observe DST: Hawaii; most of Arizona; most of Indiana; most of Saskatchewan, Canada; Puerto Rico; Virgin Islands and most of Mexico.

Universal Time (UT). Astronomical events are expressed in Universal Time, which is the Standard Time at the Old Royal Observatory in Greenwich, England. The location of the Old Royal Observatory was chosen to be longitude 0° in 1884. The beginning of every new day starts here.

Universal Time is not adjusted for Daylight-Saving Time. Expressed using the 24-hour clock, Universal Time must be converted to obtain Local Standard Time.

Coordinated Universal Time (UTC). In North America, the WWV radio station in Fort Collins, Colorado and the CHU radio station in Ottawa, Ontario, Canada broadcast Universal Time 24 hours a day on shortwave radio frequencies. The broadcasting of this time is known as Coordinated Universal Time. The abbreviation UTC was adopted from the French word order.

Coordinated Universal Time
Broadcast Frequencies & Internet Sources

Signal Origination	Station and Location	Shortwave Broadcast Frequencies
US	WWV at Fort Collins, Colorado Internet Equivalent: http://nist.time.gov	2.5, 5, 10 & 20 MHz
Canada	CHU at Ottawa, Ontario Internet Equivalent: http://time5.nrc.ca/webclock_e.shtml	3.330, 7.335 & 14.670 MHz

Time

These radio broadcasts use tones to mark the seconds and an automated voice announcement at the start of each minute. Amateur and professional astronomers use UTC for the accurate timing of astronomical events.

Greenwich Mean Time (GMT). Universal Time was originally referred to as Greenwich Mean Time. The term Universal Time was adopted in 1928 by the International Astronomical Union. UT is still occasionally referred to as GMT.

Twilight, Dawn & Dusk

Twilight is the time before sunrise and after sunset. It represents the transition period between day and night. Before sunrise, the twilight period is commonly referred to as dawn and after sunset it is called dusk. Twilight is caused by the scattering of sunlight from the atmosphere. There are three recognized twilight periods which are described below.

Civil Twilight. The period beginning at sunset and ending when the Sun is 6 arc angle degrees (12 Sun diameters) below the horizon. In the morning, before the Sun rises, Civil twilight begins when the Sun is 6 degrees below the horizon and ends at sunrise. Civil twilight is the last or first time of the day when "normal" daylight activities can be conducted.

Twilight Rules of Thumb

CIVIL Twilight	**Ends 30 minutes after Sunset**
	Starts 30 minutes before Sunrise
NAUTICAL Twilight	**Ends 60 minutes after Sunset**
	Starts 60 minutes before Sunrise
ASTRONOMICAL Twilight	**Ends 90 minutes after Sunset**
	Starts 90 minutes before Sunrise

Nautical Twilight. Begins in the morning or ends in the evening when the the Sun is 12 degrees below the horizon. The horizon at sea is not visible when the Sun is 12 degrees below the horizon. The brighter stars and planets are noticeable at this time.

Astronomical Twilight. The Sun must be 18 degrees below the horizon for Astronomical twilight to end in the evening and

Converting UT Time

begin in the morning. When the Sun is 18 or more degrees below the horizon, everyone would agree it is night and all astronomical objects are visible.

Working with Universal Time (UT)
If you read any astronomical literature, including the popular monthly astronomy magazines, you will quickly discover that Universal Time is often used to express the occurrence of astronomical events. This is done to avoid confusion with time zones. But, what is the equivalent local standard time for your location? Depending on the actual Universal Time, and your location, you could witness an astronomical event as much as a day before the Universal Time noted for the event.

There are several factors that must be taken into consideration when changing Universal Time to local standard time. First is the Time Zone difference between your location and Greenwich. Second is the consideration for Daylight-Saving Time. Third is that the local standard time date may be one day prior to the UT date; and lastly, 24-hour UT time must be converted to 12-hour time.

Advisory Note: At the printing of this book, Washington is considering a change in the start/stop dates of DST.

Changing UT to Local Standard Time

a₁ From the last Sunday in October to the first Saturday in April, find your location on the map on the next page and note the **BLUE** Time Zone number.

or

a₂ From the first Sunday in April to the last Saturday in October, note the **GREEN DST number** in parentheses if your location observes Daylight-Saving Time (DST).

b Subtract the Time Zone number (or DST number) from the Universal Time. Subtract **whole hours** only.

c If the Time Zone number is larger than the UT hour, then first add 24 to the UT hour and *then* subtract the Time Zone number from this larger number. When 24 is added to the UT time, the *date* of the local standard time will be *one day prior* to the UT date.

d Use the vertical conversion table on page 302 to change 24-hour to 12-hour time.

Standard Time Zones

Universal Time Zone Differences

The boxed numbers next to the Time Zones indicate the difference in hours of Local Standard Time from Universal Time. *The number in parentheses is the difference during Daylight-Saving Time.*

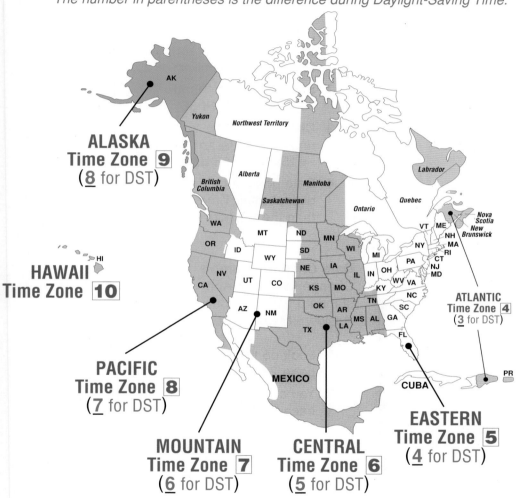

ALASKA
Time Zone **9**
(**8** for DST)

HAWAII
Time Zone **10**

PACIFIC
Time Zone **8**
(**7** for DST)

MOUNTAIN
Time Zone **7**
(**6** for DST)

CENTRAL
Time Zone **6**
(**5** for DST)

EASTERN
Time Zone **5**
(**4** for DST)

ATLANTIC
Time Zone **4**
(**3** for DST)

The following locations DO NOT observe Daylight-Saving Time.
Hawaii, Most of Arizona, Most of Indiana,
Most of Saskatchewan, Puerto Rico, Virgin Islands, Most of Mexico.

TO BEGIN CHANGING Universal Time (UT) to your Local Standard Time, first _**subtract**_ the *BLUE number* for your Time Zone from the UT, however, *USE the GREEN DST number* during Daylight-Saving Time that is in effect from Spring through Fall. See the facing page for more details.

Time Zones

301

Converting UT Time

24-Hour to 12-Hour Conversion Chart

24 Hour	12 Hour
0[1]	12 A.M.[2] (MIDNIGHT)
1	1 A.M.
2	2 A.M.
3	3 A.M.
4	4 A.M.
5	5 A.M.
6	6 A.M.
7	7 A.M.
8	8 A.M.
9	9 A.M.
10	10 A.M.
11	11 A.M.
12	12 P.M.[2] (NOON)
13	1 P.M.
14	2 P.M.
15	3 P.M.
16	4 P.M.
17	5 P.M.
18	6 P.M.
19	7 P.M.
20	8 P.M.
21	9 P.M.
22	10 P.M.
23	11 P.M.

[1]0 hour & 12 a.m. have the same calendar date.
[2]You may encounter differing uses of a.m. and p.m. associated with Noon and Midnight in different sources.

Basic Example

Change the UT of August 4, 19:56 to local standard time if you are in New York.
Answer: August 4, 3:56 p.m.

1. Look up the Time Zone number on page 301 for New York (in this case, use the DST number) → **4**

2. Subtract 4 from 19:56
   → 19:56 − 4 = **15:56**

3. Change 15:56 to 12-hour time by referring to the chart on this page
   → 15:56 = **3:56 p.m.**

4. Date does not have to be changed because the Time Zone number is less than the UT hour of 19.

Date Change Example

Change the UT of April 1, 2:38 to local standard time if you are in San Diego.
Answer: March 31, 6:38 p.m.

1. Look up the Time Zone number on page 283 for San Diego → **8**

2. You cannot subtract 8 from 2:38 because 8 is larger than 2, so add 24 to 2:38 → **26:38**

3. Now subtract 8 from 26:38
   → 26:38 − 8 = **18:38**

4. Change 18:38 to 12-hour time by referring to the chart on this page
   → 18:38 = **6:38 p.m.**

5. **Date changes to March 31** because subtracting 8 from 2:38 UT backs into the previous day. When-ever you add 24 to the UT, the local date will always be one day prior to the UT date.

Converting UT Time

Practical Example

You will be visiting a friend just outside Chicago during the first half of October. Hoping for clear skies, you want to observe the variable star Algol dim to magnitude 3.4 (see page 267 in the Deep Sky Object section of this field guide). You consult the popular monthly astronomy magazine *Sky & Telescope* and find that for the first part of October, Algol will reach minima on the following dates and times:

Minima of Algol from *Sky & Telescope*	Chicago Time Zone	UT Converted to Local Standard Time
October 3, 4:05 UT	−5	October 2, 11:05 p.m.
October 6, 0:54 UT	−5	October 5, 7:54 p.m.
October 8, 21:43 UT	−5	October 8, 4:43 p.m.
October 11, 18:31 UT	−5	October 11, 1:31 p.m.

Will you be able to observe Algol dim? By converting the four UT dates, you discover that October 2nd and 5th are the only dates that will allow viewing of the minima. The other minima occur during daylight. On October 5th, the Sun sets at 5:30 p.m. and astronomical twilight ends around 7 p.m., which will, weather permitting, provide a good hour to view Algol's magnitude dip from its binary partner. If the weather is nice, you can sit outside in a chair and leisurely watch Algol since it will be low in the sky. Or, you could stay up later on the 2nd and observe the complete cycle with Algol higher up in the sky.

Changing Local Standard Time to UT Time

a Find your Time Zone or DST number using the map on page 301.

b Add the Time Zone or DST number to your local time — *add it to the **HOUR** number only*.

c Add 12 to the hour number <u>if it is p.m.</u> at your location.

d If the hour number is less than 24, your conversion is complete and your date is the same date as UT. HOWEVER, if the hour number is 24 or larger, subtract 24 from the hour AND advance your local *date* by one day to get the correct UT date.

Using the Sunrise & Sunset Tables

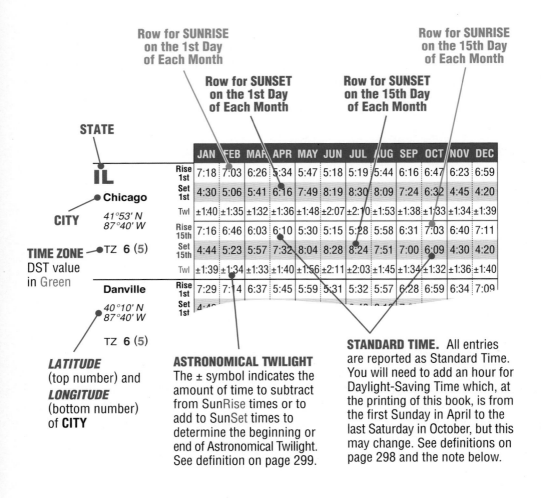

Row for SUNRISE on the 1st Day of Each Month

Row for SUNRISE on the 15th Day of Each Month

Row for SUNSET on the 1st Day of Each Month

Row for SUNSET on the 15th Day of Each Month

STATE

IL

● Chicago

CITY *41°53' N 87°40' W*

TIME ZONE ● TZ **6** (5)
DST value
in Green

Danville

40°10' N 87°40' W

TZ **6** (5)

		JAN	FEB	MAR	APR	MAY	JUN	JUL	AUG	SEP	OCT	NOV	DEC
	Rise 1st	7:18	7:03	6:26	5:34	5:47	5:18	5:19	5:44	6:16	6:47	6:23	6:59
	Set 1st	4:30	5:06	5:41	6:16	7:49	8:19	8:30	8:09	7:24	6:32	4:45	4:20
	Twl	±1:40	±1:35	±1:32	±1:36	±1:48	±2:07	±2:10	±1:53	±1:38	±1:33	±1:34	±1:39
	Rise 15th	7:16	6:46	6:03	6:10	5:30	5:15	5:28	5:58	6:31	7:03	6:40	7:11
	Set 15th	4:44	5:23	5:57	7:32	8:04	8:28	8:24	7:51	7:00	6:09	4:30	4:20
	Twl	±1:39	±1:34	±1:33	±1:40	±1:56	±2:11	±2:03	±1:45	±1:34	±1:32	±1:36	±1:40
	Rise 1st	7:29	7:14	6:37	5:45	5:59	5:31	5:32	5:57	6:28	6:59	6:34	7:09
	Set 1st	4:40											

LATITUDE (top number) and **LONGITUDE** (bottom number) of **CITY**

ASTRONOMICAL TWILIGHT The ± symbol indicates the amount of time to subtract from SunRise times or to add to SunSet times to determine the beginning or end of Astronomical Twilight. See definition on page 299.

STANDARD TIME. All entries are reported as Standard Time. You will need to add an hour for Daylight-Saving Time which, at the printing of this book, is from the first Sunday in April to the last Saturday in October, but this may change. See definitions on page 298 and the note below.

NOTES

General. The sunrise and sunset times in these tables are accurate to within a few minutes. The exact time of sunrise and sunset is dependent on your location and varies because of leap year and atmospheric refraction. These tables were designed to provide reasonable accuracy for determining the beginning and end of the day. Cities were selected based on population as well as geographic considerations.

Daylight-Saving Time Change? There is often discussion in Washington about changing the beginning and ending dates of Daylight-Saving Time. So, to avoid any future confusion, all of the sunrise and sunset times in this book are reported in Standard Time.

Instructions

Sunrises & Sunsets

Alabama/Alaska

		JAN	FEB	MAR	APR	MAY	JUN	JUL	AUG	SEP	OCT	NOV	DEC
AL **Birmingham** 33°31′ N 86°50′ W TZ **6** (5)	Rise 1st	6:52	6:44	6:16	5:35	4:59	4:38	4:41	5:00	5:21	5:42	6:06	6:33
	Set 1st	4:50	5:19	5:44	6:08	6:30	6:52	7:01	6:47	6:13	5:32	4:55	4:39
	Twl	±1:33	±1:27	±127	±1:29	±1:37	±1:47	±1:49	±1:40	±1:30	±1:27	±1:29	±1:32
	Rise 15th	6:52	6:31	5:58	5:17	4:47	4:37	4:48	5:10	5:31	5:52	6:19	6:44
	Set 15th	5:02	5:32	5:55	6:18	6:41	6:59	6:58	6:33	5:54	5:14	4:45	4:41
	Twl	±1:32	±1:27	±1:27	±1:32	±1:42	±1:49	±1:45	±1:36	±1:28	±1:27	±1:30	±1:33
Mobile 30°41′ N 88°03′ W TZ **6** (5)	Rise 1st	6:50	6:44	6:19	5:41	5:08	4:50	4:53	5:10	5:29	5:48	6:07	6:32
	Set 1st	5:02	5:28	5:51	6:11	6:31	6:50	6:59	6:47	6:15	5:38	5:04	4:51
	Twl	±1:30	±1:26	±1:24	±1:25	±1:32	±1:42	±1:42	±1:35	±1:28	±1:23	±1:26	±1:29
	Rise 15th	6:50	6:33	6:02	5:25	4:58	4:49	5:00	5:19	5:36	5:55	6:18	6:42
	Set 15th	5:13	5:40	6:00	6:20	6:40	6:56	6:56	6:34	5:58	5:21	4:55	4:53
	Twl	±1:28	±1:25	±1:25	±1:28	±1:36	±1:44	±1:41	±1:32	±1:26	±1:25	±1:27	±1:30
Montgomery 32°20′ N 86°20′ W TZ **6** (5)	Rise 1st	6:47	6:40	6:13	5:34	4:59	4:39	4:42	5:00	5:20	5:39	6:02	6:29
	Set 1st	4:51	5:19	5:43	6:05	6:26	6:47	6:56	6:43	6:10	5:30	4:55	4:40
	Twl	±1:32	±1:27	±1:25	±1:28	±1:35	±1:44	±1:46	±1:38	±1:29	±1:26	±1:27	±1:31
	Rise 15th	6:47	6:28	5:56	5:16	4:47	4:38	4:49	5:09	5:29	5:49	6:15	6:39
	Set 15th	5:03	5:31	5:53	6:15	6:36	6:54	6:53	6:30	5:52	5:13	4:45	4:42
	Twl	±1:30	±1:27	±1:26	±1:30	±1:39	±1:47	±1:43	±1:34	±1:27	±1:26	±1:29	±1:32
AK **Anchorage** 61°10′ N 149°50′ W TZ **9** (8) *Note: Most of Alaska does not experience an end of twilight during the summer.s*	Rise 1st	10:13	9:20	7:59	6:22	4:50	3:36	3:28	4:33	5:52	7:07	8:28	9:46
	Set 1st	3:54	5:08	6:26	7:46	9:05	10:20	10:38	9:37	8:05	6:30	4:57	3:51
	Twl	±2:59	±2:39	±2:30	±2:59	NONE	NONE	NONE	NONE	±3:29	±2:35	±2:35	±2:56
	Rise 15th	9:56	8:41	7:16	5:38	4:12	3:21	3:52	5:09	6:27	7:43	9:06	10:09
	Set 15th	4:23	5:48	7:03	8:23	9:42	10:39	10:17	8:57	7:21	5:47	4:22	3:41
	Twl	±2:48	±2:31	±2:35	±4:39	NONE	NONE	NONE	NONE	±2:51	±2:32	±2:44	±3:02
Bethel 60°50′ N 161°50′ W TZ **9** (8)	Rise 1st	10:57	10:05	8:46	7:10	5:40	4:27	4:20	5:23	6:41	7:54	9:14	10:30
	Set 1st	4:45	5:58	7:14	8:34	9:51	11:04	11:22	10:22	8:52	7:18	5:47	4:42
	Twl	±2:57	±2:37	±2:29	±2:55	NONE	NONE	NONE	NONE	±3:23	±2:30	±2:32	±2:53

→ **Sunrises & Sunsets HAVE NOT been adjusted for Daylight-Saving Time.**

SunRISE & SET

305

Sunrises & Sunsets

Alaska/Arizona

		JAN	FEB	MAR	APR	MAY	JUN	JUL	AUG	SEP	OCT	NOV	DEC
Bethel	Rise 15th	10:41	9:27	8:03	6:27	5:02	4:13	4:44	5:59	7:15	8:30	9:52	10:53
	Set 15th	5:14	6:37	7:51	9:09	10:27	11:23	11:02	9:43	8:08	6:35	5:12	4:32
	Twl	±2:48	±2:30	±2:34	±4:06	NONE	NONE	NONE	NONE	±2:44	±2:28	±2:40	±2:59
Fairbanks	Rise 1st	10:54	9:36	8:00	6:07	4:17	2:33	2:13	3:52	5:32	7:02	8:40	10:20
64°50' N 147°50' W	Set 1st	2:57	4:35	6:09	7:45	9:22	11:09	11:36	10:01	8:08	6:18	4:29	3:01
TZ 9 (8)	Twl	±3:46	±3:03	±2:53	±3:50	NONE	NONE	NONE	NONE	NONE	NONE	±2:59	±3:31
	Rise 15th	10:26	8:49	7:09	5:16	3:28	2:02	2:54	4:38	6:14	7:45	9:28	10:53
Note: Most of Alaska does not experience an end of twilight during the summer	Set 15th	3:37	5:24	6:53	8:29	10:11	11:44	10:58	9:10	7:17	5:28	3:44	2:41
	Twl	±3:23	±2:50	±3:02	NONE	NONE	NONE	NONE	NONE	±3:27	±2:54	±3:11	±3:45
Kodiak	Rise 1st	9:53	9:12	8:04	6:38	5:19	4:20	4:16	5:07	6:12	7:16	8:24	9:28
57°30' N 152°45' W	Set 1st	4:36	5:38	6:43	7:52	8:58	9:57	10:12	9:25	8:08	6:43	5:23	4:30
TZ 9 (8)	Twl	±2:35	±2:20	±2:14	±2:32	NONE	NONE	NONE	NONE	±3:36	±2:12	±2:12	±2:25
	Rise 15th	9:41	8:40	7:25	6:00	4:48	4:10	4:34	5:36	6:41	7:46	8:56	9:47
	Set 15th	5:00	6:11	7:15	8:23	9:27	10:12	9:57	8:52	7:28	6:05	4:54	4:24
	Twl	±2:29	±2:15	±2:18	±2:58	NONE	NONE	NONE	NONE	±2:28	±2:16	±2:25	±2:36
Kotzebue	Rise 1st	12:42	10:54	9:05	7:01	4:58	2:24	NONE	4:27	6:24	8:04	9:55	11:58
66°50' N 162°40' W	Set 1st	3:09	5:17	7:03	8:51	10:41	1:24	NONE	11:25	9:15	7:15	5:14	3:23
TZ 9 (8)	Twl	±4:23	±3:21	±3:06	NONE	NONE	NONE	NONE	NONE	NONE	±3:17	±3:16	±4:05
	Rise 15th	11:57	10:00	8:09	6:05	3:58	NONE	3:03	5:23	7:11	8:52	10:51	12:48
Note: Most of Alaska does not experience an end of twilight during the summer	Set 15th	4:05	6:12	7:52	9:40	11:41	NONE	12:50	10:25	8:19	6:20	4:20	2:45
	Twl	±3:51	±3:08	±3:20	NONE	NONE	NONE	NONE	NONE	±4:03	±3:09	±3:33	±4:34
AZ	Rise 1st	7:35	7:26	6:56	6:13	5:35	5:13	5:16	5:36	5:59	6:22	6:48	7:17
Flagstaff	Set 1st	5:26	5:55	6:22	6:48	7:13	7:36	7:45	7:30	6:53	6:10	5:32	5:15
35°10' N 111°40' W	Twl	±1:34	±1:31	±1:29	±1:31	±1:39	±1:50	±1:53	±1:43	±1:33	±1:30	±1:30	±1:33
TZ 7	Rise 15th	7:35	7:13	6:37	5:54	5:23	5:12	5:24	5:47	6:10	6:33	7:02	7:28
	Set 15th	5:38	6:09	6:35	7:00	7:24	7:43	7:41	7:15	6:33	5:51	5:21	5:16
	Twl	±1:33	±1:30	±1:28	±1:33	±1:44	±1:53	±1:50	±1:38	±1:31	±1:30	±1:32	±1:36

→ **Sunrises & Sunsets HAVE NOT been adjusted for Daylight-Saving Time.**

Sunrises & Sunsets

Arizona/Arkansas

		JAN	FEB	MAR	APR	MAY	JUN	JUL	AUG	SEP	OCT	NOV	DEC
Phoenix 33°30' N 112°10' W TZ 7	Rise 1st	7:33	7:24	6:56	6:16	5:40	5:19	5:22	5:41	6:02	6:23	6:47	7:14
	Set 1st	5:32	6:00	6:25	6:49	7:11	7:33	7:42	7:28	6:53	6:12	5:36	5:20
	Twl	±1:33	±1:29	±1:27	±1:29	±1:37	±1:47	±1:50	±1:41	±1:31	±1:28	±1:26	±1:33
	Rise 15th	7:32	7:12	6:38	5:58	5:28	5:18	5:30	5:51	6:12	6:33	7:00	7:25
	Set 15th	5:44	6:13	6:36	6:59	7:22	7:40	7:39	7:14	6:34	5:54	5:26	5:22
	Twl	±1:31	±1:28	±1:27	±1:32	±1:41	±1:49	±1:45	±1:36	±1:29	±1:28	±1:30	±1:33
Tucson 32°14' N 110°59' W TZ 7	Rise 1st	7:25	7:18	6:51	6:12	5:38	5:18	5:21	5:39	5:59	6:18	6:41	7:08
	Set 1st	5:31	5:58	6:22	6:44	7:05	7:26	7:35	7:21	6:48	6:09	5:34	5:19
	Twl	±1:31	±1:27	±1:25	±1:27	±1:34	±1:43	±1:45	±1:38	±1:29	±1:26	±1:27	±1:31
	Rise 15th	7:26	7:06	6:34	5:55	5:26	5:17	5:28	5:48	6:08	6:28	6:54	7:18
	Set 15th	5:42	6:11	6:32	6:54	7:15	7:32	7:32	7:08	6:30	5:51	5:24	5:21
	Twl	±1:29	±1:26	±1:26	±1:29	±1:38	±1:46	±1:42	±1:34	±1:27	±1:26	±1:29	±1:32
Yuma 32°45' N 114°37' W TZ 7	Rise 1st	7:41	7:33	7:06	6:26	5:51	5:31	5:34	5:52	6:13	6:33	6:56	7:23
	Set 1st	5:44	6:11	6:36	6:59	7:20	7:42	7:50	7:37	7:03	6:23	5:47	5:32
	Twl	±1:32	±1:28	±1:26	±1:28	±1:35	±1:45	±1:48	±1:24	±1:30	±1:27	±1:28	±1:31
	Rise 15th	7:41	7:21	6:49	6:09	5:39	5:30	5:41	6:02	6:22	6:43	7:09	7:34
	Set 15th	5:55	6:24	6:47	7:09	7:31	7:48	7:47	7:23	6:44	6:05	5:37	5:34
	Twl	±1:31	±1:27	±1:25	±1:31	±1:39	±1:47	±1:45	±1:35	±1:28	±1:27	±1:30	±1:32
AR **El Dorado** 33°10' N 92°40' W TZ 6 (5)	Rise 1st	7:14	7:06	6:39	5:59	5:23	5:03	5:05	5:24	5:45	6:05	6:29	6:56
	Set 1st	5:15	5:43	6:08	6:31	6:53	7:15	7:24	7:10	6:36	5:55	5:19	5:03
	Twl	±1:32	±1:28	±1:26	±1:24	±1:35	±1:45	±1:36	±1:40	±1:30	±1:27	±1:28	±1:32
	Rise 15th	7:14	6:54	6:21	5:41	5:11	5:01	5:12	5:33	5:54	6:15	6:42	7:07
	Set 15th	5:26	5:56	6:19	6:41	87:03	7:21	7:21	6:56	6:17	5:37	5:09	5:05
	Twl	±1:32	±1:27	±1:26	±1:32	±1:41	±1:49	±1:44	±1:35	±1:28	±1:27	±1:30	±1:33
Fort Smith 35°25' N 94°25' W TZ 6 (5)	Rise 1st	7:27	7:17	6:48	6:04	5:26	5:04	5:06	5:26	5:50	6:13	6:39	7:08
	Set 1st	5:16	5:46	6:13	6:39	7:04	7:27	7:37	7:21	6:45	6:02	5:23	5:05
	Twl	±1:35	±1:30	±1:29	±1:31	±1:40	±1:51	±1:54	±1:43	±1:33	±1:29	±1:30	±1:34

➜ **Sunrises & Sunsets HAVE NOT been adjusted for Daylight-Saving Time.**

SunRISE & SET

Sunrises & Sunsets

Arkansas/California

		JAN	FEB	MAR	APR	MAY	JUN	JUL	AUG	SEP	OCT	NOV	DEC
Fort Smith	Rise 15th	7:26	7:04	6:29	5:45	5:13	5:02	5:14	5:37	6:00	6:24	6:53	7:19
TZ **6** (5)	Set 15th	5:28	6:00	6:25	6:51	7:15	7:34	7:33	7:07	6:25	5:43	5:11	5:06
	Twl	±1:34	±1:30	±1:29	±1:33	±1:45	±1:54	±1:50	±1:38	±1:30	±1:29	±1:32	±1:36
Little Rock	Rise 1st	7:17	7:08	6:39	5:56	5:19	4:57	4:59	5:19	5:42	6:04	6:30	6:58
34°41′ N	Set 1st	5:09	5:38	6:05	6:30	6:54	7:17	7:26	7:11	6:36	5:53	5:15	4:58
92°10′ W	Twl	±1:34	±1:30	±1:27	±1:30	±1:37	±1:49	±1:51	±1:42	±1:32	±1:28	±1:29	±1:33
TZ **6** (5)	Rise 15th	7:16	6:55	6:20	5:38	5:06	4:55	5:07	5:29	5:52	6:15	6:43	7:09
	Set 15th	5:21	5:52	6:17	6:41	7:05	7:24	7:23	6:57	6:16	5:35	5:04	5:00
	Twl	±1:33	±1:29	±1:27	±1:33	±1:44	±1:51	±1:47	±1:37	±1:29	±1:28	±1:31	±1:33
CA **Fresno**	Rise 1st	7:12	7:01	6:30	5:45	4:05	4:42	4:44	5:05	5:31	5:55	6:23	6:54
	Set 1st	4:54	5:25	5:54	6:22	6:48	7:13	7:22	7:06	6:27	5:42	5:02	4:43
36°47′ N	Twl	±1:37	±1:33	±1:30	±1:33	±1:42	±1:55	±1:58	±1:46	±1:36	±1:32	±1:32	±1:37
119°50′ W	Rise 15th	7:11	6:47	6:10	5:25	4:52	4:40	4:52	5:17	5:42	6:07	6:38	7:05
TZ **8** (7)	Set 15th	5:07	5:40	6:07	6:34	7:00	7:20	7:18	6:50	6:07	5:23	4:50	4:44
	Twl	±1:35	±1:31	±1:30	±1:36	±1:48	±1:58	±1:54	±1:41	±1:32	±1:31	±1:34	±1:38
Los Angeles	Rise 1st	6:59	6:50	6:21	5:40	5:04	4:43	4:45	5:04	5:27	5:48	6:13	6:41
34°00′ N	Set 1st	4:55	5:24	5:50	6:14	6:37	6:59	7:08	6:54	6:18	5:37	5:00	4:44
118°10′ W	Twl	±1:33	±1:28	±1:26	±1:29	±1:37	±1:47	±1:49	±1:40	±1:31	±1:28	±1:29	±1:32
TZ **8** (7)	Rise 15th	6:58	6:37	6:03	5:22	4:51	4:41	4:53	5:15	5:36	5:58	6:26	6:51
	Set 15th	5:07	5:37	6:01	6:25	6:48	7:06	7:05	6:40	5:59	5:19	4:49	4:45
	Twl	±1:32	±1:28	±1:27	±1:31	±1:41	±1:50	±1:46	±1:35	±1:29	±1:27	±1:31	±1:33
Redding	Rise 1st	7:33	7:19	6:43	5:53	5:08	4:41	4:43	5:07	5:37	6:06	6:40	7:14
40°30′ N	Set 1st	4:54	5:28	6:01	6:35	7:06	7:34	7:44	7:24	6:41	5:51	5:06	4:44
122°25′ W	Twl	±1:42	±1:38	±1:35	±1:37	±1:50	±2:08	±2:12	±1:57	±1:42	±1:36	±1:38	±1:41
TZ **8** (7)	Rise 15th	7:31	7:03	6:21	5:31	4:53	4:39	4:52	5:21	5:51	6:21	6:56	7:26
	Set 15th	5:08	5:45	6:17	6:49	7:20	7:42	7:39	7:07	6:18	5:29	4:52	4:44
	Twl	±1:41	±1:36	±1:35	±1:43	±1:58	±2:13	±2:06	±1:49	±1:38	±1:36	±1:40	±1:43

→ **Sunrises & Sunsets HAVE NOT been adjusted for Daylight-Saving Time.**

SunRISE & SET

Sunrises & Sunsets

California/Colorado

		JAN	FEB	MAR	APR	MAY	JUN	JUL	AUG	SEP	OCT	NOV	DEC
Sacramento 38°33' N 121°30' W TZ **8** (7)	Rise 1st	7:24	7:11	6:38	5:51	5:09	4:43	4:45	5:08	5:35	6:02	6:33	7:05
	Set 1st	4:56	5:28	5:59	6:30	6:58	7:25	7:34	7:16	6:36	6:48	5:06	4:45
	Twl	±1:39	±1:35	±1:32	±1:35	±1:45	±2:00	±2:04	±1:51	±1:38	±1:34	±1:34	±1:39
	Rise 15th	7:22	6:57	6:17	5:30	4:54	4:41	4:54	5:20	5:48	6:15	6:48	7:17
	Set 15th	5:09	5:44	6:13	6:43	7:11	7:32	7:30	7:00	6:14	5:28	4:53	4:46
	Twl	±1:37	±1:33	±1:32	±1:39	±1:52	±2:04	±1:58	±1:44	±1:35	±1:33	±1:37	±1:39
San Diego 32°43' N 117°10' W TZ **8** (7)	Rise 1st	6:51	6:43	6:16	5:36	5:01	4:41	4:44	5:02	5:23	5:43	6:06	6:33
	Set 1st	4:53	5:21	5:46	6:09	6:30	6:52	7:00	6:46	6:13	5:33	4:57	4:42
	Twl	±1:33	±1:28	±1:26	±1:28	±1:35	±1:45	±1:48	±1:39	±1:30	±1:27	±1:28	±1:32
	Rise 15th	6:51	6:31	5:58	5:18	4:49	4:40	4:51	5:12	5:32	5:53	6:19	6:43
	Set 15th	5:05	5:34	5:56	6:19	6:40	6:58	6:57	6:33	5:54	5:15	4:47	4:44
	Twl	±1:31	±1:27	±1:27	±1:31	±1:41	±1:47	±1:45	±1:35	±1:28	±1:27	±1:30	±1:32
San Francisco 37°47' N 122°30' W TZ **8** (7)	Rise 1st	7:25	7:14	6:41	5:55	5:14	4:49	4:52	5:13	5:40	6:06	6:35	7:07
	Set 1st	5:02	5:34	6:04	6:33	7:00	7:26	7:36	7:18	6:39	5:52	5:11	4:51
	Twl	±1:38	±1:34	±1:31	±1:34	±1:45	±1:59	±2:01	±1:49	±1:37	±1:33	±1:33	±1:38
	Rise 15th	7:24	6:59	6:21	5:34	5:00	4:47	5:00	5:25	5:52	6:18	6:50	7:18
	Set 15th	5:15	5:49	6:17	6:45	7:13	7:33	7:31	7:02	6:17	5:32	4:58	4:52
	Twl	±1:36	±1:33	±1:32	±1:39	±1:50	±2:02	±1:57	±1:44	±1:35	±1:33	±1:35	±1:39
CO **Denver** 39°45' N 105°00' W TZ **7** (6)	Rise 1st	7:21	7:08	6:33	5:44	5:00	4:34	4:36	4:59	5:28	5:56	6:29	7:02
	Set 1st	4:46	5:20	5:52	6:24	6:54	7:22	7:32	7:13	6:31	5:42	4:58	4:36
	Twl	±1:41	±1:37	±1:34	±1:37	±1:49	±2:05	±2:08	±1:55	±1:41	±1:35	±1:36	±1:40
	Rise 15th	7:19	6:52	6:11	5:22	4:45	4:31	4:45	5:12	5:41	6:10	6:45	7:14
	Set 15th	5:00	5:37	6:07	6:38	7:08	7:30	7:27	6:56	6:08	5:20	4:44	4:36
	Twl	±1:40	±1:34	±1:34	±1:41	±1:56	±2:10	±2:03	±1:47	±1:37	±1:35	±1:39	±1:42
Grand Junction 39°00' N 108°30' W TZ **7** (6)	Rise 1st	7:33	7:20	6:46	5:58	5:16	4:50	4:52	5:15	5:43	6:10	6:42	7:14
	Set 1st	5:03	5:36	6:07	6:38	7:07	7:34	7:44	7:25	6:44	5:56	5:13	4:52
	Twl	±1:39	±1:34	±1:33	±1:36	±1:47	±2:02	±2:05	±1:53	±1:39	±1:34	±1:35	±1:39

➜ **Sunrises & Sunsets HAVE NOT been adjusted for Daylight-Saving Time.**

309

Sunrises & Sunsets

Florida/Georgia

		JAN	FEB	MAR	APR	MAY	JUN	JUL	AUG	SEP	OCT	NOV	DEC
Miami	Rise 15th	7:09	6:56	6:30	5:58	5:35	5:29	5:39	5:54	6:07	6:20	6:39	7:00
	Set 15th	5:52	6:14	6:30	6:44	6:59	7:14	7:15	6:56	6:25	5:53	5:32	5:32
	Twl	±1:24	±1:22	±1:19	±1:24	±1:30	±1:34	±1:32	±1:26	±1:21	±1:21	±1:24	±1:26
Orlando	Rise 1st	7:18	7:14	6:51	6:16	5:45	5:28	5:32	5:47	6:04	6:19	6:38	7:01
28°30′ N	Set 1st	5:40	6:05	6:26	6:44	7:01	7:19	7:27	7:16	6:47	6:12	5:41	5:29
81°25′ W	Twl	±1:28	±1:25	±1:22	±1:23	±1:29	±1:37	±1:39	±1:33	±1:25	±1:22	±1:23	±1:27
TZ **5** (4)	Rise 15th	7:19	7:04	6:35	6:00	5:35	5:28	5:38	5:55	6:11	6:26	6:48	7:11
	Set 15th	5:51	6:16	6:34	6:51	7:09	7:25	7:25	7:05	6:31	5:56	5:32	5:31
	Twl	±1:27	±1:23	±1:23	±1:26	±1:34	±1:38	±1:37	±1:29	±1:23	±1:23	±1:26	±1:29
St. Petersburg	Rise 1st	7:22	7:17	6:55	6:21	5:51	5:35	5:38	5:54	6:09	6:23	6:42	7:04
27°45′ N	Set 1st	5:47	6:11	6:31	6:48	7:05	7:22	7:31	7:20	6:52	6:17	5:47	5:35
82°40′ W	Twl	±1:27	±1:24	±1:16	±1:23	±1:29	±1:36	±1:37	±1:31	±1:24	±1:21	±1:23	±1:27
TZ **5** (4)	Rise 15th	7:23	7:08	6:40	6:06	5:42	5:34	5:45	6:01	6:16	6:31	6:52	7:14
	Set 15th	5:58	6:22	6:39	6:56	7:13	7:28	7:28	7:09	6:35	6:02	5:39	5:38
	Twl	±1:26	±1:22	±1:22	±1:25	±1:32	±1:37	±1:36	±1:28	±1:23	±1:22	±1:25	±1:27
Tallahassee	Rise 1st	7:34	7:28	7:03	6:26	5:54	5:35	5:38	5:55	6:14	6:30	6:51	7:16
30°25′ N	Set 1st	5:48	6:14	6:36	6:56	7:15	7:34	7:43	7:31	7:00	6:22	5:49	5:36
84°15′ W	Twl	±1:29	±1:25	±1:23	±1:25	±1:32	±1:40	±1:42	±1:35	±1:27	±1:24	±1:26	±1:29
TZ **5** (4)	Rise 15th	7:35	7:17	6:47	6:10	5:43	5:34	5:45	6:04	6:21	6:39	7:03	7:26
	Set 15th	5:59	6:25	6:45	7:05	7:24	7:41	7:41	7:19	6:43	6:06	5:40	5:38
	Twl	±1:28	±1:25	±1:24	±1:28	±1:36	±1:42	±1:39	±1:30	±1:25	±1:24	±1:27	±1:30
GA **Albany**	Rise 1st	7:37	7:30	7:04	6:25	5:51	5:32	5:35	5:53	6:12	6:30	6:53	7:19
	Set 1st	5:44	6:11	6:35	6:56	7:17	7:37	7:46	7:33	7:01	6:22	5:47	5:33
31°40′ N	Twl	±1:31	±1:27	±1:25	±1:27	±1:34	±1:43	±1:44	±1:36	±1:28	±1:25	±1:27	±1:30
84°10′ W	Rise 15th	7:37	7:19	6:47	6:08	5:40	5:31	5:42	6:02	6:21	6:40	7:05	7:29
TZ **5** (4)	Set 15th	5:56	6:23	6:45	7:06	7:26	7:43	7:43	7:20	6:43	6:05	5:38	5:35
	Twl	±1:29	±1:26	±1:25	±1:29	±1:38	±1:46	±1:41	±1:33	±1:26	±1:25	±1:28	±1:31

➡ **Sunrises & Sunsets HAVE NOT been adjusted for Daylight-Saving Time.**

SunRISE & SET

Georgia

		JAN	FEB	MAR	APR	MAY	JUN	JUL	AUG	SEP	OCT	NOV	DEC
Atlanta	Rise 1st	7:43	7:34	7:06	6:25	5:49	5:28	5:31	5:49	6:11	6:32	6:57	7:24
33°50' N 84°24' W	Set 1st	5:40	6:09	6:34	6:58	7:21	7:43	7:52	7:38	7:03	6:22	5:45	5:29
	Twl	±1:33	±1:28	±1:27	±1:29	±1:37	±1:47	±1:50	±1:41	±1:32	±1:28	±1:29	±1:32
TZ 5 (4)	Rise 15th	7:42	7:22	6:48	6:07	5:37	5:27	5:38	5:59	6:21	6:42	7:10	7:35
	Set 15th	5:52	6:22	6:45	7:09	7:32	7:50	7:49	7:24	6:44	6:04	5:35	5:31
	Twl	±1:32	±1:28	±1:27	±1:32	±1:42	±1:50	±1:46	±1:36	±1:29	±1:27	±1:30	±1:33
Augusta	Rise 1st	7:32	7:24	6:56	6:16	5:40	5:19	5:22	5:40	6:02	6:22	6:47	7:14
33°29' N 81°59' W	Set 1st	5:31	5:59	6:25	6:48	7:11	7:33	7:42	7:28	6:53	6:13	5:36	5:20
	Twl	±1:33	±1:29	±1:26	±1:29	±1:37	±1:47	±1:49	±1:40	±1:31	±1:27	±1:28	±1:32
TZ 5 (4)	Rise 15th	7:32	7:12	6:39	5:58	5:28	5:18	5:29	5:50	6:11	6:33	6:59	7:25
	Set 15th	5:43	6:13	6:36	6:59	7:21	7:39	7:39	7:14	6:34	5:54	5:25	5:22
	Twl	±1:32	±1:27	±1:26	±1:31	±1:41	±1:49	±1:45	±1:35	±1:29	±1:28	±1:31	±1:32
Macon	Rise 1st	7:37	7:30	7:03	6:23	5:47	5:27	5:30	5:48	6:09	6:29	6:52	7:19
32°50' N 83°37' W	Set 1st	5:39	6:07	6:32	6:55	7:16	7:38	7:47	7:33	6:59	6:19	5:44	5:28
	Twl	±1:32	±1:28	±1:26	±1:28	±1:35	±1:45	±1:47	±1:39	±1:30	±1:27	±1:27	±1:31
TZ 5 (4)	Rise 15th	7:37	7:18	6:45	6:05	5:36	5:26	5:37	5:58	6:18	6:39	7:05	7:30
	Set 15th	5:51	6:20	6:42	7:05	7:27	7:44	7:44	7:20	6:41	6:02	5:33	5:30
	Twl	±1:31	±1:27	±1:26	±1:31	±1:40	±1:47	±1:44	±1:34	±1:27	±1:26	±1:30	±1:32
Savannah	Rise 1st	7:25	7:18	6:52	6:13	5:38	5:19	5:22	5:39	5:59	6:18	6:41	7:07
32°04' N 81°04' W	Set 1st	5:31	5:58	6:22	6:44	7:05	7:26	7:35	7:21	6:49	6:09	5:34	5:20
	Twl	±1:31	±1:27	±1:25	±1:27	±1:34	±1:43	±1:45	±1:38	±1:28	±1:26	±1:27	±1:30
TZ 5 (4)	Rise 15th	7:25	7:07	6:35	5:56	5:27	5:18	5:29	5:49	6:08	6:28	6:53	7:17
	Set 15th	5:42	6:11	6:32	6:54	7:15	7:32	7:32	7:08	6:30	5:52	5:24	5:21
	Twl	±1:30	±1:26	±1:26	±1:29	±1:38	±1:45	±1:42	±1:33	±1:27	±1:26	±1:29	±1:32
Waycross	Rise 1st	7:28	7:22	6:57	6:19	5:45	5:26	5:29	5:46	6:06	6:23	6:45	7:10
31°12' N 82°25' W	Set 1st	5:38	6:05	6:28	6:49	7:09	7:29	7:38	7:25	6:53	6:15	5:41	5:27
TZ 5 (4)	Twl	±1:31	±1:27	±1:25	±1:26	±1:32	±1:42	±1:44	±1:36	±1:28	±1:24	±1:26	±1:30

SunRISE & SET

➜ **Sunrises & Sunsets HAVE NOT been adjusted for Daylight-Saving Time.**

Sunrises & Sunsets

Georgia/Hawaii/Idaho

		JAN	FEB	MAR	APR	MAY	JUN	JUL	AUG	SEP	OCT	NOV	DEC
Waycross	Rise 15th	7:29	7:11	6:40	6:02	5:34	5:25	5:36	5:55	6:14	6:32	6:57	7:21
TZ **5** (4)	Set 15th	5:50	6:17	6:38	6:58	7:18	7:35	7:35	7:13	6:36	5:58	5:31	5:29
	Twl	±1:28	±1:26	±1:24	±1:29	±1:38	±1:44	±1:41	±1:32	±1:26	±1:25	±1:28	±1:31
HI	Rise 1st	7:08	7:09	6:52	6:24	6:00	5:49	5:53	6:05	6:15	6:23	6:35	6:53
Honolulu	Set 1st	6:01	6:22	6:36	6:46	6:57	7:10	7:18	7:10	6:47	6:19	5:55	5:49
21°19' N	Twl	±1:23	±1:20	±1:18	±1:18	±1:23	±1:28	±1:29	±1:26	±1:20	±1:17	±1:19	±1:21
157°52' W	Rise 15th	7:12	7:02	6:40	6:12	5:53	5:49	5:58	6:10	6:19	6:27	6:43	7:01
TZ **10**	Set 15th	6:11	6:30	6:41	6:51	7:03	7:15	7:16	7:01	6:34	6:07	5:50	5:52
	Twl	±1:21	±1:17	±1:18	±1:20	±1:26	±1:30	±1:29	±1:23	±1:19	±1:18	±1:21	±1:23
ID	Rise 1st	8:18	8:01	7:21	6:26	5:37	5:06	5:07	5:34	6:09	6:43	7:21	7:59
Boise	Set 1st	5:19	5:56	6:34	7:12	7:47	8:20	8:30	8:07	7:20	6:25	5:35	5:09
43°43' N	Twl	±1:51	±1:45	±1:42	±1:47	±2:03	±2:27	±2:35	±2:09	±1:49	±1:42	±1:44	±1:50
116°09' W	Rise 15th	8:15	7:43	6:57	6:02	5:20	5:03	5:17	5:50	6:24	6:59	7:39	8:11
TZ **7** (6)	Set 15th	5:34	6:16	6:51	7:29	8:03	8:28	8:24	7:48	6:55	6:01	5:19	5:09
	Twl	±1:49	±1:42	±1:43	±1:52	±2:14	±2:36	±2:23	±1:58	±1:44	±1:42	±1:47	±1:51
Idaho Falls	Rise 1st	8:01	7:44	7:04	6:09	5:21	4:50	4:51	5:18	5:52	6:26	7:04	7:41
43°30' N	Set 1st	5:03	5:40	6:17	6:55	7:30	8:02	8:13	7:50	7:03	6:09	5:19	4:53
112°01' W	Twl	±1:47	±1:42	±1:39	±1:44	±2:00	±2:24	±2:29	±2:08	±1:48	±1:40	±1:42	±1:47
TZ **7** (6)	Rise 15th	7:58	7:26	6:40	5:45	5:03	4:46	5:01	5:33	6:08	6:42	7:22	7:54
	Set 15th	5:18	5:59	6:35	7:12	7:46	8:11	8:07	7:31	6:38	5:45	5:03	4:52
	Twl	±1:46	±1:40	±1:40	±1:49	±2:09	±2:30	±2:20	±1:56	±1:43	±1:40	±1:44	±1:49
Twin Falls	Rise 1st	8:08	7:52	7:13	6:20	5:35	5:03	5:05	5:30	6:03	6:35	7:12	7:48
42°30' N	Set 1st	5:16	5:52	6:28	7:04	7:38	8:09	8:19	7:58	7:12	6:19	5:31	5:06
114°30' W	Twl	±1:46	±1:41	±1:38	±1:42	±1:56	±2:18	±2:23	±2:02	±1:46	±1:39	±1:39	±1:45
TZ **7** (6)	Rise 15th	8:05	7:34	6:50	5:57	5:16	5:00	5:14	5:45	6:18	6:51	7:29	8:01
	Set 15th	5:31	6:10	6:45	7:20	7:53	8:17	8:13	7:39	6:47	5:56	5:16	5:06
	Twl	±1:43	±1:39	±1:38	±1:47	±2:06	±2:24	±2:16	±1:54	±1:42	±1:38	±1:42	±1:46

→ **Sunrises & Sunsets HAVE NOT been adjusted for Daylight-Saving Time.**

SunRISE & SET

Sunrises & Sunsets

Illinois

		JAN	FEB	MAR	APR	MAY	JUN	JUL	AUG	SEP	OCT	NOV	DEC
IL **Chicago** 41°53' N 87°40' W TZ 6 (5)	Rise 1st	7:18	7:03	6:26	5:34	4:47	4:18	4:19	4:44	5:16	5:47	6:23	6:59
	Set 1st	4:30	5:06	5:41	6:16	6:49	7:19	7:30	7:09	6:24	5:32	4:45	4:20
	Twl	±1:45	±1:40	±1:37	±1:41	±1:54	±2:14	±2:19	±2:00	±1:45	±1:38	±1:39	±1:45
	Rise 15th	7:16	6:46	6:03	5:10	4:30	4:15	4:28	4:58	5:31	6:03	6:40	7:11
	Set 15th	4:44	5:23	5:57	6:32	7:04	7:28	7:24	6:51	6:00	5:09	4:30	4:20
	Twl	±1:44	±1:38	±1:38	±1:45	±2:03	±2:21	±2:13	±1:52	±1:40	±1:38	±1:41	±1:45
Danville 40°10' N 87°40' W TZ 6 (5)	Rise 1st	7:13	6:59	6:24	5:34	4:50	4:23	4:25	4:49	5:18	5:47	6:20	6:54
	Set 1st	4:36	5:10	5:43	6:15	6:46	7:14	7:24	7:05	6:22	5:33	4:48	4:26
	Twl	±1:41	±1:37	±1:34	±1:37	±1:49	±2:06	±2:11	±1:55	±1:42	±1:35	±1:36	±1:40
	Rise 15th	7:11	6:44	6:02	5:12	4:35	4:21	4:34	5:02	5:32	6:01	6:36	7:06
	Set 15th	4:50	5:27	5:58	6:30	7:00	7:22	7:19	6:47	5:59	5:11	4:34	4:26
	Twl	±1:40	±1:35	±1:34	±1:42	±1:57	±2:11	±2:05	±1:49	±1:38	±1:35	±1:39	±1:42
Moline 41°30' N 90°30' W TZ 6 (5)	Rise 1st	7:29	7:14	6:37	5:45	4:59	4:31	4:32	4:57	5:28	5:59	6:34	7:09
	Set 1st	4:43	5:18	5:53	6:27	7:00	7:29	7:40	7:19	6:35	5:44	4:57	4:33
	Twl	±1:44	±1:39	±1:36	±1:41	±1:53	±2:13	±2:16	±2:00	±1:43	±1:37	±1:39	±1:44
	Rise 15th	7:26	6:57	6:14	5:22	4:43	4:28	4:41	5:11	5:42	6:14	6:51	7:21
	Set 15th	4:57	5:36	6:09	6:42	7:14	7:38	7:34	7:02	6:11	5:21	4:42	4:33
	Twl	±1:42	±1:37	±1:37	±1:46	±2:03	±2:17	±2:10	±1:50	±1:39	±1:37	±1:41	±1:44
Mount Vernon 38°19' N 88°55' W TZ 6 (5)	Rise 1st	7:13	7:01	6:27	5:41	4:59	4:34	4:36	4:58	5:25	5:52	6:22	6:54
	Set 1st	4:46	5:18	5:49	6:19	6:46	7:14	7:24	7:05	6:25	5:38	4:56	4:36
	Twl	±1:39	±1:34	±1:32	±1:35	±1:46	±2:00	±2:02	±1:51	±1:38	±1:33	±1:34	±1:38
	Rise 15th	7:11	6:46	6:07	5:20	4:44	4:32	4:44	5:10	5:37	6:05	6:36	7:06
	Set 15th	5:00	5:34	6:03	6:32	7:00	7:22	7:19	6:48	6:04	5:18	4:43	4:36
	Twl	±1:36	±1:33	±1:32	±1:39	±1:52	±2:02	±1:58	±1:45	±1:35	±1:33	±1:36	±1:40
Rockford 42°20' N 89°00' W TZ 6 (5)	Rise 1st	7:25	7:10	6:32	5:39	4:51	4:22	4:23	4:48	5:21	5:53	6:29	7:05
	Set 1st	4:34	5:10	5:46	6:22	6:55	7:26	7:37	7:16	6:30	5:38	4:50	4:25
	Twl	±1:46	±1:41	±1:37	±1:41	±1:56	±2:17	±2:21	±2:02	±1:44	±1:38	±1:40	±1:44

➡ **Sunrises & Sunsets HAVE NOT been adjusted for Daylight-Saving Time.**

Sunrises & Sunsets

Illinois/Indiana/Iowa

		JAN	FEB	MAR	APR	MAY	JUN	JUL	AUG	SEP	OCT	NOV	DEC
Rockford	Rise 15th	7:23	6:53	6:08	5:15	5435	4:19	4:33	5:03	5:36	6:09	6:47	7:18
	Set 15th	4:49	5:28	6:02	6:38	7:11	7:34	7:31	6:57	6:06	5:14	4:34	4:24
	Twl	±1:43	±1:39	±1:38	±1:46	±2:04	±2:23	±2:14	±1:53	±1:41	±1:38	±1:42	±1:46
Springfield *39°48′ N* *89°40′ W* TZ **6** (5)	Rise 1st	7:20	7:07	6:32	5:43	4:59	4:33	4:34	4:57	5:27	5:55	6:27	7:01
	Set 1st	4:45	5:18	5:51	6:23	6:53	7:21	7:31	7:12	6:30	5:41	4:57	4:35
	Twl	±1:41	±1:37	±1:34	±1:37	±1:49	±2:05	±2:09	±1:54	±1:41	±1:35	±1:35	±1:40
	Rise 15th	7:18	6:51	6:10	5:21	4:44	4:30	4:43	5:11	5:40	6:09	6:43	7:13
	Set 15th	4:58	5:35	6:06	6:37	7:07	7:29	7:26	6:55	6:07	5:19	4:43	4:35
	Twl	±1:40	±1:35	±1:33	±1:42	±1:56	±2:10	±2:03	±1:47	±1:37	±1:35	±1:38	±1:42
IN **Indianapolis** *39°42′ N* *86°10′ W* TZ **5**	Rise 1st	8:06	7:52	7:18	6:29	5:45	5:19	5:21	5:44	6:13	6:41	7:13	7:47
	Set 1st	5:31	6:05	6:37	7:09	7:39	8:07	8:16	7:58	7:16	6:27	5:43	5:21
	Twl	±1:41	±1:36	±1:33	±1:37	±1:49	±2:04	±2:09	±1:53	±1:40	±1:35	±1:35	±1:40
	Rise 15th	8:04	7:37	6:56	6:07	5:30	5:16	5:29	5:57	6:26	6:55	7:29	7:59
	Set 15th	5:45	6:21	6:52	7:23	7:53	8:14	8:12	7:41	6:53	6:05	5:29	5:21
	Twl	±1:39	±1:35	±1:33	±1:38	±1:55	±2:09	±2:03	±1:41	±1:37	±1:35	±1:38	±1:42
South Bend *41°38′ N* *86°20′ W* TZ **5**	Rise 1st	8:12	7:57	7:20	6:28	5:42	5:13	5:15	5:40	6:11	6:42	7:18	7:53
	Set 1st	5:26	6:01	6:36	7:11	7:44	8:13	8:23	8:03	7:18	6:27	5:40	5:16
	Twl	±1:44	±1:39	±1:36	±1:40	±1:53	±2:14	±2:18	±2:00	±1:45	±1:37	±1:39	±1:44
	Rise 15th	8:10	7:41	6:57	6:05	5:26	5:10	5:24	5:54	6:26	6:58	7:35	8:05
	Set 15th	5:40	6:19	6:52	7:26	7:58	8:21	8:18	7:45	6:54	6:04	5:25	5:16
	Twl	±1:43	±1:37	±1:37	±1:45	±2:03	±2:19	±2:11	±1:51	±1:40	±1:37	±1:41	±1:45
IA **Davenport** *41°30′ N* *90°40′ W* TZ **6** (5)	Rise 1st	7:29	7:14	6:37	5:45	4:59	4:31	4:32	4:57	5:28	5:59	6:34	7:09
	Set 1st	4:43	5:18	5:53	6:27	7:00	7:29	7:40	7:19	6:35	5:44	4:57	4:33
	Twl	±1:45	±1:40	±1:36	±1:41	±1:54	±2:14	±2:18	±2:00	±1:44	±1:38	±1:40	±1:44
	Rise 15th	7:26	6:57	6:14	5:22	4:43	4:28	4:41	5:11	5:42	6:14	5:51	6:21
	Set 15th	4:57	5:36	6:09	6:42	7:14	7:38	7:34	7:02	6:11	5:21	4:42	4:33
	Twl	±1:43	±1:38	±1:38	±1:46	±2:03	±2:19	±2:12	±1:51	±1:40	±1:38	±1:42	±1:45

➞ **Sunrises & Sunsets HAVE NOT been adjusted for Daylight-Saving Time.**

SunRISE & SET

Sunrises & Sunsets

Iowa/Kansas

		JAN	FEB	MAR	APR	MAY	JUN	JUL	AUG	SEP	OCT	NOV	DEC
Des Moines	Rise 1st	7:41	7:26	6:49	5:58	5:11	5:43	4:44	5:09	5:40	6:11	6:46	7:22
41°35' N 93°37' W	Set 1st	4:55	5:30	6:05	6:40	7:12	7:42	7:52	7:32	6:48	5:56	5:09	4:45
	Twl	±1:45	±1:40	±1:36	±1:40	±1:54	±2:14	±2:18	±2:00	±1:44	±1:37	±1:39	±1:44
TZ 6 (5)	Rise 15th	7:39	7:10	6:26	5:35	4:55	4:40	4:53	5:23	5:55	6:26	7:03	7:34
	Set 15th	5:09	5:48	6:21	6:55	7:27	7:50	7:47	7:14	6:24	5:33	4:54	4:45
	Twl	±1:43	±1:37	±1:37	±1:45	±2:02	±2:19	±2:11	±1:51	±1:39	±1:38	±1:41	±1:45
Mason City	Rise 1st	7:45	7:28	6:49	5:55	5:06	4:36	4:37	5:03	5:37	6:10	6:48	7:25
43°09' N 93°12' W	Set 1st	4:48	5:25	6:02	6:39	7:14	7:46	7:56	7:34	6:48	5:54	5:05	4:39
	Twl	±1:47	±1:42	±1:39	±1:43	±1:58	±2:22	±2:27	±2:06	±1:46	±1:40	±1:40	±1:46
TZ 6 (5)	Rise 15th	7:42	7:11	6:25	5:31	4:49	4:32	4:47	5:18	5:52	6:26	7:06	7:38
	Set 15th	5:03	5:44	6:19	6:56	7:30	7:54	7:50	7:16	6:23	5:30	4:49	4:38
	Twl	±1:45	±1:40	±1:40	±1:48	±2:09	±2:29	±2:19	±1:55	±1:42	±1:40	±1:43	±1:48
Sioux City	Rise 1st	7:56	7:40	7:01	6:08	5:21	4:51	4:52	5:18	5:51	6:23	6:59	7:36
42°32' N 96°25' W	Set 1st	5:03	5:39	6:15	6:52	7:26	7:57	8:07	7:46	7:00	6:07	5:19	4:54
	Twl	±1:46	±1:41	±1:38	±1:41	±1:55	±2:17	±2:23	±2:03	±1:46	±1:39	±1:40	±1:45
TZ 6 (5)	Rise 15th	7:53	7:23	6:38	5:45	5:04	4:48	5:02	5:32	6:05	6:39	7:17	7:48
	Set 15th	5:18	5:58	6:32	7:08	7:41	8:05	8:01	7:27	6:36	5:44	5:03	4:53
	Twl	±1:44	±1:38	±1:39	±1:46	±2:06	±2:24	±2:16	±1:54	±1:41	±1:38	±1:43	±1:46
KS **Kansas City**	Rise 1st	7:38	7:25	6:51	6:03	5:20	4:55	4:57	5:20	5:48	6:15	6:46	7:19
	Set 1st	5:07	5:40	6:12	6:43	7:12	7:39	7:48	7:30	6:49	6:01	5:18	4:57
39°00' N 94°40' W	Twl	±1:40	±1:36	±1:32	±1:35	±1:46	±2:01	±2:05	±1:52	±1:39	±1:34	±1:34	±1:39
TZ 6 (5)	Rise 15th	7:36	7:10	6:30	5:42	5:06	4:52	5:05	5:32	6:00	6:28	7:02	7:31
	Set 15th	5:21	5:56	6:26	6:56	7:25	7:46	7:44	7:13	6:27	5:40	5:05	4:57
	Twl	±1:37	±1:34	±1:33	±1:40	±1:53	±2:06	±2:00	±1:46	±1:36	±1:34	±1:37	±1:40
Oakley	Rise 1st	8:03	7:50	7:16	6:26	5:45	5:19	5:21	5:44	6:12	6:40	8:11	7:44
39°08' N 100°51' W	Set 1st	5:32	6:05	6:36	7:07	7:37	8:04	8:13	7:55	7:14	6:26	6:42	6:21
TZ 6 (5)	Twl	±1:40	±1:35	±1:33	±1:36	±1:46	±2:01	±2:05	±1:52	±1:38	±1:34	±1:35	±1:40

➜ **Sunrises & Sunsets HAVE NOT been adjusted for Daylight-Saving Time.**

SunRISE & SET

317

Sunrises & Sunsets

Kansas/Kentucky

		JAN	FEB	MAR	APR	MAY	JUN	JUL	AUG	SEP	OCT	NOV	DEC
Oakley	Rise 15th	8:01	7:35	6:55	6:06	5:30	5:17	5:30	5:57	6:25	6:53	7:27	7:56
	Set 15th	5:45	6:21	6:51	7:21	7:50	8:11	8:09	7:38	6:52	6:04	5:29	5:22
	Twl	±1:38	±1:34	±1:32	±1:39	±1:53	±2:06	±2:00	±1:46	±1:35	±1:34	±1:38	±1:40
Salina	Rise 1st	7:49	7:36	7:02	6:15	5:32	5:07	5:09	5:31	5:59	6:26	6:57	7:30
38°50′ N 97°40′ W	Set 1st	5:19	5:52	6:23	6:54	7:23	7:50	7:59	7:41	7:00	6:13	5:29	5:09
	Twl	±1:40	±1:36	±1:33	±1:36	±1:47	±2:02	±2:06	±1:52	±1:39	±1:34	±1:36	±1:39
TZ 6 (5)	Rise 15th	7:47	7:21	6:41	5:53	5:18	5:04	5:17	5:44	6:12	6:40	7:13	7:41
	Set 15th	5:33	6:08	6:37	7:07	7:36	7:57	7:54	7:24	6:38	5:51	5:16	5:09
	Twl	±1:38	±1:34	±1:33	±1:40	±1:54	±2:06	±2:01	±1:47	±1:36	±1:35	±1:38	±1:41
Wichita	Rise 1st	7:45	7:33	7:01	6:15	5:34	5:09	5:11	5:33	6:00	6:25	6:55	7:26
37°40′ N 97°20′ W	Set 1st	5:22	5:53	6:23	6:52	7:20	7:45	7:55	7:38	6:58	6:12	5:31	5:11
	Twl	±1:39	±1:36	±1:33	±1:36	±1:45	±1:59	±2:02	±1:50	±1:39	±1:34	±1:34	±1:39
TZ 6 (5)	Rise 15th	7:43	7:19	6:40	5:54	5:20	5:07	5:20	5:45	6:11	6:38	7:10	7:37
	Set 15th	5:35	6:09	6:37	7:05	7:32	7:53	7:50	7:22	6:37	5:52	5:18	5:12
	Twl	±1:37	±1:33	±1:32	±1:38	±1:52	±2:02	±1:59	±1:44	±1:35	±1:33	±1:36	±1:40
KY **Bowling Green**	Rise 1st	6:59	6:48	6:16	5:31	4:51	4:28	4:30	4:51	5:17	5:41	6:10	6:40
	Set 1st	4:40	5:11	5:40	6:08	6:35	7:00	7:09	6:52	6:14	5:29	4:48	4:29
	Twl	±1:37	±1:33	±1:30	±1:33	±1:42	±1:55	±1:59	±1:48	±1:36	±1:31	±1:32	±1:37
37°00′ N 86°25′ W	Rise 15th	6:58	6:34	5:56	5:11	4:38	4:25	4:38	5:03	5:28	5:54	6:24	6:52
TZ 6 (5)	Set 15th	4:53	5:26	5:53	6:21	6:47	7:07	7:05	6:37	5:53	5:09	4:36	4:30
	Twl	±1:35	±1:31	±1:30	±1:36	±1:48	±2:00	±1:54	±1:41	±1:32	±1:31	±1:34	±1:38
Lexington	Rise 1st	7:54	7:43	7:10	6:23	5:42	5:17	5:19	5:41	6:08	6:34	7:04	7:36
38°06′ N 84°30′ W	Set 1st	5:29	6:01	6:32	7:01	7:29	7:55	8:05	7:47	7:07	6:21	5:39	5:19
	Twl	±1:37	±1:34	±1:32	±1:37	±1:49	±2:06	±2:09	±1:55	±1:40	±1:33	±1:33	±1:36
TZ 5 (4)	Rise 15th	7:53	7:28	6:49	6:02	5:27	5:15	5:27	5:53	6:20	6:47	7:19	7:47
	Set 15th	5:42	6:17	6:45	7:14	7:42	8:03	8:00	7:31	6:46	6:00	5:26	5:19
	Twl	±1:36	±1:32	±1:33	±1:41	±1:56	±2:10	±2:04	±1:48	±1:36	±1:33	±1:35	±1:38

→ **Sunrises & Sunsets HAVE NOT been adjusted for Daylight-Saving Time.**

SunRISE & SET

Sunrises & Sunsets

Kentucky/Louisiana

		JAN	FEB	MAR	APR	MAY	JUN	JUL	AUG	SEP	OCT	NOV	DEC
Louisville	Rise 1st	8:00	7:48	7:15	6:28	5:46	5:21	5:23	5:46	6:13	6:39	7:09	7:41
38° 15' N	Set 1st	5:34	6:06	6:36	7:06	7:34	8:01	8:10	7:53	7:13	6:26	5:43	5:23
85° 45' W	Twl	±1:39	±1:35	±1:32	±1:35	±1:45	±2:00	±2:03	±1:50	±1:37	±1:33	±1:34	±1:38
TZ 5 (4)	Rise 15th	7:58	7:33	6:54	6:07	5:32	5:19	5:32	5:58	6:25	6:52	7:24	7:53
	Set 15th	5:47	6:22	6:50	7:19	7:47	8:08	8:06	7:36	6:51	6:05	5:31	5:24
	Twl	±1:37	±1:32	±1:32	±1:39	±1:52	±2:03	±1:58	±1:44	±1:35	±1:33	±1:35	±1:39
LA **Alexandria**	Rise 1st	7:09	7:03	6:37	5:59	5:25	5:06	5:09	5:27	5:46	6:04	6:26	6:51
	Set 1st	5:18	5:45	6:08	6:29	6:49	7:10	7:18	7:06	6:34	5:55	5:21	5:07
31° 20' N	Twl	±1:31	±1:27	±1:25	±1:26	±1:33	±1:41	±1:44	±1:36	±1:28	±1:25	±1:26	±1:30
92° 30' W	Rise 15th	7:09	6:52	6:20	5:42	5:14	5:05	5:16	5:35	5:54	6:13	6:37	7:01
TZ 6 (5)	Set 15th	5:30	5:57	6:18	6:39	6:59	7:16	7:16	6:53	6:16	5:38	5:12	5:09
	Twl	±1:28	±1:26	±1:25	±1:28	±1:38	±1:44	±1:41	±1:32	±1:26	±1:25	±1:28	±1:31
Baton Rouge	Rise 1st	7:01	6:56	6:31	5:54	5:21	5:03	5:06	5:22	5:41	5:58	6:19	6:44
	Set 1st	5:15	5:41	6:03	6:23	6:42	7:02	7:11	6:59	6:27	5:50	5:17	5:03
30° 30' N	Twl	±1:30	±1:26	±1:24	±1:25	±1:32	±1:40	±1:42	±1:35	±1:28	±1:23	±1:25	±1:29
91° 05' W	Rise 15th	7:02	6:45	6:14	5:37	5:10	5:02	5:12	5:31	5:49	6:07	6:30	6:54
TZ 6 (5)	Set 15th	5:26	5:53	6:13	6:32	6:52	7:08	7:08	6:46	6:10	5:33	5:07	5:05
	Twl	±1:28	±1:24	±1:24	±1:28	±1:36	±1:42	±1:39	±1:32	±1:25	±1:25	±1:28	±1:30
New Orleans	Rise 1st	6:56	6:51	6:26	5:50	5:18	5:00	5:03	5:19	5:37	5:54	6:14	6:38
30° 00' N	Set 1st	5:12	5:38	5:59	6:19	6:38	6:57	7:05	6:54	6:23	5:46	5:13	5:00
90° 05' W	Twl	±1:29	±1:25	±1:24	±1:25	±1:31	±1:39	±1:41	±1:34	±1:27	±1:23	±1:25	±1:29
TZ 6 (5)	Rise 15th	6:57	6:40	6:10	5:34	5:07	4:59	5:09	5:28	5:45	6:02	6:25	6:48
	Set 15th	5:23	5:49	6:09	6:27	6:47	8:03	7:03	6:41	6:06	5:30	5:04	5:02
	Twl	±1:27	±1:25	±1:23	±1:28	±1:35	±1:42	±1:39	±1:32	±1:25	±1:24	±1:27	±1:30
Port Arthur	Rise 1st	7:12	7:06	6:42	6:05	5:33	5:15	5:18	5:35	5:53	6:09	6:30	6:54
30° 00' N	Set 1st	5:27	5:53	6:15	6:35	6:53	7:13	7:21	7:09	6:39	6:02	5:29	5:16
94° 00' W	Twl	±1:28	±1:26	±1:24	±1:24	±1:32	±1:39	±1:41	±1:34	±1:27	±1:23	±1:25	±1:29
TZ 6 (5)													

→ **Sunrises & Sunsets HAVE NOT been adjusted for Daylight-Saving Time.**

Sunrises & Sunsets

Louisiana/Maine

		JAN	FEB	MAR	APR	MAY	JUN	JUL	AUG	SEP	OCT	NOV	DEC
Port Arthur	Rise 15th	7:13	6:56	6:26	5:49	5:23	5:14	5:25	5:43	6:01	6:18	6:41	7:04
TZ **6** (5)	Set 15th	5:39	6:05	6:24	6:43	7:02	7:19	7:19	6:57	6:21	5:45	5:20	5:18
	Twl	±1:27	±1:24	±1:24	±1:28	±1:36	±1:41	±1:39	±1:30	±1:24	±1:24	±1:27	±1:30
Shreveport	Rise 1st	7:17	7:10	6:43	6:04	5:29	5:09	5:12	5:30	5:50	6:09	6:33	6:59
32°30' N	Set 1st	5:21	5:48	6:13	6:35	6:57	7:18	7:27	7:13	6:40	6:00	5:25	5:10
93°50' W	Twl	±1:32	±1:28	±1:26	±1:28	±1:34	±1:44	±1:46	±1:38	±1:29	±1:26	±1:27	±1:31
TZ **6** (5)	Rise 15th	7:17	6:58	6:26	5:46	5:17	5:08	5:19	5:39	5:59	6:19	6:45	7:10
	Set 15th	5:33	6:01	6:23	6:45	7:07	7:24	7:24	7:00	6:22	5:43	5:15	5:11
	Twl	±1:29	±1:27	±1:26	±1:30	±1:39	±1:47	±1:40	±1:34	±1:27	±1:26	±1:29	±1:37
ME	Rise 1st	7:13	6:54	6:13	5:16	4:25	3:52	3:53	4:21	4:57	5:33	6:13	6:53
Bangor	Set 1st	4:05	4:44	5:23	6:03	6:40	7:14	7:25	7:01	6:12	5:16	4:24	3:56
44°48' N	Twl	±1:51	±1:46	±1:40	±1:45	±2:02	±2:30	±2:42	±2:15	±1:50	±1:43	±1:44	±1:50
68°42' W	Rise 15th	7:09	6:36	5:47	4:51	4:07	3:48	4:03	4:37	5:14	5:51	6:33	7:06
TZ **5** (4)	Set 15th	4:21	5:04	5:41	6:21	6:57	7:23	7:18	6:41	5:46	4:50	4:07	3:55
	Twl	±1:51	±1:42	±1:40	±1:51	±2:14	±2:41	±2:30	±2:03	±1:45	±1:42	±1:50	±1:55
Calais	Rise 1st	7:08	6:50	6:07	5:10	4:18	3:45	3:46	4:14	4:51	5:28	6:08	6:48
45°11' N	Set 1st	3:58	4:37	5:17	5:57	6:36	7:10	7:20	6:56	6:07	5:10	4:17	3:49
67°20' W	Twl	±1:51	±1:46	±1:42	±1:47	±2:04	±2:36	±2:45	±2:14	±1:52	±1:43	±1:45	±1:50
TZ **5** (4)	Rise 15th	7:05	6:30	5:42	4:44	4:00	3:41	3:56	4:31	5:08	5:45	6:28	7:02
	Set 15th	4:14	4:57	5:36	6:15	6:52	7:19	7:14	6:36	5:40	4:44	4:00	3:46
	Twl	±1:48	±1:43	±1:42	±1:54	±2:18	±2:47	±2:32	±2:02	±1:48	±1:43	±1:48	±1:54
Portland	Rise 1st	7:15	6:58	6:17	5:22	4:33	4:02	4:03	4:30	5:05	5:39	6:17	6:55
43°40' N	Set 1st	4:15	4:52	5:30	6:08	6:44	7:16	7:26	7:04	6:16	5:22	4:32	4:05
70°15' W	Twl	±1:48	±1:43	±1:39	±1:44	±1:59	±2:24	±2:31	±2:07	±1:49	±1:41	±1:42	±1:47
TZ **5** (4)	Rise 15th	7:11	6:40	5:53	4:58	4:16	3:59	4:13	4:46	5:20	5:55	6:35	7:08
	Set 15th	4:30	5:11	5:47	6:25	7:00	7:24	7:20	6:44	5:51	4:57	4:16	4:05
	Twl	±1:46	±1:41	±1:41	±1:49	±2:10	±2:33	±2:21	±1:58	±1:44	±1:41	±1:44	±1:49

→ **Sunrises & Sunsets HAVE NOT been adjusted for Daylight-Saving Time.**

SunRISE & SET

Maine/Maryland/Massachusetts

		JAN	FEB	MAR	APR	MAY	JUN	JUL	AUG	SEP	OCT	NOV	DEC
Presque Isle	Rise 1st	7:17	6:56	6:11	5:11	4:17	4342	3:42	4:12	4:52	5:30	6:14	6:56
46°40′ N	Set 1st	3:55	4:38	5:18	6:01	6:42	7:18	7:29	7:03	6:11	5:12	4:17	3:46
68°00′ W	Twl	±1:55	±1:46	±1:44	±1:51	±2:10	±2:51	±3:03	±2:22	±1:56	±1:47	±1:47	±1:53
TZ **5** (4)	Rise 15th	7:12	6:36	5:45	4:45	3:58	3:38	3:54	4:30	5:10	5:49	6:34	7:10
	Set 15th	4:11	4:57	5:38	6:20	7:00	7:27	7:22	6:42	5:44	4:45	3:59	3:45
	Twl	±1:53	±1:46	±1:45	±1:58	±2:26	±3:08	±2:45	±2:08	±1:50	±1:46	±1:50	±1:55
MD **Baltimore**	Rise 1st	7:26	7:14	6:39	5:51	5:08	4:42	4:43	5:06	5:35	6:02	6:34	7:07
	Set 1st	4:54	5:27	5:59	6:30	7:00	7:27	7:37	7:19	6:37	5:49	5:05	4:44
39°18′ N	Twl	±1:40	±1:36	±1:33	±1:37	±1:47	±2:03	±2:07	±1:52	±1:39	±1:34	±1:35	±1:39
76°37′ W	Rise 15th	7:25	6:58	6:18	5:30	4:53	4:39	4:52	5:19	5:48	6:16	6:50	7:19
TZ **5** (4)	Set 15th	5:08	5:43	6:13	6:44	7:13	7:35	7:32	7:02	6:15	5:28	4:52	4:44
	Twl	±1:38	±1:35	±1:34	±1:40	±1:55	±2:07	±2:02	±1:46	±1:36	±1:34	±1:38	±1:41
Cumberland	Rise 1st	7:36	7:23	6:48	5:59	5:16	4:49	4:51	5:14	5:43	6:11	6:43	7:16
39°40′ N	Set 1st	5:01	5:35	6:07	6:39	7:09	7:37	7:47	7:28	6:46	5:58	5:13	4:51
78°43′ W	Twl	±1:41	±1:36	±1:34	±1:37	±1:48	±2:04	±2:08	±1:54	±1:41	±1:34	±1:35	±1:40
TZ **5** (4)	Rise 15th	7:34	7:07	6:27	5:38	5:01	4:46	5:00	5:27	5:56	6:25	6:59	7:29
	Set 15th	5:15	5:51	6:22	6:53	7:22	7:44	7:42	7:11	6:24	5:36	4:59	4:52
	Twl	±1:40	±1:35	±1:33	±1:41	±1:56	±2:09	±2:03	±1:46	±1:36	±1:34	±1:39	±1:41
MA **Boston**	Rise 1st	7:14	6:58	6:20	5:27	4:39	4:10	4:11	4:37	5:10	5:41	6:18	6:54
	Set 1st	4:23	4:59	5:34	6:10	6:44	7:15	7:25	7:04	6:18	5:26	4:38	4:13
42°20′ N	Twl	±1:45	±1:40	±1:37	±1:41	±1:55	±2:16	±2:21	±2:02	±1:45	±1:38	±1:40	±1:44
71°00′ W	Rise 15th	7:11	6:41	5:56	5:03	4:23	4:07	4:21	4:52	5:24	5:57	6:35	7:07
TZ **5** (4)	Set 15th	4:37	5:17	5:51	6:26	6:59	7:23	7:19	6:45	5:54	5:02	4:22	4:13
	Twl	±1:43	±1:38	±1:38	±1:46	±2:04	±2:22	±2:14	±1:53	±1:39	±1:38	±1:42	±1:45
New Bedford	Rise 1st	7:11	6:55	6:19	5:26	4:39	4:10	4:13	4:37	5:09	5:41	6:17	6:51
41°40′ N	Set 1st	4:24	4:58	5:34	6:10	6:42	7:11	7:22	7:01	6:16	5:25	4:37	4:14
70°52′ W	Twl	±1:44	±1:40	±1:36	±1:39	±1:53	±2:14	±2:18	±1:59	±1:45	±1:38	±1:40	±1:44
TZ **5** (4)													

➔ **Sunrises & Sunsets HAVE NOT been adjusted for Daylight-Saving Time.**

SunRISE & SET

Sunrises & Sunsets

Massachusetts/Michigan

		JAN	FEB	MAR	APR	MAY	JUN	JUL	AUG	SEP	OCT	NOV	DEC
New Bedford	Rise 15th	7:08	6:40	5:56	5:03	4:23	4:07	4:21	4:51	5:24	5:57	6:33	7:04
	Set 15th	4:37	5:17	5:51	6:24	6:56	7:20	7:16	6:43	5:54	5:02	4:22	4:14
	Twl	±1:44	±1:37	±1:37	±1:46	±2:03	±2:18	±2:11	±1:52	±1:38	±1:38	±1:42	±1:45
Springfield 42°08' N 72°37' W TZ 5 (4)	Rise 1st	7:19	7:03	6:26	5:33	4:46	4:17	4:18	4:44	5:16	5:48	6:24	6:59
	Set 1st	4:30	5:05	5:41	6:16	6:50	7:20	7:30	7:09	6:24	5:32	4:44	4:20
	Twl	±1:45	±1:40	±1:37	±1:41	±1:54	±2:16	±2:21	±2:02	±1:45	±1:38	±1:40	±1:44
	Rise 15th	7:16	6:46	6:02	5:10	4:30	4:14	4:28	4:58	5:31	6:03	6:41	7:12
	Set 15th	4:44	5:23	5:57	6:32	7:05	7:28	7:25	6:51	6:00	5:09	4:29	4:19
	Twl	±1:43	±1:38	±1:38	±1:46	±2:04	±2:22	±2:14	±1:52	±1:41	±1:38	±1:42	±1:46
MI **Cadillac** 44°16' N 85°25' W TZ 5 (4)	Rise 1st	8:17	8:00	7:19	6:23	5:33	5:01	5:02	5:29	6:05	6:40	7:19	7:57
	Set 1st	5:14	5:52	6:30	7:09	7:46	8:19	8:29	8:06	7:18	6:22	5:31	5:04
	Twl	±1:49	±1:43	±1:40	±1:45	±2:01	±2:28	±2:36	±2:11	±1:49	±1:42	±1:44	±1:48
	Rise 15th	8:14	7:41	6:54	5:58	5:15	4:57	5:12	5:45	6:21	6:57	7:38	8:11
	Set 15th	5:29	6:11	6:48	7:26	8:02	8:27	8:23	7:46	6:52	5:57	5:15	5:03
	Twl	±1:47	±1:41	±1:41	±1:52	±2:13	±2:38	±2:25	±2:00	±1:45	±1:42	±1:45	±1:50
Cheboygan 45°38' N 84°29' W TZ 5 (4)	Rise 1st	8:19	7:59	7:16	6:18	5:26	4:52	4:53	5:22	5:59	6:36	7:18	7:58
	Set 1st	5:05	5:45	6:25	7:06	7:45	8:20	8:31	8:06	7:16	6:18	5:25	4:56
	Twl	±1:52	±1:46	±1:43	±1:49	±2:07	±2:40	±2:49	±2:15	±1:53	±1:45	±1:46	±1:51
	Rise 15th	8:15	7:40	6:50	5:52	5:07	4:48	5:03	5:38	6:16	6:55	7:38	8:12
	Set 15th	5:21	6:05	6:44	7:25	8:03	8:29	8:24	7:45	6:49	5:52	5:07	4:55
	Twl	±1:49	±1:44	±1:44	±1:54	±2:20	±2:53	±2:36	±2:05	±1:48	±1:44	±1:49	±1:53
Detroit 42°23' N 83°05' W TZ 5 (4)	Rise 1st	8:02	7:46	7:08	6:15	5:27	4:58	4:59	5:25	5:58	6:30	7:06	7:42
	Set 1st	5:11	5:47	6:22	6:58	7:32	8:03	8:13	7:52	7:06	6:14	5:25	5:01
	Twl	±1:45	±1:40	±1:38	±1:42	±1:56	±2:16	±2:22	±2:02	±1:46	±1:38	±1:41	±1:45
	Rise 15th	7:59	7:29	6:44	5:51	5:11	4:55	5:09	5:40	6:12	6:45	7:23	7:55
	Set 15th	5:25	6:05	6:39	7:14	7:47	8:11	8:07	7:33	6:42	5:50	5:10	5:00
	Twl	±1:43	±1:38	±1:38	±1:47	±2:06	±2:24	±2:15	±1:54	±1:42	±1:39	±1:42	±1:46

→ **Sunrises & Sunsets HAVE NOT been adjusted for Daylight-Saving Time.**

SunRISE & SET

Sunrises & Sunsets

Michigan/Minnesota

		JAN	FEB	MAR	APR	MAY	JUN	JUL	AUG	SEP	OCT	NOV	DEC
Lansing 42°47' N 84°40' W TZ 5 (4)	Rise 1st	8:09	7:53	7:14	6:21	5:33	5:03	5:04	5:30	6:03	6:36	7:13	7:50
	Set 1st	5:16	5:52	6:28	7:05	7:39	8:11	8:21	7:59	7:13	6:20	5:31	5:06
	Twl	±1:46	±1:41	±1:38	±1:42	±1:57	±2:19	±2:24	±2:04	±1:46	±1:39	±1:40	±1:45
	Rise 15th	8:06	7:36	6:51	5:57	5:16	5:00	5:14	5:45	6:19	6:52	7:31	8:02
	Set 15th	5:30	6:11	6:45	7:21	7:55	8:19	8:15	7:40	6:48	5:56	5:16	5:05
	Twl	±1:44	±1:38	±1:39	±1:48	±2:07	±2:26	±2:17	±1:56	±1:43	±1:39	±1:42	±1:48
Marquette 46°30' N 87°21' W TZ 5 (4)	Rise 1st	8:32	8:12	7:28	6:29	5:36	5:00	5:02	5:30	6:10	6:48	7:30	8:13
	Set 1st	5:13	5:55	6:36	7:18	7:58	8:35	8:46	8:19	7:28	6:29	5:35	5:04
	Twl	±1:55	±1:47	±1:44	±1:51	±2:11	±2:49	±3:00	±2:17	±1:51	±1:42	±1:45	±1:53
	Rise 15th	8:29	7:52	7:02	6:03	5:17	4:56	5:13	5:49	6:28	7:07	7:52	8:27
	Set 15th	5:29	6:16	6:56	7:37	8:17	8:44	8:39	7:58	7:00	6:03	5:17	5:04
	Twl	±1:53	±1:44	±1:45	±1:58	±2:25	±3:05	±2:40	±2:03	±1:46	±1:42	±1:47	±1:54
Sault Sainte Marie 46°27' N 84°22' W TZ 5 (4)	Rise 1st	8:21	8:01	7:17	6:17	5:23	4:48	4:49	5:19	5:58	6:36	7:19	8:01
	Set 1st	5:01	5:42	6:24	7:07	7:47	8:23	8:34	8:08	7:16	6:17	5:22	4:52
	Twl	±1:55	±1:48	±1:44	±1:50	±2:10	±2:48	±2:59	±2:21	±1:56	±1:47	±1:48	±1:53
	Rise 15th	8:17	7:41	6:50	5:50	5:04	4:44	5:00	5:36	6:16	6:55	7:39	8:15
	Set 15th	5:18	6:03	6:44	7:25	8:05	8:32	8:27	7:47	6:49	5:51	5:04	4:51
	Twl	±1:52	±1:45	±1:45	±1:58	±2:25	±3:04	±2:42	±2:05	±1:48	±1:43	±1:51	±1:55
MN **Duluth** 46°48' N 92°10' W TZ 6 (5)	Rise 1st	7:54	7:33	6:49	5:48	4:54	4:18	4:18	4:49	5:28	6:07	6:51	7:33
	Set 1st	4:31	5:12	5:54	6:38	7:19	7:55	8:06	7:41	6:48	5:49	4:53	4:22
	Twl	±1:55	±1:49	±1:45	±1:51	±2:11	±2:53	±3:07	±2:22	±1:56	±1:47	±1:48	±1:54
	Rise 15th	7:49	7:13	6:22	5:21	4:34	4:14	4:30	5:06	5:46	6:26	7:11	7:47
	Set 15th	4:47	5:33	6:14	6:57	7:37	8:05	7:59	7:19	6:21	5:22	4:35	4:21
	Twl	±1:53	±1:46	±1:46	±1:58	±2:28	±3:11	±2:46	±2:08	±1:50	±1:46	±1:50	±1:55
International Falls 48°36' N 93°25' W TZ 6 (5)	Rise 1st	8:06	7:43	6:55	5:52	4:54	4:16	4:15	4:48	5:31	6:13	7:00	7:45
	Set 1st	4:29	5:12	5:57	6:44	7:28	8:08	8:19	7:51	6:56	5:53	4:54	4:21
	Twl	±2:00	±1:53	±1:49	±1:56	±2:21	±3:29	NONE	±2:35	±2:01	±1:50	±1:51	±1:58

➜ **Sunrises & Sunsets HAVE NOT been adjusted for Daylight-Saving Time.**

Sunrises & Sunsets

Minnesota/Mississippi

		JAN	FEB	MAR	APR	MAY	JUN	JUL	AUG	SEP	OCT	NOV	DEC
International Falls	Rise 15th	8:01	7:21	6:27	6:23	4:33	4:11	4:27	5:07	5:50	6:34	7:22	7:59
Note: Some Minnesota locations do not experience an end of twilight during the summer	Set 15th	4:46	5:35	6:19	8:05	7:48	8:18	8:11	7:28	6:26	5:25	4:34	4:18
	Twl	±1:57	±1:51	±1:51	±2:05	±2:42	NONE	±3:13	±2:16	±1:55	±1:49	±1:56	±2:01
Minneapolis	Rise 1st	7:52	7:33	6:51	5:54	5:03	4:30	4:31	4:59	5:35	6:11	6:52	7:31
44°58' N 93°20' W	Set 1st	4:43	5:21	6:01	6:41	7:19	7:53	8:04	7:40	6:51	5:54	5:02	4:33
	Twl	±1:50	±1:46	±1:42	±1:47	±2:04	±2:34	±2:42	±2:13	±1:51	±1:43	±1:44	±1:51
TZ **6** (5)	Rise 15th	7:48	7:14	6:26	5:29	4:44	4:26	4:41	5:15	5:52	6:29	7:11	7:45
	Set 15th	4:58	5:41	6:19	6:59	7:36	8:02	7:57	7:20	6:24	5:29	4:45	4:32
	Twl	±1:49	±1:43	±1:43	±1:53	±2:16	±2:44	±2:30	±2:01	±1:46	±1:42	±1:47	±1:51
MS **Biloxi**	Rise 1st	6:52	6:47	6:22	5:45	5:12	4:54	4:57	5:14	5:32	5:49	6:10	6:35
	Set 1st	5:06	5:32	5:54	6:14	6:34	6:53	7:02	6:50	6:18	5:41	5:08	4:54
30°24' N 88°53' W	Twl	±1:30	±1:26	±1:24	±1:25	±1:31	±1:40	±1:42	±1:35	±1:28	±1:23	±1:25	±1:30
TZ **6** (5)	Rise 15th	6:53	6:36	6:06	5:28	5:01	4:53	5:04	5:22	5:40	5:58	6:21	6:45
	Set 15th	5:17	5:44	6:04	6:23	6:43	6:59	6:59	6:37	6:01	5:25	4:59	4:57
	Twl	±1:28	±1:24	±1:24	±1:28	±1:36	±1:42	±1:39	±1:32	±1:26	±1:24	±1:27	±1:30
Jackson	Rise 1st	7:02	6:55	6:28	5:49	5:14	4:55	4:58	5:15	5:36	5:55	6:18	6:44
32°20' N 90°10' W	Set 1st	5:07	5:34	5:58	6:21	6:42	7:03	7:12	6:58	6:25	5:46	5:11	4:55
	Twl	±1:31	±1:28	±1:26	±1:27	±1:34	±1:43	±1:45	±1:38	±1:29	±1:26	±1:26	±1:31
TZ **6** (5)	Rise 15th	7:02	6:43	6:11	5:32	5:03	4:53	5:05	5:25	5:44	6:04	6:30	6:55
	Set 15th	5:18	5:47	6:09	6:30	6:52	7:09	7:09	6:45	6:07	5:28	5:00	4:57
	Twl	±1:30	±1:26	±1:25	±1:30	±1:38	±1:47	±1:43	±1:33	±1:27	±1:26	±1:29	±1:32
Meridian	Rise 1st	6:56	6:49	6:22	5:43	5:08	4:49	4:51	5:09	5:30	5:49	6:12	6:38
32°20' N 88°42' W	Set 1st	5:01	5:28	5:52	6:15	6:36	6:57	7:06	6:52	6:19	5:40	5:05	4:49
	Twl	±1:31	±1:28	±1:26	±1:27	±1:34	±1:43	±1:46	±1:38	±1:29	±1:26	±1:27	±1:31
TZ **6** (5)	Rise 15th	6:56	6:38	6:05	5:26	4:57	4:47	4:59	5:19	5:39	5:58	6:24	6:49
	Set 15th	5:12	5:41	6:03	6:24	6:46	7:03	7:03	6:39	6:01	5:22	4:54	4:51
	Twl	±1:30	±1:26	±1:25	±1:30	±1:38	±1:47	±1:43	±1:34	±1:27	±1:26	±1:29	±1:32

➡ **Sunrises & Sunsets HAVE NOT been adjusted for Daylight-Saving Time.**

SunRISE & SET

Sunrises & Sunsets

Mississippi/Missouri

		JAN	FEB	MAR	APR	MAY	JUN	JUL	AUG	SEP	OCT	NOV	DEC
Natchez	Rise 1st	7:05	6:59	6:33	5:54	5:21	5:01	5:04	5:22	5:41	5:59	6:22	6:47
31°35' N 91°25' W	Set 1st	5:13	5:40	6:04	6:25	6:46	7:06	7:15	7:02	6:30	5:51	5:17	5:02
	Twl	±1:31	±1:27	±1:25	±1:26	±1:32	±1:43	±1:44	±1:36	±1:28	±1:25	±1:26	±1:30
TZ **6** (5)	Rise 15th	7:06	6:47	6:16	5:37	5:09	5:00	5:11	5:31	5:50	6:09	6:34	6:58
	Set 15th	5:25	5:53	6:14	6:34	6:55	7:12	7:12	6:49	6:12	5:34	5:07	5:04
	Twl	±1:29	±1:25	±1:25	±1:29	±1:38	±1:45	±1:41	±1:32	±1:26	±1:25	±1:28	±1:31
Tupelo	Rise 1st	7:01	6:52	6:24	5:42	5:05	4:44	4:46	5:06	5:28	5:49	6:15	6:43
34°15' N 88°42' W	Set 1st	4:56	5:25	5:51	6:16	6:39	7:02	7:11	6:56	6:21	5:39	5:02	4:45
	Twl	±1:34	±1:29	±1:27	±1:29	±1:37	±1:48	±1:50	±1:42	±1:32	±1:28	±1:29	±1:33
TZ **6** (5)	Rise 15th	7:01	6:40	6:05	5:24	4:53	4:42	4:54	5:16	5:38	6:00	6:28	6:53
	Set 15th	5:08	5:38	6:03	6:26	6:50	7:08	7:07	6:42	6:02	5:21	4:51	4:47
	Twl	±1:33	±1:29	±1:27	±1:33	±1:42	±1:51	±1:47	±1:36	±1:29	±1:28	±1:31	±1:34
MO **Kansas City**	Rise 1st	7:37	7:25	6:51	6:03	5:20	4:54	4:56	5:19	5:47	6:14	6:46	7:18
39°03' N 94°30' W	Set 1st	5:07	5:39	6:11	6:42	7:11	7:38	7:48	7:30	6:49	6:01	5:18	4:56
	Twl	±1:39	±1:36	±1:33	±1:36	±1:47	±2:02	±2:05	±1:52	±1:38	±1:33	±1:34	±1:39
TZ **6** (5)	Rise 15th	7:36	7:10	6:30	5:42	5:06	4:52	5:05	5:32	6:00	6:28	7:01	7:30
	Set 15th	5:20	5:56	6:25	6:56	7:24	7:46	7:43	7:13	6:27	5:40	5:04	4:57
	Twl	±1:38	±1:33	±1:33	±1:39	±1:54	±2:06	±2:00	±1:46	±1:35	±1:33	±1:37	±1:40
St. Joseph	Rise 1st	7:41	7:27	6:53	6:04	5:20	4:53	4:55	5:18	5:47	6:15	6:48	7:21
39°46' N 94°50' W	Set 1st	5:06	5:39	6:11	6:43	7:14	7:41	7:51	7:33	6:51	6:02	5:17	4:55
	Twl	±1:40	±1:37	±1:34	±1:37	±1:48	±2:05	±2:09	±1:54	±1:40	±1:34	±1:36	±1:41
TZ **6** (5)	Rise 15th	7:39	7:12	6:31	5:42	5:05	4:51	5:04	5:31	6:00	6:30	7:04	7:33
	Set 15th	5:19	5:56	6:26	6:57	7:27	7:49	7:47	7:16	6:28	5:40	5:04	4:56
	Twl	±1:40	±1:34	±1:34	±1:42	±1:56	±2:09	±2:03	±1:46	±1:37	±1:35	±1:38	±1:42
St. Louis	Rise 1st	7:19	7:07	6:33	5:46	5:04	4:38	4:40	5:02	5:30	5:57	6:28	7:00
38°40' N 90°12' W	Set 1st	4:50	5:23	5:54	6:24	6:53	7:20	7:29	7:11	6:31	5:44	5:01	4:39
TZ **6** (5)	Twl	±1:40	±1:35	±1:32	±1:36	±1:46	±2:01	±2:04	±1:51	±1:38	±1:33	±1:34	±1:39

➡ **Sunrises & Sunsets HAVE NOT been adjusted for Daylight-Saving Time.**

SunRISE & SET

Sunrises & Sunsets

Missouri/Montana

		JAN	FEB	MAR	APR	MAY	JUN	JUL	AUG	SEP	OCT	NOV	DEC
St. Louis	Rise 15th	7:17	6:52	6:12	6:25	4:49	4:36	4:48	5:15	5:42	6:10	6:43	7:11
	Set 15th	5:04	5:39	6:08	7:38	7:06	7:27	7:25	6:55	6:09	5:23	4:48	4:41
	Twl	±1:40	±1:33	±1:32	±1:39	±1:53	±2:05	±1:59	±1:44	±1:35	±1:33	±1:36	±1:39
Springfield	Rise 1st	7:27	7:16	6:45	5:59	5:19	4:55	4:57	5:18	5:44	6:09	6:38	7:09
37°15' N	Set 1st	5:07	5:38	6:07	5:36	7:03	7:28	7:38	7:21	6:42	5:57	5:16	4:56
93°20' W	Twl	±1:38	±1:34	±1:31	±1:34	±1:43	±1:57	±1:59	±1:47	±1:37	±1:31	±1:32	±1:37
TZ 6 (5)	Rise 15th	7:26	7:02	6:25	5:39	5:05	4:52	5:05	5:30	5:55	6:21	6:52	7:20
	Set 15th	5:20	5:53	6:21	6:48	7:15	7:35	7:34	7:05	6:21	5:37	5:03	4:57
	Twl	±1:35	±1:32	±1:31	±1:37	±1:50	±2:00	±1:55	±1:42	±1:33	±1:31	±1:34	±1:38
MT **Bonners Ferry**	Rise 1st	8:38	8:15	7:27	6:23	5:25	4:47	4:47	5:20	5:03	6:45	7:32	8:17
	Set 1st	5:01	5:44	6:30	7:17	8:01	8:40	8:51	8:23	7:27	6:24	5:25	4:52
48°38' N	Twl	±1:59	±1:53	±1:49	±1:55	±2:20	±3:31	NONE	±2:35	±2:02	±1:51	±1:52	±1:58
116°21' W	Rise 15th	8:33	7:53	6:58	5:54	5:04	4:42	4:59	5:39	6:22	7:06	7:54	8:31
TZ 7 (6)	Set 15th	5:18	6:07	6:51	7:37	8:20	8:50	8:43	8:00	6:58	5:56	5:06	4:50
Note: Some Montana locations do not experience an end of twilight during the summer	Twl	±1:56	±1:51	±1:51	±2:05	±2:43	NONE	±3:13	±2:16	±1:55	±1:50	±1:55	±2:01
Bozeman	Rise 1st	8:05	7:45	7:02	6:04	5:11	4:38	4:39	5:08	5:45	6:23	7:04	7:45
45°40' N	Set 1st	4:51	5:31	6:11	6:53	7:31	8:06	8:17	7:52	7:02	6:04	5:10	4:42
111°00' W	Twl	±1:52	±1:46	±1:43	±1:47	±2:07	±2:40	±2:49	±2:17	±1:52	±1:45	±1:46	±1:51
TZ 7 (6)	Rise 15th	8:01	7:26	6:36	5:38	4:53	4:34	4:49	5:25	6:03	6:41	7:24	7:58
	Set 15th	5:07	5:51	6:30	7:11	7:49	8:15	8:10	7:32	6:35	5:38	4:53	4:41
	Twl	±1:50	±1:44	±1:44	±1:55	±2:21	±2:53	±2:34	±2:04	±1:48	±1:44	±1:49	±1:53
Glendive	Rise 1st	7:45	7:24	6:38	5:37	4:43	4:07	4:07	4:38	5:18	5:58	6:42	7:24
47°07' N	Set 1st	4:20	5:01	5:44	6:28	7:10	7:47	7:58	7:31	6:38	5:38	4:42	4:11
104°40' W	Twl	±1:56	±1:50	±1:46	±1:52	±2:12	±2:57	±3:13	±2:23	±1:57	±1:48	±1:49	±1:55
TZ 7 (6)	Rise 15th	7:40	7:03	6:11	5:10	4:23	4:02	4:19	4:56	5:36	6:17	7:03	7:38
	Set 15th	4:37	5:23	6:05	6:48	7:28	7:56	7:50	7:09	6:10	5:11	4:24	4:10
	Twl	±1:53	±1:48	±1:46	±1:59	±2:30	±3:19	±2:47	±2:08	±1:49	±1:47	±1:51	±1:57

→ **Sunrises & Sunsets HAVE NOT been adjusted for Daylight-Saving Time.**

SunRISE & SET

Sunrises & Sunsets

Montana/Nebraska

		JAN	FEB	MAR	APR	MAY	JUN	JUL	AUG	SEP	OCT	NOV	DEC
Great Falls 47°27'N 111°12'W TZ 7 (6)	Rise 1st	8:12	7:51	7:05	6:03	5:08	4:32	4:32	5:03	5:44	6:24	7:09	7:52
	Set 1st	4:45	5:27	6:10	6:55	7:37	8:14	8:25	7:58	7:05	6:04	5:07	4:36
	Twl	±1:56	±1:50	±1:46	±2:54	±2:14	±3:02	±3:21	±2:24	±1:58	±1:49	±1:50	±1:56
	Rise 15th	8:08	7:30	6:37	5:36	4:48	4:27	4:43	5:21	6:02	6:44	7:30	8:06
	Set 15th	5:02	5:49	6:31	7:15	7:55	8:24	8:18	7:36	6:36	5:37	4:49	4:34
	Twl	±1:54	±1:47	±1:48	±2:00	±2:33	±3:28	±2:51	±2:06	±1:51	±1:47	±1:52	±1:58
Helena 46°40'N 112°00'W TZ 7 (6)	Rise 1st	8:13	7:52	7:07	6:07	5:13	4:38	4:38	5:09	5:48	6:27	7:10	7:52
	Set 1st	4:51	5:32	6:14	6:57	7:38	8:14	8:25	7:59	7:07	6:07	5:12	4:42
	Twl	±1:55	±1:49	±1:45	±1:51	±2:11	±2:51	±3:04	±2:22	±1:56	±1:48	±1:48	±1:53
	Rise 15th	8:08	7:32	6:40	5:40	4:53	4:34	4:50	5:26	6:06	6:46	7:31	8:06
	Set 15th	5:08	5:53	6:34	7:16	7:56	8:24	8:18	7:38	6:39	5:41	4:54	4:41
	Twl	±1:52	±1:46	±1:46	±1:58	±2:27	±3:08	±2:43	±2:08	±1:50	±1:46	±1:51	±1:55
NE **Bassett** 42°37'N 99°30'W TZ 6 (5)	Rise 1st	8:08	7:52	7:13	6:20	5:32	5:03	5:04	5:30	6:03	6:35	7:12	7:49
	Set 1st	5:16	5:52	6:28	7:04	7:38	8:09	8:20	7:58	7:12	6:19	5:31	5:06
	Twl	±1:45	±1:40	±1:38	±1:42	±1:56	±2:18	±2:23	±2:04	±1:46	±1:39	±1:40	±1:45
	Rise 15th	8:05	7:35	6:50	5:57	5:16	5:00	5:14	5:45	6:18	6:51	7:30	8:01
	Set 15th	5:30	6:10	6:45	7:20	7:54	8:18	8:14	7:39	6:47	5:55	5:15	5:05
	Twl	±1:44	±1:39	±1:38	±1:47	±2:05	±2:25	±2:15	±1:54	±1:43	±1:39	±1:43	±1:47
Grand Island 40°59'N 98°25'W TZ 6 (5)	Rise 1st	7:59	7:44	7:08	6:17	5:32	5:04	5:05	5:30	6:01	6:30	7:05	7:39
	Set 1st	5:16	5:51	6:25	6:59	7:31	8:00	8:10	7:50	7:06	6:15	5:29	5:06
	Twl	±1:44	±1:38	±1:35	±1:39	±1:51	±2:10	±2:14	±1:58	±1:43	±1:37	±1:39	±1:42
	Rise 15th	7:56	7:28	6:45	5:54	5:16	5:01	5:15	5:44	6:14	6:45	7:21	7:52
	Set 15th	5:31	6:08	6:41	7:14	7:45	8:08	8:04	7:32	6:42	5:53	5:15	5:06
	Twl	±1:41	±1:37	±1:36	±1:43	±2:00	±2:15	±2:08	±1:50	±1:39	±1:36	±1:40	±1:44
Lincoln 40°50'N 96°42'W TZ 6 (5)	Rise 1st	7:51	7:37	7:01	6:10	5:25	4:57	4:59	5:23	5:54	6:24	6:58	7:32
	Set 1st	5:10	5:45	6:18	6:52	7:23	7:52	8:02	7:42	6:59	6:09	5:23	5:00
	Twl	±1:43	±1:38	±1:35	±1:39	±1:52	±2:10	±2:14	±1:57	±1:42	±1:36	±1:38	±1:41

➜ **Sunrises & Sunsets HAVE NOT been adjusted for Daylight-Saving Time.**

SunRISE & SET

Sunrises & Sunsets

Nebraska/Nevada

		JAN	FEB	MAR	APR	MAY	JUN	JUL	AUG	SEP	OCT	NOV	DEC
Lincoln	Rise 15th	7:49	7:21	6:38	6:48	5:09	4:55	5:08	5:37	6:08	6:38	7:14	7:44
	Set 15th	5:24	6:02	6:34	8:07	7:38	8:00	7:57	7:25	6:36	5:46	5:08	5:00
	Twl	±1:41	±1:36	±1:36	±1:43	±1:59	±2:15	±2:07	±1:49	±1:38	±1:37	±1:40	±1:43
Omaha	Rise 1st	7:50	7:35	6:58	6:07	5:21	4:53	4:55	5:19	5:51	6:21	6:56	7:30
41°15' N	Set 1st	5:06	5:41	6:15	6:49	7:21	7:51	8:01	7:41	6:57	6:06	5:19	4:56
96°00' W	Twl	±1:44	±1:38	±1:36	±1:40	±1:52	±2:11	±2:16	±1:58	±1:43	±1:37	±1:39	±1:43
TZ **6** (5)	Rise 15th	7:47	7:19	6:36	5:44	5:05	4:50	5:04	5:33	6:05	6:36	7:12	7:43
	Set 15th	5:20	5:58	6:31	7:04	7:36	7:59	7:55	7:23	6:33	5:43	5:05	4:56
	Twl	±1:42	±1:37	±1:37	±1:44	±2:01	±2:17	±2:10	±1:51	±1:39	±1:37	±1:40	±1:44
Scottsbluff	Rise 1st	7:22	7:07	6:29	5:37	4:50	4:21	4:23	4:48	5:20	5:51	6:27	7:03
41°55' N	Set 1st	4:34	5:10	5:45	6:20	6:53	7:23	7:33	7:12	6:28	5:36	4:48	4:24
103°35' W	Twl	±1:45	±1:39	±1:36	±1:41	±1:54	±2:15	±2:20	±2:01	±1:45	±1:38	±1:40	±1:44
TZ **7** (6)	Rise 15th	7:20	6:50	6:06	5:14	4:34	4:18	4:32	5:03	5:35	6:07	6:44	7:15
	Set 15th	4:49	5:28	6:01	6:36	7:08	7:31	7:28	6:54	6:04	5:13	4:33	4:24
	Twl	±1:42	±1:37	±1:38	±1:45	±2:04	±2:20	±2:12	±1:53	±1:40	±1:37	±1:42	±1:45
NV **Ely**	Rise 1st	6:59	6:46	6:12	5:24	4:41	4:15	4:17	4:40	5:08	5:36	6:07	6:40
	Set 1st	4:28	5:01	5:32	6:03	6:33	7:00	7:09	6:51	6:10	5:22	4:38	4:17
39°10' N	Twl	±1:40	±1:35	±1:33	±1:36	±1:47	±2:03	±2:07	±1:53	±1:39	±1:34	±1:35	±1:39
114°50' W	Rise 15th	6:57	6:31	5:50	5:02	4:26	4:13	4:26	4:53	5:21	5:49	6:23	6:52
TZ **8** (7)	Set 15th	4:41	5:17	5:47	6:17	6:46	7:07	7:05	6:34	5:47	4:00	4:25	4:18
	Twl	±1:38	±1:34	±1:32	±1:40	±1:54	±2:08	±2:00	±1:46	±1:37	±1:34	±1:38	±1:40
Las Vegas	Rise 1st	6:52	6:41	6:11	5:27	4:48	4:25	4:27	4:48	5:12	5:36	6:04	6:33
36°10' N	Set 1st	4:37	5:08	5:36	6:03	6:28	6:53	7:02	6:46	6:08	5:24	4:44	4:26
115°05' W	Twl	±1:35	±1:30	±1:29	±1:31	±1:40	±1:52	±1:55	±1:44	±1:34	±1:30	±1:31	±1:35
TZ **8** (7)	Rise 15th	6:51	6:28	5:51	5:07	4:34	4:23	4:35	4:59	5:23	5:48	6:18	6:45
	Set 15th	4:50	5:22	5:48	6:15	6:40	7:00	6:58	6:31	5:48	5:04	4:31	4:27
	Twl	±1:34	±1:30	±1:29	±1:35	±1:46	±1:56	±1:51	±1:40	±1:31	±1:30	±1:34	±1:37

➡ **Sunrises & Sunsets HAVE NOT been adjusted for Daylight-Saving Time.**

Nevada/New Hampshire/New Jersey

		JAN	FEB	MAR	APR	MAY	JUN	JUL	AUG	SEP	OCT	NOV	DEC
Reno	Rise 1st	7:20	7:07	6:32	5:43	5:00	4:34	4:36	4:59	5:28	5:56	6:28	7:01
39°30' N	Set 1st	4:47	5:20	5:52	6:24	6:53	7:21	7:30	7:12	6:30	5:41	4:58	4:36
119°50' W	Twl	±1:40	±1:36	±1:33	±1:36	±1:48	±2:04	±2:08	±1:53	±1:39	±1:35	±1:35	±1:40
TZ 8 (7)	Rise 15th	7:18	6:51	6:10	5:22	4:45	4:32	4:45	5:12	5:41	6:10	6:44	7:13
	Set 15th	5:00	5:36	6:07	6:37	7:07	7:28	7:26	6:55	6:07	5:20	4:44	4:37
	Twl	±1:40	±1:35	±1:33	±1:41	±1:55	±2:09	±2:02	±1:46	±1:37	±1:34	±1:38	±1:41
Winnemucca	Rise 1st	7:16	7:01	6:25	5:34	4:49	4:21	4:23	4:47	5:18	5:48	6:22	6:57
41°00' N	Set 1st	4:34	5:08	5:42	6:16	6:48	7:17	7:27	7:07	6:23	5:33	4:47	4:23
117°45' W	Twl	±1:43	±1:39	±1:36	±1:40	±1:51	±2:11	±2:15	±1:58	±1:43	±1:36	±1:38	±1:42
TZ 8 (7)	Rise 15th	7:14	6:45	6:02	5:12	4:33	4:18	4:32	5:01	5:32	6:03	6:39	7:09
	Set 15th	4:48	5:26	5:58	6:31	7:02	7:25	7:22	6:49	6:00	5:10	4:32	4:24
	Twl	±1:41	±1:36	±1:36	±1:43	±2:01	±2:16	±2:08	±1:51	±1:38	±1:37	±1:40	±1:43
NH **Berlin**	Rise 1st	7:20	7:03	6:22	5:26	4:36	4:04	4:05	4:32	5:08	5:42	6:21	7:00
44°29' N	Set 1st	4:17	4:55	5:33	6:12	6:48	7:21	7:32	7:09	6:21	5:26	4:35	4:07
71°10' W	Twl	±1:49	±1:43	±1:40	±1:46	±2:03	±2:31	±2:38	±2:12	±1:50	±1:41	±1:43	±1:49
TZ 5 (4)	Rise 15th	7:17	6:44	5:57	5:01	4:18	3:59	4:15	4:48	5:24	5:59	6:40	7:13
	Set 15th	4:32	5:14	5:51	6:29	7:06	7:30	7:26	6:50	5:55	5:01	4:18	4:07
	Twl	±1:47	±1:41	±1:42	±1:52	±2:13	±2:40	±2:27	±2:00	±1:45	±1:41	±1:45	±1:49
Manchester	Rise 1st	7:17	7:01	6:22	5:28	4:40	4:10	4:11	4:37	5:10	5:43	6:21	6:58
42°58' N	Set 1st	4:22	4:59	5:35	6:12	6:47	7:18	7:29	7:06	6:20	5:27	4:38	4:12
71°29' W	Twl	±1:47	±1:41	±1:39	±1:43	±1:57	±2:21	±2:26	±2:05	±1:47	±1:40	±1:41	±1:46
TZ 5 (4)	Rise 15th	7:14	6:43	5:58	5:04	4:23	4:06	4:21	4:52	5:26	6:00	6:38	7:10
	Set 15th	4:37	5:18	5:53	6:29	7:02	7:27	7:23	6:48	5:56	5:03	4:22	4:12
	Twl	±1:45	±1:39	±1:39	±1:48	±2:08	±2:27	±2:17	±1:56	±1:42	±1:40	±1:44	±1:48
NJ **Altantic City**	Rise 1st	7:18	7:05	6:31	4:42	4:59	4:33	4:34	4:57	5:26	5:54	6:26	6:59
39°25' N	Set 1st	4:45	5:18	5:50	5:22	6:51	7:19	7:29	7:10	6:29	5:40	4:56	4:35
74°25' W	Twl	±1:40	±1:36	±1:33	±1:36	±1:48	±2:03	±2:07	±1:53	±1:39	±1:34	±1:36	±1:39
TZ 5 (4)													

➜ **Sunrises & Sunsets HAVE NOT been adjusted for Daylight-Saving Time.**

SunRISE & SET

Sunrises & Sunsets

New Jersey/New Mexico

		JAN	FEB	MAR	APR	MAY	JUN	JUL	AUG	SEP	OCT	NOV	DEC
Atlantic City	Rise 15th	7:16	6:50	6:09	5:21	4:44	4:30	4:43	5:10	5:39	6:07	6:41	7:11
TZ **5** (4)	Set 15th	4:58	5:34	6:05	6:36	7:05	7:26	7:24	6:53	6:06	5:19	4:43	4:35
	Twl	±1:40	±1:35	±1:33	±1:40	±1:55	±2:08	±2:02	±1:46	±1:36	±1:34	±1:38	±1:42
NM	Rise 1st	7:15	7:06	6:37	5:54	5:16	4:54	4:57	5:16	5:40	6:02	6:28	6:57
Albuquerque	Set 1st	5:06	5:36	6:03	6:29	6:53	7:16	7:25	7:10	6:34	5:51	5:13	4:55
35° 05' N	Twl	±1:35	±1:30	±1:28	±1:30	±1:39	±1:50	±1:53	±1:43	±1:33	±1:29	±1:30	±1:34
106° 47' W	Rise 15th	7:15	6:53	6:18	5:35	5:03	4:52	5:04	5:27	5:50	6:13	6:42	7:08
TZ **7** (6)	Set 15th	5:19	5:50	6:15	6:40	7:04	7:23	7:22	6:56	6:14	5:32	5:01	4:57
	Twl	±1:33	±1:29	±1:28	±1:33	±1:44	±1:53	±1:49	±1:37	±1:30	±1:29	±1:32	±1:34
Clovis	Rise 1st	6:59	6:50	6:22	5:40	5:03	4:42	4:44	5:03	5:26	5:47	6:13	6:41
34° 20' N	Set 1st	4:54	5:23	5:49	6:14	6:37	7:00	7:09	6:54	6:19	5:37	4:59	4:43
103° 10' W	Twl	±1:33	±1:29	±1:27	±1:29	±1:38	±1:48	±1:51	±1:41	±1:32	±1:28	±1:29	±1:32
TZ **7** (6)	Rise 15th	6:59	6:38	6:03	5:22	4:51	4:40	4:52	5:14	5:36	5:58	6:26	6:52
	Set 15th	5:06	5:36	6:00	6:24	6:48	7:06	7:05	6:40	5:59	5:18	4:48	4:44
	Twl	±1:32	±1:29	±1:28	±1:33	±1:42	±1:51	±1:47	±1:37	±1:30	±1:28	±1:31	±1:34
Farmington	Rise 1st	7:27	7:16	6:45	6:00	5:20	4:56	4:59	5:20	5:45	6:09	6:38	7:08
36° 45' N	Set 1st	5:09	5:39	6:08	6:36	7:02	7:27	7:37	7:20	6:42	5:57	5:17	4:58
108° 28' W	Twl	±1:37	±1:34	±1:30	±1:32	±1:43	±1:56	±1:57	±1:47	±1:35	±1:31	±1:32	±1:36
TZ **7** (6)	Rise 15th	7:26	7:02	6:25	5:40	5:06	4:54	5:07	5:31	5:56	6:21	6:52	7:19
	Set 15th	5:21	5:54	6:21	6:48	7:14	7:34	7:33	7:05	6:21	5:37	5:05	4:59
	Twl	±1:36	±1:31	±1:30	±1:37	±1:49	±1:59	±1:53	±1:41	±1:32	±1:31	±1:33	±1:37
Las Cruces	Rise 1st	7:09	7:01	6:35	5:56	5:21	5:01	5:04	5:22	5:42	6:01	6:24	6:51
32° 18' N	Set 1st	5:13	5:41	6:05	6:27	6:48	7:09	7:18	7:05	6:32	5:52	5:17	5:02
106° 50' W	Twl	±1:32	±1:27	±1:26	±1:28	±1:35	±1:44	±1:46	±1:38	±1:29	±1:26	±1:27	±1:31
TZ **7** (6)	Rise 15th	7:09	6:50	6:18	5:38	5:09	5:00	5:11	5:31	5:51	6:11	6:37	7:01
	Set 15th	5:25	5:53	6:15	6:37	6:58	7:16	7:15	6:52	6:13	5:35	5:07	5:04
	Twl	±1:30	±1:27	±1:26	±1:30	±1:39	±1:46	±1:43	±1:33	±1:28	±1:26	±1:29	±1:32

→ **Sunrises & Sunsets HAVE NOT been adjusted for Daylight-Saving Time.**

Sunrises & Sunsets

New Mexico/New York

		JAN	FEB	MAR	APR	MAY	JUN	JUL	AUG	SEP	OCT	NOV	DEC
Roswell	Rise 1st	7:02	6:54	6:27	5:46	5:10	4:49	4:52	5:11	5:32	5:52	6:17	6:44
33°26' N	Set 1st	5:02	5:30	5:55	6:19	6:41	7:03	7:12	6:58	6:24	5:43	5:06	4:50
104°32' W	Twl	±1:32	±1:28	±1:27	±1:28	±1:37	±1:47	±1:48	±1:40	±1:30	±1:27	±1:28	±1:32
TZ 7 (6)	Rise 15th	7:02	6:42	6:09	5:28	4:58	4:48	4:59	5:21	5:42	6:03	6:30	6:55
	Set 15th	5:13	5:43	6:06	6:29	6:51	7:09	7:09	6:44	6:05	5:25	4:56	4:52
	Twl	±1:32	±1:27	±1:27	±1:32	±1:41	±1:49	±1:45	±1:35	±1:28	±1:27	±1:30	±1:33
NY **Albany**	Rise 1st	7:25	7:09	6:31	5:37	4:50	4:20	4:21	4:47	5:20	5:52	6:29	7:06
	Set 1st	4:33	5:09	5:45	6:21	6:55	7:26	7:37	7:15	6:29	5:36	4:48	4:23
42°35' N	Twl	±1:45	±1:40	±1:38	±1:42	±1:56	±2:18	±2:23	±2:04	±1:46	±1:39	±1:41	±1:45
73°47' W	Rise 15th	7:22	6:52	6:07	5:14	4:33	4:17	4:31	5:02	5:35	6:08	6:47	7:18
TZ 5 (4)	Set 15th	4:47	5:27	6:02	6:37	7:11	7:35	7:31	6:56	6:05	5:13	4:33	4:23
	Twl	±1:44	±1:39	±1:38	±1:47	±2:05	±2:25	±2:15	±1:55	±1:42	±1:39	±1:42	±1:46
Buffalo	Rise 1st	7:46	7:30	6:51	5:58	5:10	4:39	4:40	5:06	5:40	6:12	6:50	7:26
42°55' N	Set 1st	4:52	5:28	6:05	6:42	7:16	7:47	7:58	7:36	6:50	5:57	5:08	4:42
78°50' W	Twl	±1:46	±1:41	±1:38	±1:42	±1:57	±2:21	±2:26	±2:04	±1:46	±1:39	±1:41	±1:46
TZ 5 (4)	Rise 15th	7:44	7:13	6:28	5:34	4:52	4:36	4:50	5:21	5:55	6:29	7:07	7:39
	Set 15th	5:06	5:47	6:22	6:58	7:32	7:56	7:52	7:18	6:25	5:33	4:52	4:42
	Twl	±1:45	±1:39	±1:39	±1:48	±2:07	±2:27	±2:17	±1:55	±1:43	±1:39	±1:43	±1:47
New York City	Rise 1st	7:20	7:06	6:30	5:39	4:54	4:27	4:28	4:53	5:23	5:53	6:27	7:01
40°45' N	Set 1st	4:39	5:14	5:47	6:21	6:52	7:21	7:31	7:11	6:28	5:38	4:52	4:29
74°00' W	Twl	±1:43	±1:38	±1:35	±1:39	±1:51	±2:09	±2:14	±1:57	±1:42	±1:36	±1:38	±1:42
TZ 5 (4)	Rise 15th	7:18	6:50	6:08	5:17	4:39	4:24	4:38	5:06	5:37	6:07	6:43	7:13
	Set 15th	4:53	5:31	6:03	6:36	7:07	7:29	7:26	6:54	6:05	5:16	4:38	4:29
	Twl	±1:41	±1:36	±1:35	±1:43	±1:59	±2:14	±2:07	±1:49	±1:38	±1:36	±1:40	±1:44
Rochester	Rise 1st	7:43	7:26	6:47	5:52	5:04	4:34	4:35	5:01	5:35	6:08	6:46	7:23
43°10' N	Set 1st	4:46	5:23	6:00	6:37	7:12	7:44	7:54	7:32	6:45	5:52	5:02	4:37
77°40' W	Twl	±1:47	±1:42	±1:38	±1:43	±1:58	±2:22	±2:27	±2:06	±1:47	±1:40	±1:42	±1:46
TZ 5 (4)													

➙ **Sunrises & Sunsets HAVE NOT been adjusted for Daylight-Saving Time.**

SunRISE & SET

Sunrises & Sunsets

New York/North Carolina

		JAN	FEB	MAR	APR	MAY	JUN	JUL	AUG	SEP	OCT	NOV	DEC
Rochester	Rise 15th	7:40	7:08	6:23	5:28	4:47	4:30	4:45	5:16	5:50	6:25	7:04	7:36
	Set 15th	5:01	5:42	6:17	6:54	7:28	7:52	7:48	7:13	6:20	5:28	4:47	4:36
	Twl	±1:45	±1:39	±1:40	±1:48	±2:08	±2:29	±2:19	±1:56	±1:43	±1:40	±1:43	±1:48
Syracuse	Rise 1st	7:36	7:20	6:41	5:47	4:58	4:28	4:29	4:55	5:29	6:02	6:40	7:17
43°04' N	Set 1st	4:41	5:17	5:54	6:31	7:06	7:38	7:48	7:26	6:39	5:46	4:57	4:31
76°11' W	Twl	±1:46	±1:42	±1:38	±1:43	±1:57	±2:20	±2:27	±2:05	±1:47	±1:40	±1:41	±1:46
TZ **5** (4)	Rise 15th	7:33	7:02	6:17	5:23	4:41	4:25	4:39	5:11	5:44	6:18	6:58	7:29
	Set 15th	4:56	5:36	6:11	7:48	7:22	7:46	7:42	7:07	6:15	5:22	4:41	4:31
	Twl	±1:44	±1:39	±1:40	±1:48	±2:07	±2:28	±2:18	±1:56	±1:42	±1:40	±1:43	±1:47
Watertown	Rise 1st	7:39	7:21	6:41	5:45	4:55	4:24	4:25	4:52	5:27	6:02	6:40	7:19
43°58' N	Set 1st	4:37	5:14	5:52	6:31	7:07	7:40	7:50	7:27	6:39	5:44	4:54	4:27
75°57' W	Twl	±1:49	±1:43	±1:40	±1:45	±2:01	±2:27	±2:34	±2:09	±1:50	±1:42	±1:43	±1:48
TZ **5** (4)	Rise 15th	7:35	7:03	6:16	5:20	4:38	4:20	4:35	5:08	5:43	6:19	6:59	7:32
	Set 15th	4:52	5:34	6:10	6:48	7:23	7:48	7:44	7:08	6:14	5:20	4:38	4:27
	Twl	±1:47	±1:40	±1:41	±1:51	±2:12	±2:36	±2:24	±1:58	±1:44	±1:41	±1:44	±1:49
NC **Asheville**	Rise 1st	7:40	7:30	7:00	6:16	5:38	5:15	5:18	5:38	6:02	6:25	6:52	7:21
	Set 1st	5:28	5:58	6:25	6:52	7:17	7:41	7:50	7:34	6:57	6:14	5:35	5:17
35°39' N	Twl	±1:36	±1:31	±1:29	±1:32	±1:41	±1:51	±1:54	±1:45	±1:33	±1:29	±1:30	±1:34
82°30' W	Rise 15th	7:39	7:17	6:41	5:57	5:25	5:14	5:26	5:49	6:13	6:37	7:06	7:32
TZ **5** (4)	Set 15th	5:40	6:12	6:38	7:03	7:28	7:47	7:46	7:19	6:37	5:54	5:23	5:18
	Twl	±1:34	±1:30	±1:28	±1:35	±1:46	±1:55	±1:50	±1:38	±1:31	±1:29	±1:33	±1:36
Charlotte	Rise 1st	7:32	7:22	6:53	6:10	5:32	5:10	5:12	5:32	5:55	6:18	6:44	7:13
35°16' N	Set 1st	5:22	5:51	6:19	6:45	7:09	7:32	7:42	7:27	6:50	6:07	5:29	5:11
80°46' W	Twl	±1:34	±1:31	±1:28	±1:30	±1:39	±1:51	±1:53	±1:42	±1:33	±1:29	±1:29	±1:34
TZ **5** (4)	Rise 15th	7:31	7:10	6:34	5:51	5:19	5:08	5:20	5:43	6:06	6:29	6:58	7:24
	Set 15th	5:34	6:05	6:31	6:56	7:20	7:39	7:38	7:12	6:30	5:48	5:17	5:12
	Twl	±1:34	±1:30	±1:28	±1:33	±1:45	±1:54	±1:50	±1:38	±1:30	±1:29	±1:32	±1:36

➜ **Sunrises & Sunsets HAVE NOT been adjusted for Daylight-Saving Time.**

Sunrises & Sunsets

North Carolina/North Dakota

		JAN	FEB	MAR	APR	MAY	JUN	JUL	AUG	SEP	OCT	NOV	DEC
Kitty Hawk	Rise 1st	7:14	7:04	6:33	5:49	5:10	4:47	4:50	5:10	5:35	5:58	6:26	6:55
36°04' N *75°42' W*	Set 1st	5:00	5:30	5:58	6:25	6:50	7:14	7:24	7:08	6:30	5:46	5:07	4:49
	Twl	±1:35	±1:31	±1:29	±1:31	±1:40	±1:53	±1:55	±1:45	±1:35	±1:31	±1:31	±1:34
TZ **5** (4)	Rise 15th	7:13	6:50	6:14	5:30	4:57	4:45	4:58	5:21	5:45	6:10	6:40	7:06
	Set 15th	5:12	5:44	6:10	6:37	7:02	7:21	7:20	6:53	6:10	5:27	4:55	4:50
	Twl	±1:34	±1:30	±1:30	±1:35	±1:46	±1:57	±1:52	±1:40	±1:31	±1:30	±1:33	±1:36
Raleigh	Rise 1st	7:25	7:15	6:44	6:01	5:22	5:00	5:02	5:22	5:47	6:10	6:37	7:06
35°47' N *78°39' W*	Set 1st	5:12	5:42	6:10	6:37	7:02	7:25	7:35	7:19	6:42	5:58	5:19	5:01
	Twl	±1:35	±1:32	±1:29	±1:30	±1:39	±1:52	±1:54	±1:45	±1:34	±1:30	±1:31	±1:34
TZ **5** (4)	Rise 15th	7:24	7:01	6:25	5:42	5:09	4:58	5:10	5:33	5:57	6:21	6:51	7:17
	Set 15th	5:25	5:57	6:22	6:48	7:13	7:32	7:31	7:04	6:22	5:39	5:07	5:02
	Twl	±1:33	±1:29	±1:29	±1:35	±1:46	±1:56	±1:50	±1:39	±1:31	±1:30	±1:33	±1:37
Wilmington	Rise 1st	7:18	7:09	6:40	5:59	5:22	5:01	5:03	5:23	5:45	6:06	6:32	7:00
34°14' N *77°54' W*	Set 1st	5:13	5:42	6:08	6:33	6:56	7:18	7:27	7:13	6:37	5:56	5:18	5:02
	Twl	±1:33	±1:29	±1:27	±1:29	±1:37	±1:49	±1:51	±1:41	±1:33	±1:28	±1:30	±1:33
TZ **5** (4)	Rise 15th	7:17	6:56	6:22	5:40	5:10	4:59	5:11	5:33	5:55	6:17	6:45	7:10
	Set 15th	5:25	5:56	6:20	6:43	7:07	7:25	7:24	6:59	6:18	5:38	5:08	5:03
	Twl	±1:32	±1:28	±1:27	±1:33	±1:42	±1:51	±1:47	±1:36	±1:29	±1:27	±1:30	±1:34
Winston-Salem	Rise 1st	7:32	7:22	6:51	6:07	5:28	5:05	5:08	5:28	5:53	6:16	6:44	7:14
36°07' N *80°15' W*	Set 1st	5:18	5:48	6:16	6:43	7:09	7:33	7:42	7:26	6:49	6:04	5:25	5:07
	Twl	±1:35	±1:31	±1:29	±1:31	±1:40	±1:53	±1:56	±1:45	±1:34	±1:31	±1:31	±1:34
TZ **5** (4)	Rise 15th	7:31	7:08	6:32	5:48	5:15	5:03	5:16	5:39	6:04	6:28	6:58	7:25
	Set 15th	5:30	6:02	6:29	6:55	7:20	7:40	7:38	7:11	6:28	5:45	5:13	5:08
	Twl	±1:34	±1:31	±1:29	±1:35	±1:47	±1:56	±1:52	±1:40	±1:31	±1:30	±1:33	±1:36
ND **Bismarck**	Rise 1st	8:28	8:07	7:22	6:22	5:28	4:53	4:53	5:23	6:03	6:42	7:26	8:08
46°49' N *100°49' W*	Set 1st	5:06	5:47	6:29	6:13	7:53	8:30	8:41	8:15	7:22	6:23	5:27	4:57
TZ **6** (5)	Twl	±1:55	±1:49	±1:45	±1:51	±2:12	±2:53	±3:07	±2:23	±1:57	±1:47	±1:48	±1:53

➙ **Sunrises & Sunsets HAVE NOT been adjusted for Daylight-Saving Time.**

SunRISE & SET

333

Sunrises & Sunsets

North Dakota/Ohio

		JAN	FEB	MAR	APR	MAY	JUN	JUL	AUG	SEP	OCT	NOV	DEC
Bismarck	Rise 15th	8:24	7:47	6:56	5:55	5:08	4:48	5:04	5:41	6:21	7:01	7:46	8:22
	Set 15th	5:22	6:08	6:49	7:32	8:12	8:39	8:33	7:53	6:55	5:56	5:09	4:55
	Twl	±1:53	±1:46	±1:46	±1:59	±2:28	±3:12	±2:47	±2:09	±1:50	±1:46	±1:51	±1:56
Grand Forks	Rise 1st	8:18	7:55	7:09	6:06	5:09	4:32	4:32	5:04	5:46	6:27	7:13	7:57
48°00' N *97°03' W*	Set 1st	4:46	5:28	6:13	6:58	7:41	8:20	8:31	8:03	7:09	6:07	5:09	4:37
	Twl	±1:58	±1:52	±1:47	±1:55	±2:18	±3:12	±3:44	±2:31	±2:00	±1:50	±1:51	±1:57
TZ **6 (5)**	Rise 15th	8:13	7:34	6:41	5:38	4:49	4:27	4:44	5:23	6:05	6:48	7:35	8:11
Note: Some North Dakota locations do not experience an end of twilight during the summer	Set 15th	5:02	5:51	6:34	7:19	8:01	8:30	8:23	7:41	6:40	5:39	4:50	4:35
	Twl	±1:56	±1:49	±1:49	±2:02	±2:36	NONE	±3:02	±2:14	±1:54	±1:49	±1:54	±1:59
Williston	Rise 1st	7:45	7:22	6:35	5:32	4:35	3:58	3:58	4:30	5:12	5:54	6:40	7:24
48°10' N *103°35' W*	Set 1st	4:12	4:54	5:39	6:25	7:08	7:47	7:58	7:30	6:35	5:33	4:35	4:03
	Twl	±1:58	±1:52	±1:47	±1:54	±2:19	±3:15	±3:55	±2:32	±2:01	±1:50	±1:51	±1:57
TZ **6 (5)**	Rise 15th	7:40	7:01	6:07	5:04	4:15	3:53	4:10	4:49	5:32	6:14	7:02	7:38
Note: Some North Dakota locations do not experience an end of twilight during the summer	Set 15th	4:29	5:17	6:00	6:45	7:27	7:57	7:50	7:08	6:06	5:05	4:16	4:01
	Twl	±1:55	±1:49	±1:50	±2:03	±2:39	NONE	±3:04	±2:14	±1:55	±1:49	±1:54	±1:59
OH **Akron**	Rise 1st	7:51	7:37	7:00	6:09	5:24	4:56	4:57	5:22	5:53	6:23	6:57	7:32
	Set 1st	5:08	5:43	6:17	6:51	7:23	7:52	8:02	7:42	6:59	6:08	5:22	4:58
41°07' N *81°31' W*	Twl	±1:44	±1:39	±1:36	±1:40	±1:52	±2:11	±2:16	±1:59	±1:42	±1:37	±1:38	±1:43
TZ **5 (4)**	Rise 15th	7:49	7:20	6:38	5:47	5:08	4:53	5:07	5:36	6:07	6:38	7:14	7:44
	Set 15th	5:23	6:01	6:33	7:06	7:38	8:00	7:57	7:25	6:35	5:45	5:07	4:58
	Twl	±1:41	±1:36	±1:36	±1:44	±2:00	±2:16	±2:08	±1:50	±1:39	±1:37	±1:40	±1:44
Cincinnati	Rise 1st	7:57	7:44	7:10	6:22	5:39	5:13	5:15	5:38	6:06	6:34	7:06	7:38
39°10' N *84°26' W*	Set 1st	5:26	5:59	6:30	7:02	7:31	7:58	8:08	7:49	7:08	6:20	5:37	5:15
	Twl	±1:40	±1:36	±1:33	±1:36	±1:47	±2:03	±2:06	±1:53	±1:39	±1:34	±1:35	±1:40
TZ **5 (4)**	Rise 15th	7:56	7:29	6:49	6:01	5:24	5:11	5:24	5:51	6:19	6:48	7:21	7:50
	Set 15th	5:39	6:15	6:45	7:15	7:44	8:06	8:03	7:33	6:46	5:59	5:23	5:16
	Twl	±1:38	±1:34	±1:33	±1:40	±1:54	±2:07	±2:02	±1:46	±1:36	±1:34	±1:38	±1:40

→ **Sunrises & Sunsets HAVE NOT been adjusted for Daylight-Saving Time.**

SunRISE & SET

334

Ohio/Oklahoma

		JAN	FEB	MAR	APR	MAY	JUN	JUL	AUG	SEP	OCT	NOV	DEC
Columbus 39°57' N 83°01' W TZ **5** (4)	Rise 1st	7:54	7:40	7:05	6:16	5:32	5:05	5:07	5:31	6:00	6:28	7:01	7:35
	Set 1st	5:18	5:52	6:24	6:57	7:27	7:55	8:05	7:46	7:03	6:14	5:30	5:08
	Twl	±1:41	±1:36	±1:34	±1:36	±1:49	±2:06	±2:09	±1:54	±1:41	±1:35	±1:36	±1:40
	Rise 15th	7:52	7:25	6:43	5:54	5:17	5:03	5:16	5:44	6:13	6:43	7:17	7:47
	Set 15th	5:32	6:08	6:39	7:11	7:41	8:03	8:00	7:28	6:41	5:52	5:16	5:08
	Twl	±1:40	±1:35	±1:34	±1:42	±1:57	±2:10	±2:03	±1:48	±1:37	±1:35	±1:39	±1:42
Toledo 41°37' N 83°33' W TZ **5** (4)	Rise 1st	8:01	7:46	7:09	6:17	5:31	5:02	5:04	5:29	6:00	6:31	7:06	7:42
	Set 1st	5:15	5:50	6:25	7:00	7:32	8:02	8:12	7:52	7:07	6:16	5:29	5:05
	Twl	±1:44	±1:39	±1:36	±1:40	±1:54	±2:14	±2:18	±2:00	±1:45	±1:37	±1:39	±1:44
	Rise 15th	7:59	7:29	6:46	5:54	5:15	4:59	5:13	5:43	6:15	6:46	7:23	7:54
	Set 15th	5:29	6:08	6:41	7:15	7:47	8:10	8:07	7:34	6:43	5:53	5:14	5:05
	Twl	±1:42	±1:37	±1:37	±1:45	±2:02	±2:19	±2:11	±1:51	±1:40	±1:37	±1:41	±1:44
OK **Blackwell** 36°55' N 97°20' W TZ **6** (5)	Rise 1st	7:43	7:32	7:00	6:15	5:35	5:11	5:14	5:35	6:00	6:25	6:54	7:24
	Set 1st	5:24	5:55	6:24	6:52	7:18	7:43	7:53	7:36	6:58	6:12	5:32	5:13
	Twl	±1:37	±1:33	±1:30	±1:32	±1:43	±1:56	±1:57	±1:47	±1:36	±1:32	±1:32	±1:37
	Rise 15th	7:41	7:18	6:40	5:55	5:21	5:09	5:22	5:46	6:12	6:37	7:08	7:35
	Set 15th	5:37	6:10	6:37	7:04	7:30	7:50	7:48	7:21	6:37	5:53	5:20	5:14
	Twl	±1:35	±1:31	±1:30	±1:36	±1:49	±1:59	±1:54	±1:41	±1:32	±1:31	±1:34	±1:37
Oklahoma City 35°25' N 97°30' W TZ **6** (5)	Rise 1st	7:39	7:29	7:00	6:16	5:38	5:16	5:19	5:39	6:02	6:25	6:52	7:21
	Set 1st	5:29	5:58	6:26	6:52	7:16	7:40	7:49	7:33	6:57	6:14	5:35	5:17
	Twl	±1:34	±1:31	±1:28	±1:30	±1:40	±1:51	±1:54	±1:44	±1:33	±1:29	±1:30	±1:34
	Rise 15th	7:39	7:16	6:41	5:57	5:25	5:14	5:26	5:49	6:13	6:36	7:06	7:32
	Set 15th	5:41	6:12	6:38	7:03	7:28	7:47	7:45	7:19	6:37	5:55	5:24	5:19
	Twl	±1:33	±1:30	±1:28	±1:34	±1:44	±1:54	±1:50	±1:38	±1:30	±1:29	±1:32	±1:36
Tulsa 36°10' N 96°00' W TZ **6** (5)	Rise 1st	7:35	7:25	6:54	6:10	5:31	5:08	5:10	5:31	5:56	6:19	6:47	7:17
	Set 1st	5:21	5:51	6:19	6:46	7:12	7:36	7:45	7:29	6:52	6:07	5:28	5:09
	Twl	±1:35	±1:32	±1:29	±1:31	±1:40	±1:52	±1:56	±1:45	±1:34	±1:31	±1:31	±1:35

➤ **Sunrises & Sunsets HAVE NOT been adjusted for Daylight-Saving Time.**

SunRISE & SET

Sunrises & Sunsets

Oklahoma/Oregon

		JAN	FEB	MAR	APR	MAY	JUN	JUL	AUG	SEP	OCT	NOV	DEC
Tulsa	Rise 15th	7:34	7:11	6:35	5:51	5:18	5:06	5:18	5:42	6:07	6:31	7:01	7:28
	Set 15th	5:33	6:05	6:32	6:58	7:23	7:43	7:41	7:14	6:31	5:48	5:16	5:11
	Twl	±1:34	±1:31	±1:29	±1:35	±1:47	±1:57	±1:52	±1:40	±1:31	±1:30	±1:33	±1:36
OR **Burns** 43°40′N 119°04′W TZ **8** (7)	Rise 1st	7:30	7:13	6:32	5:38	4:48	4:17	4:19	4:46	5:20	5:54	6:32	7:10
	Set 1st	4:30	5:08	5:45	6:23	6:59	7:31	7:42	7:19	6:31	5:37	4:47	4:21
	Twl	±1:49	±1:42	±1:40	±1:45	±1:59	±2:25	±2:31	±2:07	±1:49	±1:41	±1:42	±1:47
	Rise 15th	7:27	6:55	6:08	5:13	4:31	4:14	4:29	5:01	5:36	6:11	6:51	7:23
	Set 15th	4:45	5:27	6:03	6:40	7:15	7:40	7:35	7:00	6:06	5:13	4:31	4:20
	Twl	±1:47	±1:40	±1:40	±1:49	±2:10	±2:32	±2:22	±1:57	±1:44	±1:40	±1:44	±1:49
Medford 42°20′N 122°52′W TZ **8** (7)	Rise 1st	7:41	7:25	6:46	5:54	5:06	4:37	4:39	5:04	5:37	6:09	6:45	7:21
	Set 1st	4:50	5:26	6:02	6:38	7:11	7:42	7:52	7:31	6:45	5:53	5:05	4:40
	Twl	±1:45	±1:40	±1:37	±1:41	±1:56	±2:16	±2:22	±2:02	±1:46	±1:38	±1:40	±1:45
	Rise 15th	7:38	7:08	6:23	5:30	4:50	4:34	4:48	5:19	5:52	6:25	7:03	7:34
	Set 15th	5:05	5:44	6:18	6:53	7:26	7:50	7:46	7:12	6:21	5:29	4:49	4:40
	Twl	±1:43	±1:38	±1:39	±1:47	±2:06	±2:24	±2:14	±1:54	±1:41	±1:39	±1:43	±1:45
Ontario 44°01′N 117°01′W TZ **7** (6)	Rise 1st	8:23	8:05	7:25	6:29	5:39	5:08	5:09	5:36	6:12	6:46	7:25	8:03
	Set 1st	5:21	5:59	6:37	7:15	7:52	8:24	8:35	8:12	7:24	6:29	5:38	5:11
	Twl	±1:49	±1:43	±1:40	±1:45	±2:01	±2:27	±2:33	±2:09	±1:49	±1:41	±1:43	±1:48
	Rise 15th	8:20	7:47	7:00	6:04	5:22	5:04	5:19	5:52	6:27	7:03	7:43	8:16
	Set 15th	5:36	6:18	6:55	7:32	8:08	8:33	8:28	7:52	6:58	6:04	5:22	5:11
	Twl	±1:47	±1:41	±1:40	±1:51	±2:12	±2:35	±2:24	±1:58	±1:44	±1:41	±1:45	±1:49
Portland 45°35′N 122°40′W TZ **8** (7)	Rise 1st	7:51	7:32	6:49	5:51	4:58	4:25	4:26	4:55	5:32	6:09	6:51	7:31
	Set 1st	4:38	5:18	5:58	6:39	7:18	7:52	8:03	7:38	6:48	5:51	4:57	4:29
	Twl	±1:52	±1:46	±1:42	±1:48	±2:07	±2:40	±2:49	±2:16	±1:53	±1:44	±1:46	±1:51
	Rise 15th	7:47	7:12	6:23	5:25	4:40	4:21	4:37	5:12	5:49	6:27	7:10	7:44
	Set 15th	4:54	5:38	6:17	6:57	7:35	8:01	7:56	7:18	6:21	5:25	4:40	4:28
	Twl	±1:49	±1:44	±1:44	±1:55	±2:20	±2:52	±2:35	±2:04	±1:48	±1:44	±1:49	±1:53

➙ **Sunrises & Sunsets HAVE NOT been adjusted for Daylight-Saving Time.**

Sunrises & Sunsets

Pennsylvania

		JAN	FEB	MAR	APR	MAY	JUN	JUL	AUG	SEP	OCT	NOV	DEC
PA	Rise 1st	7:49	7:34	6:56	6:03	5:16	5447	4:48	5:14	5:46	6:18	6:54	7:30
Erie	Set 1st	4:59	5:35	6:11	6:46	7:20	7:50	8:00	7:39	6:54	6:02	5:14	4:49
42°10' N	Twl	±1:46	±1:40	±1:37	±1:41	±1:55	±2:16	±2:21	±2:02	±1:45	±1:38	±1:40	±1:45
80°07' W	Rise 15th	7:46	7:17	6:32	5:40	4:59	4:44	4:58	5:28	6:01	6:33	7:11	7:42
TZ 5 (4)	Set 15th	5:14	5:53	6:27	7:02	7:35	7:58	7:55	7:21	6:30	5:39	4:59	4:49
	Twl	±1:43	±1:38	±1:38	±1:46	±2:04	±2:23	±2:14	±1:53	±1:41	±1:38	±1:42	±1:46
Harrisburg	Rise 1st	7:30	7:16	6:41	5:51	5:07	4:40	4:42	5:06	5:35	6:04	6:37	7:11
40°18' N	Set 1st	4:53	5:27	5:59	6:32	7:03	7:31	7:41	7:21	6:39	5:50	5:05	4:42
76°52' W	Twl	±1:41	±1:36	±1:35	±1:37	±1:49	±2:07	±2:11	±1:57	±1:42	±1:35	±1:36	±1:41
TZ 5 (4)	Rise 15th	7:28	7:00	6:19	5:29	4:52	4:37	4:51	5:19	5:48	6:18	6:53	7:23
	Set 15th	5:07	5:43	6:15	6:46	7:17	7:39	7:36	7:04	6:16	5:28	4:51	4:43
	Twl	±1:39	±1:35	±1:35	±1:43	±1:57	±2:12	±2:05	±1:49	±1:38	±1:35	±1:39	±1:42
Philadelphia	Rise 1st	7:22	7:09	6:34	5:44	5:01	4:34	4:36	4:59	5:28	5:57	6:30	7:03
40°00' N	Set 1st	4:46	5:20	5:53	6:25	6:55	7:23	7:33	7:14	6:32	5:43	4:58	4:36
75°10' W	Twl	±1:41	±1:37	±1:34	±1:37	±1:49	±2:07	±2:10	±1:55	±1:41	±1:35	±1:36	±1:41
TZ 5 (4)	Rise 15th	7:21	6:53	6:12	5:23	4:45	4:31	4:45	5:12	5:42	6:11	6:46	7:15
	Set 15th	5:00	5:37	6:08	6:39	7:09	7:31	7:28	6:57	6:09	5:21	4:44	4:36
	Twl	±1:40	±1:35	±1:34	±1:42	±1:57	±2:11	±2:04	±1:48	±1:37	±1:35	±1:39	±1:43
Pittsburgh	Rise 1st	7:43	7:29	6:54	6:04	5:19	4:52	4:54	5:17	5:47	6:17	6:50	7:24
40°25' N	Set 1st	5:04	5:39	6:12	6:45	7:16	7:44	7:54	7:35	6:52	6:02	5:17	4:54
79°55' W	Twl	±1:42	±1:37	±1:34	±1:37	±1:49	±2:08	±2:12	±1:56	±1:41	±1:35	±1:36	±1:41
TZ 5 (4)	Rise 15th	7:41	7:13	6:31	5:41	5:04	4:49	5:03	5:31	6:01	6:31	7:06	7:36
	Set 15th	5:18	5:56	6:27	6:59	7:30	7:52	7:49	7:17	6:29	5:40	5:03	4:54
	Twl	±1:40	±1:35	±1:34	±1:42	±1:58	±2:13	±2:06	±1:49	±1:37	±1:35	±1:39	±1:43
Scranton	Rise 1st	7:29	7:14	6:37	5:46	5:00	4:32	4:33	4:58	5:29	6:00	6:34	7:09
41°22' N	Set 1st	4:44	5:19	5:54	6:28	7:00	7:30	7:40	7:20	6:35	5:44	4:58	4:34
75°41' W	Twl	±1:44	±1:39	±1:35	±1:40	±1:53	±2:12	±2:16	±1:59	±1:44	±1:38	±1:39	±1:44
TZ 5 (4)													

➡ **Sunrises & Sunsets HAVE NOT been adjusted for Daylight-Saving Time.**

Sunrises & Sunsets

Pennsylvania/Rhode Island/South Carolina

		JAN	FEB	MAR	APR	MAY	JUN	JUL	AUG	SEP	OCT	NOV	DEC
Scranton	Rise 15th	7:26	6:58	6:14	5:23	4:44	4:29	4:42	5:12	5:43	6:15	6:51	7:22
	Set 15th	4:58	5:37	6:10	6:43	7:15	7:38	7:35	7:02	6:12	5:22	4:43	4:34
	Twl	±1:42	±1:37	±1:36	±1:45	±2:01	±2:17	±2:09	±1:51	±1:39	±1:37	±1:41	±1:44
RI **Providence** 41°50' N 71°28' W TZ **5** (4)	Rise 1st	7:14	6:58	6:21	5:29	4:42	4:13	4:15	4:40	5:12	5:43	6:18	6:54
	Set 1st	4:26	5:01	5:36	6:12	6:44	7:15	7:25	7:04	6:19	5:27	4:40	4:16
	Twl	±1:45	±1:40	±1:37	±1:40	±1:54	±2:13	±2:19	±2:01	±1:45	±1:38	±1:40	±1:44
	Rise 15th	7:11	6:41	5:58	5:06	4:26	4:10	4:24	4:54	5:26	5:58	6:36	7:06
	Set 15th	4:40	5:19	5:53	6:27	6:59	7:23	7:19	6:46	5:55	5:04	4:25	4:16
	Twl	±1:43	±1:38	±1:37	±1:45	±2:03	±2:20	±2:13	±1:53	±1:40	±1:38	±1:42	±1:45
SC **Charleston** 32°47' N 79°56' W TZ **5** (4)	Rise 1st	7:22	7:15	6:48	6:08	5:33	5:13	5:15	5:33	5:54	6:14	6:37	7:04
	Set 1st	5:25	5:52	6:17	6:40	7:01	7:23	7:32	7:18	6:45	6:05	5:29	5:13
	Twl	±1:32	±1:28	±1:26	±1:28	±1:36	±1:45	±1:47	±1:39	±1:29	±1:26	±1:27	±1:32
	Rise 15th	7:22	7:03	6:30	5:50	5:21	5:11	5:22	5:43	6:03	6:24	6:50	7:15
	Set 15th	5:36	6:05	6:28	6:50	7:12	7:29	7:29	7:05	6:26	5:47	5:19	5:15
	Twl	±1:31	±1:27	±1:26	±1:30	±1:40	±1:47	±1:44	±1:34	±1:28	±1:26	±1:29	±1:32
Columbia 34°00' N 81°00' W TZ **5** (4)	Rise 1st	7:30	7:21	6:53	6:12	5:35	5:14	5:16	5:35	5:58	6:18	6:43	7:11
	Set 1st	5:26	5:55	6:20	6:45	7:08	7:30	7:39	7:25	6:50	6:08	5:31	5:15
	Twl	±1:33	±1:29	±1:28	±1:29	±1:37	±1:47	±1:50	±1:40	±1:32	±1:28	±1:29	±1:32
	Rise 15th	7:29	7:09	6:35	5:53	5:23	5:12	5:24	5:45	6:07	6:29	6:56	7:22
	Set 15th	5:38	6:08	6:32	6:55	7:18	7:37	7:36	7:11	6:31	5:50	5:21	5:16
	Twl	±1:32	±1:28	±1:27	±1:33	±1:43	±1:50	±1:46	±1:36	±1:28	±1:28	±1:30	±1:34
Myrtle Beach 33°43' N 78°50' W TZ **5** (4)	Rise 1st	7:20	7:12	6:44	6:03	5:27	5:06	5:08	5:27	5:49	6:10	6:34	7:02
	Set 1st	5:18	5:46	6:12	6:36	6:59	7:21	7:30	7:16	6:41	6:00	5:23	5:07
	Twl	±1:33	±1:29	±1:27	±1:29	±1:37	±1:47	±1:49	±1:40	±1:30	±1:27	±1:28	±1:32
	Rise 15th	7:20	7:00	6:26	5:45	5:15	5:04	5:16	5:37	5:59	6:20	6:47	7:13
	Set 15th	5:30	6:00	6:23	6:46	7:09	7:27	7:27	7:02	6:22	5:42	5:12	5:08
	Twl	±1:32	±1:28	±1:27	±1:32	±1:42	±1:49	±1:46	±1:35	±1:28	±1:27	±1:31	±1:33

→ **Sunrises & Sunsets HAVE NOT been adjusted for Daylight-Saving Time.**

SunRISE & SET

Sunrises & Sunsets

South Dakota

		JAN	FEB	MAR	APR	MAY	JUN	JUL	AUG	SEP	OCT	NOV	DEC
SD Aberdeen	Rise 1st	8:14	7:55	7:12	6:14	5:22	4:49	4:49	5:18	5:56	6:32	7:14	7:54
45°30' N 98°30' W	Set 1st	5:02	5:41	6:21	7:02	7:41	8:16	8:26	8:02	7:11	6:14	5:21	4:52
	Twl	±1:51	±1:46	±1:43	±1:49	±2:05	±2:38	±2:48	±2:15	±1:53	±1:45	±1:46	±1:51
TZ 6 (5)	Rise 15th	8:10	7:36	6:46	5:48	5:03	4:45	5:00	5:35	6:13	6:51	7:33	8:07
	Set 15th	5:17	6:01	6:40	7:21	7:58	8:25	8:20	7:41	6:45	5:48	5:04	4:51
	Twl	±1:50	±1:44	±1:44	±1:54	±2:20	±2:50	±2:34	±2:04	±1:48	±1:44	±1:48	±1:53
Mitchell	Rise 1st	8:06	7:48	7:08	6:13	5:24	4:53	4:54	5:21	5:56	6:30	7:08	7:46
43°40' N 98°00' W	Set 1st	5:06	5:43	6:21	6:59	7:35	8:07	8:17	7:55	7:07	6:13	5:23	4:56
	Twl	±1:49	±1:43	±1:39	±1:44	±1:59	±2:24	±2:31	±2:07	±1:49	±1:40	±1:42	±1:47
TZ 6 (5)	Rise 15th	8:02	7:30	6:44	5:49	5:07	4:50	5:04	5:37	6:12	6:46	7:26	7:59
	Set 15th	5:21	6:03	6:39	7:16	7:51	8:15	8:11	7:35	6:42	5:48	5:07	4:56
	Twl	±1:46	±1:40	±1:40	±1:49	±2:10	±2:33	±2:21	±1:58	±1:44	±1:41	±1:44	±1:49
Pierre	Rise 1st	8:17	7:59	7:18	6:22	5:32	5:00	5:01	5:29	6:04	6:39	7:19	7:57
44°23' N 100°20' W	Set 1st	5:13	5:51	6:30	7:09	7:46	8:19	8:29	8:06	7:17	6:22	5:31	5:03
	Twl	±1:50	±1:43	±1:40	±1:45	±2:01	±2:30	±2:38	±2:11	±1:50	±1:42	±1:43	±1:50
TZ 6 (5)	Rise 15th	8:14	7:41	6:53	5:57	5:14	4:57	5:11	5:45	6:21	6:57	7:37	8:10
	Set 15th	5:28	6:11	6:48	7:26	8:02	8:27	8:23	7:46	6:52	5:57	5:14	5:03
	Twl	±1:48	±1:41	±1:41	±1:52	±2:14	±2:39	±2:26	±2:00	±1:45	±1:42	±1:46	±1:50
Rapid City	Rise 1st	7:27	7:09	6:28	5:33	4:43	4:12	4:13	4:40	5:15	5:50	6:28	7:07
44°00' N 103°00' W	Set 1st	4:25	5:02	5:40	6:19	6:55	7:28	7:38	7:15	6:27	5:32	4:42	4:15
	Twl	±1:49	±1:43	±1:40	±1:45	±2:01	±2:27	±2:34	±2:09	±1:50	±1:42	±1:43	±1:48
TZ 7 (6)	Rise 15th	7:23	6:51	6:04	5:08	4:25	4:08	4:23	4:56	5:31	6:07	6:47	7:20
	Set 15th	4:40	5:22	5:58	6:36	7:11	7:36	7:32	6:56	6:02	5:08	4:26	4:14
	Twl	±1:47	±1:41	±1:41	±1:51	±2:13	±2:36	±2:24	±1:58	±1:44	±1:41	±1:45	±1:50
Sioux Falls	Rise 1st	8:00	7:43	7:03	6:08	5:19	4:48	4:49	5:16	5:50	6:24	7:02	7:40
43°35' N 96°40' W	Set 1st	5:01	5:38	6:15	6:53	7:29	8:01	8:11	7:49	7:01	6:07	5:17	4:51
TZ 6 (5)	Twl	±1:48	±1:42	±1:40	±1:45	±1:59	±2:25	±2:31	±2:08	±1:49	±1:41	±1:43	±1:47

→ Sunrises & Sunsets HAVE NOT been adjusted for Daylight-Saving Time.

SunRISE & SET

339

Sunrises & Sunsets

South Dakota/Tennessee

		JAN	FEB	MAR	APR	MAY	JUN	JUL	AUG	SEP	OCT	NOV	DEC
Sioux Falls	Rise 15th	7:57	7:25	6:38	5:43	5:01	4:44	4:59	5:31	6:06	6:41	7:21	7:53
	Set 15th	5:16	5:57	6:33	7:10	7:45	8:09	8:05	7:30	6:36	5:43	5:01	4:50
	Twl	±1:46	±1:40	±1:40	±1:49	±2:10	±2:32	±2:22	±1:57	±1:44	±1:41	±1:45	±1:49
TN **Chattanooga** 35°02′ N 85°17′ W TZ **5** (4)	Rise 1st	7:49	7:40	7:11	6:28	5:50	5:28	5:31	5:50	6:14	6:36	7:02	7:31
	Set 1st	5:40	6:10	6:37	7:02	7:27	7:50	7:59	7:44	7:08	6:25	5:47	5:29
	Twl	±1:35	±1:30	±1:28	±1:31	±1:39	±1:50	±1:53	±1:43	±1:33	±1:29	±1:30	±1:34
	Rise 15th	7:49	7:27	6:52	6:09	5:38	5:27	5:38	6:01	6:24	6:47	7:16	7:42
	Set 15th	5:53	6:24	6:49	7:14	7:38	7:57	7:56	7:29	6:48	6:06	5:36	5:31
	Twl	±1:33	±1:29	±1:28	±1:33	±1:44	±1:53	±1:48	±1:38	±1:30	±1:29	±1:31	±1:34
Knoxville 35°58′ N 83°57′ W TZ **5** (4)	Rise 1st	7:46	7:36	7:06	6:22	5:43	5:21	5:23	5:43	6:08	6:31	6:58	7:28
	Set 1st	5:33	6:03	6:31	6:58	7:23	7:47	7:56	7:41	7:04	6:20	5:40	5:22
	Twl	±1:35	±1:31	±1:29	±1:31	±1:40	±1:52	±1:55	±1:44	±1:33	±1:29	±1:31	±1:34
	Rise 15th	7:46	7:23	6:47	6:03	5:30	5:19	5:31	5:54	6:18	6:42	7:12	7:39
	Set 15th	5:45	6:17	6:43	7:09	7:35	7:54	7:53	7:26	6:43	6:00	5:28	5:23
	Twl	±1:34	±1:30	±1:30	±1:36	±1:46	±1:55	±1:49	±1:40	±1:31	±1:30	±1:33	±1:36
Memphis 35°07′ N 90°00′ W TZ **6** (5)	Rise 1st	7:08	6:59	6:30	5:47	5:09	4:47	4:49	5:09	5:33	5:55	6:21	6:50
	Set 1st	4:59	5:29	5:56	6:21	6:46	7:09	7:18	7:03	6:27	5:44	5:06	4:48
	Twl	±1:34	±1:30	±1:28	±1:31	±1:39	±1:50	±1:53	±1:43	±1:33	±1:29	±1:29	±1:34
	Rise 15th	7:08	6:46	6:11	5:28	4:56	4:45	4:57	5:20	5:43	6:06	6:35	7:01
	Set 15th	5:11	5:43	6:08	6:33	6:57	7:16	7:15	6:49	6:07	5:25	4:54	4:49
	Twl	±1:34	±1:29	±1:28	±1:33	±1:44	±1:53	±1:49	±1:38	±1:30	±1:29	±1:32	±1:35
Nashville 36°12′ N 86°46′ W TZ **6** (5)	Rise 1st	6:58	6:48	6:18	5:33	4:54	4:31	4:33	4:54	5:19	5:42	6:10	6:40
	Set 1st	4:43	5:14	5:42	6:09	6:35	6:59	7:08	6:52	6:15	5:31	4:51	4:33
	Twl	±1:36	±1:31	±1:29	±1:32	±1:40	±1:54	±1:56	±1:45	±1:34	±1:30	±1:31	±1:35
	Rise 15th	6:58	6:35	5:58	5:14	4:41	4:29	4:41	5:05	5:29	5:54	6:24	6:51
	Set 15th	4:56	5:28	5:54	6:21	6:46	7:06	7:04	6:37	5:55	5:11	4:39	4:34
	Twl	±1:34	±1:31	±1:30	±1:35	±1:47	±1:57	±1:52	±1:40	±1:31	±1:30	±1:33	±1:36

→ **Sunrises & Sunsets HAVE NOT been adjusted for Daylight-Saving Time.**

Sunrises & Sunsets

Texas

		JAN	FEB	MAR	APR	MAY	JUN	JUL	AUG	SEP	OCT	NOV	DEC
TX Corpus Christi 27°50' N 97°28' W TZ **6** (5)	Rise 1st	7:21	7:17	6:54	6:20	5:50	5:34	5:37	5:53	6:09	6:23	6:41	7:04
	Set 1st	5:46	6:11	6:30	6:48	7:04	7:22	7:30	7:19	6:51	6:16	5:46	5:34
	Twl	±1:27	±1:23	±1:22	±1:23	±1:29	±1:36	±1:38	±1:32	±1:24	±1:21	±1:23	±1:27
	Rise 15th	7:22	7:07	6:40	6:05	5:41	5:33	5:44	6:00	6:15	6:30	6:51	7:13
	Set 15th	5:57	6:21	6:39	6:55	7:12	7:27	7:28	7:08	6:35	6:01	5:38	5:37
	Twl	±1:26	±1:23	±1:21	±1:25	±1:32	±1:38	±1:35	±1:28	±1:22	±1:22	±1:25	±1:27
Dallas 32°50' N 96°50' W TZ **6** (5)	Rise 1st	7:30	7:22	6:55	6:15	5:40	5:20	5:23	5:41	6:02	6:21	6:45	7:12
	Set 1st	5:32	6:00	6:24	6:47	7:09	7:30	7:39	7:26	6:52	6:12	5:36	5:21
	Twl	±1:32	±1:28	±1:27	±1:29	±1:35	±1:46	±1:47	±1:38	±1:30	±1:27	±1:28	±1:31
	Rise 15th	7:30	7:10	6:38	5:58	5:28	5:19	5:30	5:51	6:11	6:31	6:57	7:22
	Set 15th	5:44	6:13	6:35	6:57	7:19	7:37	7:36	7:12	6:33	5:54	5:26	5:23
	Twl	±1:31	±1:27	±1:26	±1:32	±1:41	±1:47	±1:45	±1:35	±1:28	±1:27	±1:29	±1:32
El Paso 31°50' N 106°30' W TZ **7** (6)	Rise 1st	7:06	6:59	6:33	5:55	5:20	5:01	5:04	5:22	5:41	6:00	6:22	6:48
	Set 1st	5:13	5:40	6:04	6:26	6:46	7:07	7:16	7:03	6:30	5:51	5:16	5:02
	Twl	±1:31	±1:27	±1:25	±1:27	±1:34	±1:43	±1:45	±1:37	±1:29	±1:25	±1:27	±1:30
	Rise 15th	7:07	6:48	6:16	5:37	5:09	5:00	5:11	5:31	5:50	6:09	6:34	6:59
	Set 15th	5:25	5:53	6:14	6:35	6:56	7:13	7:13	6:50	6:12	5:34	5:07	5:04
	Twl	±1:29	±1:26	±1:25	±1:29	±1:38	±1:45	±1:42	±1:32	±1:27	±1:25	±1:28	±1:31
Houston 29°50' N 95°20' W TZ **6** (5)	Rise 1st	7:17	7:11	6:47	6:11	5:39	5:21	5:24	5:41	5:58	6:15	6:35	6:59
	Set 1st	5:33	5:59	6:21	6:40	6:58	7:17	7:26	7:14	6:44	6:07	5:35	5:21
	Twl	±1:29	±1:25	±1:23	±1:24	±1:32	±1:40	±1:41	±1:34	±1:27	±1:23	±1:24	±1:29
	Rise 15th	7:18	7:01	6:31	5:55	5:28	5:20	5:31	5:49	6:06	6:23	6:46	7:09
	Set 15th	5:44	6:10	6:30	6:48	7:07	7:24	7:24	7:02	6:27	5:51	5:26	5:24
	Twl	±1:28	±1:24	±1:23	±1:28	±1:36	±1:41	±1:38	±1:30	±1:25	±1:24	±1:26	±1:29
Lubbock 33°40' N 101°53' W TZ **6** (5)	Rise 1st	7:52	7:44	7:16	6:35	5:59	5:38	5:41	6:00	6:21	6:42	7:07	7:34
	Set 1st	5:50	6:19	6:44	7:08	7:31	7:53	8:02	7:48	7:13	6:32	5:55	5:39
	Twl	±1:33	±1:29	±1:27	±1:29	±1:37	±1:47	±1:49	±1:40	±1:31	±1:27	±1:29	±1:32

➡ **Sunrises & Sunsets HAVE NOT been adjusted for Daylight-Saving Time.**

SunRISE & SET

341

Sunrises & Sunsets

Texas/Utah

		JAN	FEB	MAR	APR	MAY	JUN	JUL	AUG	SEP	OCT	NOV	DEC
Lubbock	Rise 15th	7:52	7:32	6:58	6:17	5:47	5:37	5:48	6:10	6:31	6:52	7:19	7:45
	Set 15th	6:02	6:32	6:55	7:19	7:41	7:59	7:59	7:34	6:54	6:13	5:45	5:41
	Twl	±1:32	±1:28	±1:27	±1:31	±1:42	±1:49	±1:45	±1:35	±1:29	±1:28	±1:30	±1:33
San Angelo	Rise 1st	7:41	7:35	7:09	6:31	5:57	5:38	5:41	5:58	6:18	6:36	6:58	7:24
31°30′ N 100°30′ W	Set 1st	5:50	6:17	6:40	6:01	7:22	7:42	7:51	7:38	7:06	6:27	5:53	5:39
	Twl	±1:31	±1:27	±1:25	±1:26	±1:33	±1:43	±1:43	±1:36	±1:28	±1:25	±1:26	±1:30
TZ 6 (5)	Rise 15th	7:42	7:24	6:52	6:14	5:46	5:37	5:48	6:07	6:26	6:45	7:10	7:34
	Set 15th	6:01	6:29	6:50	7:11	7:31	7:48	7:48	7:25	6:48	6:10	5:43	5:41
	Twl	±1:29	±1:26	±1:25	±1:29	±1:38	±1:45	±1:41	±1:33	±1:26	±1:25	±1:28	±1:31
San Antonio	Rise 1st	7:29	7:24	7:00	6:24	5:52	5:35	5:38	5:54	6:11	6:27	6:47	7:11
29°30′ N 98°30′ W	Set 1st	5:47	6:12	6:34	6:53	7:11	7:29	7:38	7:26	6:56	6:20	5:48	5:35
	Twl	±1:28	±1:25	±1:23	±1:24	±1:30	±1:40	±1:40	±1:34	±1:26	±1:22	±1:24	±1:28
TZ 6 (5)	Rise 15th	7:30	7:13	6:44	6:08	5:42	5:34	5:44	6:02	6:19	6:36	6:58	7:21
	Set 15th	5:58	6:23	6:42	7:01	7:19	7:35	7:36	7:15	6:39	6:04	5:39	5:37
	Twl	±1:27	±1:24	±1:24	±1:27	±1:35	±1:41	±1:37	±1:29	±1:24	±1:23	±1:26	±1:30
UT **Cedar City**	Rise 1st	7:48	7:36	7:03	6:17	5:36	5:12	5:14	5:36	6:02	6:28	6:58	7:29
37°41′ N 113°03′ W	Set 1st	5:25	5:56	6:26	6:55	7:23	7:48	7:58	7:40	7:01	6:15	5:34	5:14
	Twl	±1:38	±1:34	±1:31	±1:34	±1:44	±1:58	±2:00	±1:48	±1:37	±1:32	±1:32	±1:37
TZ 7 (6)	Rise 15th	7:46	7:22	6:43	5:57	5:22	5:10	5:23	5:48	6:14	6:41	7:13	7:40
	Set 15th	5:38	6:12	6:40	7:08	7:35	7:56	7:53	7:25	6:40	5:55	5:21	5:15
	Twl	±1:36	±1:32	±1:31	±1:37	±1:50	±2:04	±1:57	±1:43	±1:34	±1:32	±1:35	±1:38
Richfield	Rise 1st	7:47	7:34	7:00	6:12	5:30	5:05	5:07	5:29	5:57	6:24	6:55	7:28
38°50′ N 112°00′ W	Set 1st	5:17	5:50	6:21	6:52	7:21	7:47	7:57	7:39	6:58	6:10	5:27	5:07
	Twl	±1:40	±1:35	±1:32	±1:35	±1:46	±2:00	±2:05	±1:51	±1:39	±1:34	±1:35	±1:39
TZ 7 (6)	Rise 15th	7:45	7:19	6:39	5:51	5:15	5:02	5:15	5:42	6:10	6:38	7:11	7:39
	Set 15th	5:31	6:06	6:35	7:05	7:34	7:55	7:52	7:22	6:36	5:49	5:14	5:07
	Twl	±1:36	±1:33	±1:33	±1:40	±1:53	±2:06	±2:01	±1:46	±1:36	±1:34	±1:36	±1:40

→ Sunrises & Sunsets HAVE NOT been adjusted for Daylight-Saving Time.

Sunrises & Sunsets

Utah/Vermont/Virginia

		JAN	FEB	MAR	APR	MAY	JUN	JUL	AUG	SEP	OCT	NOV	DEC
Salt Lake City	Rise 1st	7:52	7:37	7:01	6:11	5:26	4:59	5:00	5:24	5:55	6:24	6:58	7:33
	Set 1st	5:11	5:46	6:19	6:53	7:24	7:53	8:03	7:43	7:00	6:09	5:24	5:01
40°45' N *111°58' W*	Twl	±1:43	±1:38	±1:35	±1:39	±1:51	±2:09	±2:14	±1:57	±1:42	±1:37	±1:38	±1:42
TZ **7** (6)	Rise 15th	7:50	7:21	6:39	5:49	5:10	4:56	5:09	5:38	6:08	6:39	7:15	7:45
	Set 15th	5:25	6:03	6:35	7:07	7:36	8:01	7:58	7:25	6:36	5:47	5:09	5:01
	Twl	±1:41	±1:36	±1:36	±1:44	±2:02	±2:14	±2:07	±1:50	±1:39	±1:36	±1:41	±1:44
VT **Barre**	Rise 1st	7:26	7:08	6:27	5:31	4:41	4:09	4:10	4:38	5:13	5:48	6:27	7:06
	Set 1st	4:22	5:00	5:38	6:17	6:54	7:27	7:37	7:14	6:26	5:31	4:40	4:12
44°15' N *72°30' W*	Twl	±1:49	±1:43	±1:41	±1:46	±2:01	±2:28	±2:36	±2:11	±1:50	±1:41	±1:43	±1:48
TZ **5** (4)	Rise 15th	7:22	6:49	6:02	5:06	4:23	4:06	4:20	4:53	5:29	6:05	6:46	7:19
	Set 15th	4:37	5:19	5:56	6:35	7:10	7:36	7:31	6:55	6:00	5:06	4:23	4:12
	Twl	±1:47	±1:42	±1:42	±1:51	±2:14	±2:37	±2:25	±1:59	±1:45	±1:41	±1:45	±1:49
Burlington	Rise 1st	7:29	7:11	6:30	5:34	4:43	4:11	4:12	4:40	5:18	5:51	6:30	7:09
44°27' N *73°14' W*	Set 1st	4:24	5:02	5:41	6:20	6:57	7:31	7:41	7:18	6:29	5:33	4:42	4:15
TZ **5** (4)	Twl	±1:50	±1:44	±1:41	±1:46	±2:02	±2:29	±2:37	±2:11	±1:50	±1:43	±1:44	±1:49
	Rise 15th	7:26	6:53	6:05	5:09	4:25	4:08	4:22	4:56	5:32	6:08	6:49	7:22
	Set 15th	4:39	5:22	5:59	6:38	7:14	7:39	7:35	6:58	6:03	5:08	4:25	4:14
	Twl	±1:48	±1:42	±1:42	±1:51	±2:13	±2:39	±2:26	±2:00	±1:45	±1:43	±1:46	±1:50
VA **Norfolk**	Rise 1st	7:18	7:07	6:36	5:51	5:11	4:48	4:50	5:11	5:36	6:00	6:29	6:59
	Set 1st	5:00	5:31	6:00	6:27	6:54	7:18	7:28	7:11	6:33	5:48	5:08	4:49
36°40' N *76°15' W*	Twl	±1:37	±1:33	±1:29	±1:32	±1:41	±1:54	±1:57	±1:47	±1:35	±1:31	±1:32	±1:37
TZ **5** (4)	Rise 15th	7:17	6:53	6:16	5:31	4:58	4:46	4:58	5:22	5:47	6:13	6:43	7:10
	Set 15th	5:13	5:46	6:13	6:40	7:06	7:25	7:24	6:56	6:12	5:28	4:56	4:50
	Twl	±1:35	±1:31	±1:29	±1:35	±1:47	±1:58	±1:53	±1:41	±1:32	±1:31	±1:34	±1:38
Richmond	Rise 1st	7:25	7:13	6:41	5:55	5:14	4:50	4:52	5:14	5:40	6:05	6:35	7:06
37°33' N *77°27' W*	Set 1st	5:03	5:34	6:04	6:33	7:00	7:26	7:35	7:18	6:39	5:53	5:11	4:52
TZ **5** (4)	Twl	±1:37	±1:34	±1:31	±1:34	±1:43	±1:57	±2:00	±1:49	±1:37	±1:32	±1:33	±1:37

→ **Sunrises & Sunsets HAVE NOT been adjusted for Daylight-Saving Time.**

Sunrises & Sunsets

Virginia/Washington

		JAN	FEB	MAR	APR	MAY	JUN	JUL	AUG	SEP	OCT	NOV	DEC
Richmond	Rise 15th	7:23	6:59	6:21	5:35	5:00	4:48	5:01	5:26	5:52	6:18	6:50	7:17
	Set 15th	5:16	5:49	6:17	6:45	7:12	7:33	7:31	7:02	6:17	5:32	4:59	4:53
	Twl	±1:35	±1:32	±1:31	±1:37	±1:50	±2:01	±1:55	±1:43	±1:35	±1:32	±1:35	±1:38
Roanoke	Rise 1st	7:34	7:23	6:51	6:05	5:25	5:01	5:03	5:24	5:50	6:15	6:44	7:15
37° 19' N	Set 1st	5:13	5:44	6:14	6:42	7:09	7:35	7:44	7:27	6:48	6:03	5:22	5:02
79° 55' W	Twl	±1:38	±1:34	±1:30	±1:34	±1:43	±1:56	±1:59	±1:48	±1:37	±1:31	±1:32	±1:37
TZ **5** (4)	Rise 15th	7:33	7:09	6:31	5:45	5:11	4:59	5:11	5:36	6:02	6:28	6:59	7:27
	Set 15th	5:26	6:00	6:27	6:55	7:22	7:42	7:40	7:12	6:27	5:43	5:09	5:03
	Twl	±1:36	±1:31	±1:31	±1:37	±1:49	±2:00	±1:55	±1:41	±1:34	±1:31	±1:35	±1:38
WA **Bellingham**	Rise 1st	8:03	7:39	6:51	5:47	4:49	4:11	4:11	4:44	5:27	6:10	6:57	7:42
48° 45' N	Set 1st	4:25	5:08	5:54	6:41	7:25	8:05	8:16	7:48	6:51	5:48	4:49	4:16
122° 27' W	Twl	±2:00	±1:53	±1:50	±1:56	±2:21	±3:35	NONE	±2:36	±2:03	±1:52	±1:52	±2:00
TZ **8** (7)	Rise 15th	7:57	7:17	6:23	5:19	4:28	4:06	4:23	5:03	5:47	6:30	7:19	7:56
Note: Some Washington locations do not experience an end of twilight during the summer	Set 15th	4:42	5:31	6:16	7:02	7:45	8:15	8:08	7:24	6:22	5:20	4:30	4:14
	Twl	±1:58	±1:51	±1:50	±2:05	±2:44	NONE	±3:15	±2:18	±1:56	±1:50	±1:55	±2:01
Seattle	Rise 1st	7:58	7:36	6:49	5:48	4:52	4:16	4:16	4:47	5:28	6:08	6:53	7:37
47° 41' N	Set 1st	4:29	5:11	5:55	6:40	7:22	7:59	8:10	7:43	6:49	5:48	4:51	4:19
122° 15' W	Twl	±1:57	±1:50	±1:46	±1:53	±2:15	±3:07	±3:29	±2:28	±1:59	±1:49	±1:50	±1:57
TZ **8** (7)	Rise 15th	7:53	7:15	6:22	5:20	4:32	4:11	4:27	5:05	5:47	6:29	7:15	7:51
	Set 15th	4:46	5:33	6:15	6:59	7:40	8:09	8:03	7:21	6:21	5:21	4:33	4:18
	Twl	±1:54	±1:47	±1:48	±2:02	±2:35	±3:40	±2:56	±2:12	±1:53	±1:48	±1:52	±1:58
Spokane	Rise 1st	7:38	7:16	6:30	5:28	4:32	3:55	3:56	4:27	5:08	5:49	6:34	7:17
47° 45' N	Set 1st	4:09	4:51	5:35	6:20	7:02	7:40	7:51	7:24	6:30	5:28	4:32	4:00
117° 25' W	Twl	±1:57	±1:50	±1:46	±1:54	±2:16	±3:08	±3:31	±2:29	±1:59	±1:50	±1:50	±1:56
TZ **8** (7)	Rise 15th	7:33	6:55	6:02	5:00	4:12	3:51	4:07	4:45	5:27	6:09	6:55	7:32
	Set 15th	4:26	5:13	5:55	6:40	7:21	7:49	7:43	7:02	6:01	5:01	4:13	3:58
	Twl	±1:54	±1:48	±1:49	±2:02	±2:35	±3:46	±2:58	±2:12	±1:53	±1:48	±1:52	±1:58

→ **Sunrises & Sunsets HAVE NOT been adjusted for Daylight-Saving Time.**

SunRISE & SET

Sunrises & Sunsets

Washington/West Virginia/Wisconsin

		JAN	FEB	MAR	APR	MAY	JUN	JUL	AUG	SEP	OCT	NOV	DEC
Yakima	Rise 1st	7:47	7:26	6:41	5:41	4:47	4:12	4:12	4:43	5:22	6:01	6:44	7:26
46°42' N	Set 1st	4:25	5:06	5:48	6:31	7:12	7:48	7:59	7:33	6:41	5:41	4:46	4:16
120°30' W	Twl	±1:55	±1:49	±1:45	±1:51	±2:11	±2:52	±3:05	±2:22	±1:56	±1:48	±1:48	±1:53
TZ **8** (7)	Rise 15th	7:42	7:06	6:14	5:14	4:27	4:08	4:24	5:00	5:40	6:20	7:05	7:40
	Set 15th	4:41	5:27	6:08	6:51	7:30	7:58	7:52	7:12	6:13	5:15	4:28	4:15
	Twl	±1:53	±1:46	±1:46	±1:57	±2:27	±3:09	±2:45	±2:08	±1:50	±1:46	±1:51	±1:55
WV **Charleston**	Rise 1st	7:44	7:32	6:58	6:11	5:29	5:04	5:06	5:28	5:56	6:22	6:53	7:25
	Set 1st	5:16	5:49	6:20	6:50	7:18	7:45	7:55	7:37	6:56	6:09	5:26	5:06
38°24' N	Twl	±1:40	±1:35	±1:32	±1:35	±1:45	±2:00	±2:03	±1:50	±1:38	±1:33	±1:34	±1:39
81°36' W	Rise 15th	7:43	7:17	6:38	5:50	5:15	5:02	5:14	5:41	6:08	6:36	7:08	7:37
TZ **5** (4)	Set 15th	5:30	6:05	6:34	7:03	7:31	7:52	7:50	7:20	6:34	5:48	5:13	5:07
	Twl	±1:37	±1:33	±1:32	±1:39	±1:52	±2:04	±1:58	±1:40	±1:35	±1:33	±1:36	±1:39
Wheeling	Rise 1st	7:45	7:31	6:56	6:07	5:23	4:56	4:58	5:21	5:51	6:19	6:52	7:26
40°02' N	Set 1st	5:08	5:42	6:15	6:47	7:18	7:46	7:56	7:36	6:54	6:05	5:20	4:58
80°41' W	Twl	±1:41	±1:37	±1:34	±1:37	±1:49	±2:06	±2:09	±1:55	±1:41	±1:35	±1:36	±1:41
TZ **5** (4)	Rise 15th	7:43	7:16	6:34	5:45	5:07	4:53	5:06	5:34	6:04	6:33	7:08	7:38
	Set 15th	5:22	5:59	6:30	7:01	7:31	7:53	7:51	7:19	6:31	5:43	5:06	4:58
	Twl	±1:40	±1:35	±1:34	±1:42	±1:57	±2:11	±2:04	±1:48	±1:38	±1:35	±1:39	±1:43
WI **Eau Claire**	Rise 1st	7:44	7:25	6:44	5:47	4:56	4:23	4:24	4:52	5:28	6:04	6:44	7:23
	Set 1st	4:36	5:14	5:54	6:34	7:11	7:45	7:56	7:32	6:43	5:47	4:55	4:27
44°46' N	Twl	±1:51	±1:46	±1:41	±1:46	±2:03	±2:32	±2:39	±2:12	±1:50	±1:42	±1:44	±1:50
91°30' W	Rise 15th	7:40	7:07	6:19	5:22	4:38	4:20	4:34	5:08	5:45	6:21	7:03	7:37
TZ **6** (5)	Set 15th	4:51	5:34	6:12	6:51	7:28	7:54	7:49	7:12	6:17	5:22	4:38	4:26
	Twl	±1:49	±1:43	±1:42	±1:53	±2:15	±2:42	±2:29	±2:01	±1:45	±1:42	±1:47	±1:51
Green Bay	Rise 1st	7:29	7:11	6:30	5:33	4:43	4:10	4:11	4:39	5:15	5:50	6:29	7:08
44°30' N	Set 1st	4:23	5:01	5:40	6:19	6:56	7:30	7:41	7:17	6:29	5:33	4:41	4:14
88°00' W	Twl	±1:50	±1:44	±1:41	±1:46	±2:02	±2:31	±2:37	±2:11	±1:49	±1:42	±1:44	±1:49
TZ **6** (5)													

➤ **Sunrises & Sunsets HAVE NOT been adjusted for Daylight-Saving Time.**

Sunrises & Sunsets

Wisconsin

		JAN	FEB	MAR	APR	MAY	JUN	JUL	AUG	SEP	OCT	NOV	DEC
Green Bay	Rise 15th	7:25	6:52	6:05	5:08	4:25	4:07	4:21	4:55	5:31	6:07	6:48	7:22
	Set 15th	4:38	5:21	5:58	6:37	7:13	7:39	7:34	6:57	6:03	5:08	4:25	4:13
	Twl	±1:48	±1:42	±1:42	±1:52	±2:14	±2:40	±2:27	±2:00	±1:45	±1:42	±1:45	±1:50
Ironwood	Rise 1st	7:45	7:24	6:40	5:40	4:47	4:12	4:12	4:41	5:21	5:59	6:42	7:24
46°30' N *90°10' W*	Set 1st	4:24	5:05	5:47	6:30	7:10	7:46	7:57	7:32	6:40	5:41	4:46	4:15
	Twl	±1:55	±1:48	±1:44	±1:50	±2:10	±2:50	±3:01	±2:21	±1:55	±1:46	±1:47	±1:53
TZ **6** (5)	Rise 15th	7:40	7:04	6:14	5:14	4:27	4:07	4:23	4:59	5:38	6:18	7:02	7:38
	Set 15th	4:40	5:26	6:06	6:48	7:28	7:55	7:50	7:11	6:12	5:14	4:28	4:14
	Twl	±1:53	±1:45	±1:46	±1:58	±2:25	±3:06	±2:43	±2:07	±1:50	±1:45	±1:50	±1:55
Madison	Rise 1st	7:29	7:13	6:34	5:40	4:51	4:21	4:22	4:48	5:22	5:55	6:32	7:09
43°05' N *89°25' W*	Set 1st	4:33	5:10	5:47	6:24	6:59	7:30	7:41	7:19	6:33	5:39	4:50	4:24
	Twl	±1:47	±1:42	±1:38	±1:43	±1:57	±2:21	±2:27	±2:05	±1:46	±1:39	±1:41	±1:46
TZ **6** (5)	Rise 15th	7:26	6:55	6:10	5:16	4:34	4:18	4:32	5:03	5:37	6:11	6:50	7:22
	Set 15th	4:48	5:29	6:04	6:40	7:15	7:39	7:35	7:00	6:08	5:15	4:34	4:23
	Twl	±1:45	±1:39	±1:40	±1:49	±2:07	±2:28	±2:18	±1:56	±1:42	±1:39	±1:43	±1:48
Milwaukee	Rise 1st	7:24	7:07	6:28	5:34	4:46	4:15	4:16	4:42	5:16	5:49	6:27	7:04
43°09' N *87°58' W*	Set 1st	4:27	5:04	5:41	6:18	6:53	7:25	7:35	7:14	6:27	5:33	4:44	4:18
	Twl	±1:47	±1:42	±1:39	±1:43	±1:58	±2:22	±2:27	±2:05	±1:46	±1:40	±1:41	±1:46
TZ **6** (5)	Rise 15th	7:21	6:50	6:04	5:10	4:28	4:12	4:26	4:57	5:31	6:05	6:45	7:17
	Set 15th	4:42	5:23	5:58	6:35	7:09	7:33	7:30	6:55	6:02	5:09	4:28	4:17
	Twl	±1:45	±1:40	±1:40	±1:48	±2:09	±2:29	±2:18	±1:55	±1:43	±1:40	±1:43	±1:48
Wausau	Rise 1st	7:37	7:18	6:37	5:40	4:48	4:15	4:16	4:44	5:21	5:57	6:37	7:16
44°57' N *89°40' W*	Set 1st	4:28	5:07	5:46	6:26	7:04	7:38	7:49	7:25	6:36	5:39	4:47	4:19
	Twl	±1:51	±1:45	±1:42	±1:47	±2:04	±2:34	±2:42	±2:13	±1:51	±1:43	±1:44	±1:50
TZ **6** (5)	Rise 15th	7:33	7:00	6:11	5:14	4:30	4:11	4:26	5:00	5:37	6:14	6:56	7:30
	Set 15th	4:43	5:27	6:05	6:44	7:21	7:47	7:42	7:05	6:10	5:14	4:30	4:18
	Twl	±1:49	±1:42	±1:42	±1:53	±2:17	±2:44	±2:31	±2:02	±1:45	±1:42	±1:47	±1:51

➜ **Sunrises & Sunsets HAVE NOT been adjusted for Daylight-Saving Time.**

Sunrises & Sunsets

Wyoming/Puerto Rico/Canada

		JAN	FEB	MAR	APR	MAY	JUN	JUL	AUG	SEP	OCT	NOV	DEC
WY	Rise 1st	7:44	7:26	6:44	5:48	4:58	4:26	4:27	4:55	5:30	6:05	6:45	7:24
Buffalo	Set 1st	4:39	5:17	5:56	6:35	7:12	7:45	7:55	7:32	6:43	5:48	4:56	4:29
44°25' N	Twl	±1:50	±1:44	±1:40	±1:46	±2:01	±2:30	±2:38	±2:11	±1:50	±1:42	±1:44	±1:49
106°50' W	Rise 15th	7:40	7:07	6:19	5:23	4:40	4:22	4:37	5:11	5:47	6:23	7:04	7:37
TZ **7** (6)	Set 15th	4:54	5:37	6:14	6:52	7:28	7:54	7:49	7:12	6:18	5:23	4:40	4:28
	Twl	±1:48	±1:41	±1:41	±1:52	±2:14	±2:39	±2:27	±2:00	±1:45	±1:42	±1:45	±1:51
Casper	Rise 1st	7:36	7:20	6:41	5:47	4:59	4:29	4:31	4:57	5:30	6:03	6:40	7:17
42°52' N	Set 1st	4:42	5:19	5:55	6:32	7:06	7:38	7:48	7:26	6:40	5:46	4:57	4:32
106°20' W	Twl	±1:50	±1:43	±1:38	±1:42	±1:57	±2:19	±2:25	±2:04	±1:46	±1:40	±1:42	±1:46
TZ **7** (6)	Rise 15th	7:33	7:02	6:17	5:23	4:42	4:26	4:40	5:12	5:45	6:19	6:58	7:29
	Set 15th	4:57	5:37	6:12	6:48	7:22	7:46	7:42	7:07	6:15	5:23	4:42	4:32
	Twl	±1:44	±1:39	±1:39	±1:48	±2:07	±2:26	±2:17	±1:55	±1:42	±1:39	±1:43	±1:47
Rock Springs	Rise 1st	7:44	7:29	6:51	5:59	5:13	4:45	4:46	5:11	5:43	6:14	6:49	7:24
41°40' N	Set 1st	4:57	5:33	6:07	6:42	7:15	7:45	7:55	7:34	6:50	5:58	5:11	4:47
109°10' W	Twl	±1:45	±1:39	±1:37	±1:41	±1:53	±2:13	±2:19	±2:01	±1:44	±1:38	±1:39	±1:44
TZ **7** (6)	Rise 15th	7:41	7:12	6:28	5:36	4:57	4:42	4:56	5:25	5:57	6:29	7:06	7:37
	Set 15th	5:12	5:50	6:24	6:58	7:30	7:53	7:49	7:16	6:26	5:35	4:56	4:47
	Twl	±1:42	±1:38	±1:37	±1:45	±2:02	±2:19	±2:11	±1:52	±1:39	±1:38	±1:41	±1:45
Puerto Rico	Rise 1st	6:57	6:58	6:44	6:19	5:57	5:47	5:52	6:02	6:10	6:15	6:24	6:40
San Juan	Set 1st	6:00	6:19	6:30	6:38	6:46	6:57	7:05	6:59	6:39	6:13	5:52	5:47
18°28' N	Twl	±1:21	±1:18	±1:17	±1:17	±1:21	±1:26	±1:27	±1:23	±1:18	±1:16	±1:18	±1:20
66°08' W	Rise 15th	7:00	6:52	6:33	6:08	5:51	5:48	5:56	6:06	6:12	6:18	6:31	6:49
TZ **4**	Set 15th	6:08	6:25	6:34	6:42	6:51	7:02	7:04	6:52	6:27	6:02	5:47	5:51
	Twl	±1:21	±1:17	±1:16	±1:18	±1:24	±1:27	±1:26	±1:19	±1:17	±1:17	±1:20	±1:21
Canada	Rise 1st	8:40	8:13	7:21	6:12	5:10	4:28	4:27	5:02	5:50	6:37	7:29	8:18
Calgary	Set 1st	4:41	5:28	6:18	7:10	7:59	8:42	8:54	8:23	7:22	6:15	5:11	4:33
51°0' N	Twl	±2:07	±1:59	±1:55	±2:03	±2:36	NONE	NONE	±2:58	±2:10	±1:56	±1:58	±2:06
114°10' W													
TZ **7** (6)													

➜ **Sunrises & Sunsets HAVE NOT been adjusted for Daylight-Saving Time.**

Sunrises & Sunsets

Canada

		JAN	FEB	MAR	APR	MAY	JUN	JUL	AUG	SEP	OCT	NOV	DEC
Calgary	Rise 15th	8:33	7:49	6:51	5:42	4:47	4:22	4:40	5:24	6:12	7:00	7:53	8:33
	Set 15th	4:59	5:53	6:42	7:33	8:20	8:53	8:45	7:58	6:51	5:44	4:49	4:30
	Twl	±2:05	±1:56	±1:56	±2:14	±3:15	NONE	NONE	±2:29	±2:01	±1:56	±2:01	±2:08
Chicoutimi	Rise 1st	7:36	7:14	6:26	5:23	4:25	3:47	3:47	4:19	5:01	5:44	6:30	7:15
48°28' N	Set 1st	4:00	4:43	5:28	6:15	6:59	7:38	7:50	7:22	6:26	5:24	4:25	3:52
71°05' W	Twl	±1:59	±1:52	±1:50	±1:55	±2:19	NONE	NONE	±2:34	±2:02	±1:50	±1:51	±1:59
TZ **5** (4)	Rise 15th	7:31	6:52	5:58	4:54	4:04	3:42	3:58	4:38	5:21	6:04	6:52	7:29
Note: Some locations in Canada do not experience an end of twilight during the summer	Set 15th	4:17	5:06	5:50	6:35	7:18	7:48	7:42	6:59	5:57	4:55	4:05	3:50
	Twl	±1:56	±1:50	±1:50	±2:05	±2:42	NONE	±3:09	±2:15	±1:55	±1:50	±1:54	±1:59
Edmonton	Rise 1st	8:50	8:19	7:22	6:07	4:59	4:12	4:09	4:50	5:43	6:36	7:33	8:27
53°30' N	Set 1st	4:25	5:17	6:12	7:10	8:04	8:53	9:06	8:30	7:24	6:11	5:01	4:19
113°30' W	Twl	±2:16	±2:06	±2:01	±2:12	±3:02	NONE	NONE	NONE	±2:21	±2:03	±2:05	±2:14
TZ **7** (6)	Rise 15th	8:42	7:53	6:49	6:34	4:33	4:04	4:24	5:13	6:08	7:01	8:00	8:44
	Set 15th	4:45	5:45	6:38	7:36	8:28	9:05	8:55	8:02	6:50	5:38	4:37	4:14
	Twl	±2:13	±2:03	±2:04	±2:26	NONE	NONE	NONE	±2:49	±2:09	±2:02	±2:09	±2:17
Halifax	Rise 1st	7:51	7:33	6:52	5:56	5:05	4:32	4:33	5:01	5:37	6:12	6:52	7:31
44°38' N	Set 1st	4:45	5:23	6:02	6:42	7:19	7:52	8:03	7:40	6:51	5:55	5:03	4:36
63°35' W	Twl	±1:50	±1:44	±1:41	±1:46	±2:03	±2:32	±2:39	±2:12	±1:50	±1:42	±1:44	±1:49
TZ **4** (3)	Rise 15th	7:48	7:15	6:27	5:31	4:47	4:28	4:43	5:17	5:53	6:29	7:11	7:44
Note: Some locations in Canada do not experience an end of twilight during the summer	Set 15th	5:00	5:43	6:20	6:59	7:35	8:01	7:57	7:20	6:25	5:30	4:47	4:35
	Twl	±1:48	±1:42	±1:42	±1:52	±2:16	±2:42	±2:28	±2:00	±1:45	±1:42	±1:45	±1:50
Kamloops	Rise 1st	8:03	7:37	6:45	5:37	4:36	3:54	3:54	4:28	5:15	6:02	6:53	7:41
50°40' N	Set 1st	4:07	4:54	5:43	6:34	7:22	8:05	8:17	7:46	6:46	5:39	4:36	4:00
120°20' W	Twl	±2:07	±1:58	±1:54	±2:02	±2:34	NONE	NONE	±2:54	±2:09	±1:56	±1:58	±2:04
TZ **8** (7)	Rise 15th	7:57	7:13	6:15	5:07	4:13	3:48	4:07	4:51	5:38	6:26	7:17	7:56
	Set 15th	4:25	5:18	6:06	6:57	7:44	8:16	8:07	7:20	6:15	5:09	4:15	3:57
	Twl	±2:04	±1:56	±1:56	±2:12	±3:08	NONE	NONE	±2:30	±2:00	±1:54	±2:00	±2:06

→ **Sunrises & Sunsets HAVE NOT been adjusted for Daylight-Saving Time.**

SunRISE & SET

Sunrises & Sunsets

Canada

		JAN	FEB	MAR	APR	MAY	JUN	JUL	AUG	SEP	OCT	NOV	DEC
Montreal	Rise 1st	7:35	7:16	6:33	5:35	4:43	4:09	4:09	4:38	5:15	5:52	6:34	7:14
45°31′ N	Set 1st	4:21	5:01	5:41	6:22	7:01	7:36	7:47	7:23	6:32	5:35	4:42	4:13
73°34′ W	Twl	±1:52	±1:47	±1:43	±1:48	±2:06	±2:39	±2:48	±2:15	±1:53	±1:44	±1:45	±1:51
TZ **5** (4)	Rise 15th	7:31	6:56	6:07	5:09	4:24	4:05	4:20	4:55	5:33	6:10	6:53	7:28
	Set 15th	4:37	5:21	6:00	6:40	7:18	7:45	7:40	7:02	6:06	5:09	4:24	4:11
	Twl	±1:50	±1:44	±1:44	±1:55	±2:20	±2:51	±2:34	±2:03	±1:47	±1:44	±1:48	±1:53
Prince George	Rise 1st	8:30	7:58	7:00	5:44	4:35	3:47	3:44	4:25	5:20	6:13	7:12	8:07
	Set 1st	4:01	4:53	5:49	6:47	7:43	8:33	8:46	8:09	7:02	5:48	4:37	3:54
53°55′ N	Twl	±2:17	±2:08	±2:02	±2:14	±3:08	NONE	NONE	NONE	±2:23	±2:04	±2:06	±2:15
122°50′ W	Rise 15th	8:21	7:31	6:26	5:11	4:09	3:39	3:59	4:50	5:45	6:39	7:39	8:24
TZ **8** (7)	Set 15th	4:21	5:21	6:16	7:13	8:08	8:45	8:35	7:41	6:27	5:14	4:12	3:49
Note: Some locations in Canada do not experience an end of twilight during the summer	Twl	±2:14	±2:04	±2:04	±2:30	NONE	NONE	NONE	±2:53	±2:12	±2:04	±2:11	±2:19
Quebec	Rise 1st	7:30	7:10	6:25	5:24	4:30	3:54	3:54	4:24	5:04	5:43	6:27	7:09
46°52′ N	Set 1st	4:07	4:48	5:30	6:14	6:55	7:32	7:43	7:17	6:25	5:25	4:29	3:58
71°13′ W	Twl	±1:55	±1:49	±1:46	±1:51	±2:12	±2:53	±3:08	±2:23	±1:56	±1:47	±1:48	±1:55
TZ **5** (4)	Rise 15th	7:26	6:49	5:58	4:58	4:10	3:50	4:05	4:42	5:22	6:03	6:48	7:23
	Set 15th	4:23	5:09	5:50	6:33	7:13	7:41	7:36	6:56	5:57	4:58	4:11	3:57
	Twl	±1:53	±1:47	±1:47	±1:58	±2:28	NONE	±2:47	±2:08	±1:50	±1:46	±1:51	±1:55
Regina	Rise 1st	8:59	8:33	7:42	6:35	6:33	5:52	5:51	6:26	7:13	7:59	7:49	8:37
50°27′ N	Set 1st	5:05	5:51	6:40	7:31	9:18	10:01	10:13	9:42	8:43	7:37	5:34	4:58
104°35′ W	Twl	±2:05	±1:58	±1:54	±2:02	±2:32	NONE	NONE	±2:52	±2:08	±1:54	±1:57	±2:04
TZ **6** (5)	Rise 15th	8:53	8:10	7:12	7:05	6:11	5:46	6:04	6:47	7:34	8:21	8:13	8:52
Note: Some locations in Canada do not experience an end of twilight during the summer	Set 15th	5:23	6:16	7:03	8:53	9:40	10:12	10:04	9:18	8:12	7:07	5:13	4:55
	Twl	±2:03	±1:55	±1:55	±2:12	±3:04	NONE	NONE	±2:26	±2:00	±1:53	±1:59	±2:06
Rouyn-Noranda	Rise 1st	8:07	7:44	6:57	5:54	4:57	4:19	4:19	4:51	5:34	6:15	7:02	7:46
	Set 1st	4:32	5:16	6:00	6:47	7:30	8:09	8:20	7:53	6:57	5:55	4:57	4:24
48°20′ N 79°00′ W	Twl	±1:59	±1:51	±1:49	±1:55	±2:19	±3:20	NONE	±2:33	±2:02	±1:50	±1:51	±1:58
TZ **5** (4)													

➡ **Sunrises & Sunsets HAVE NOT been adjusted for Daylight-Saving Time.**

SunRISE & SET

Sunrises & Sunsets

Canada

		JAN	FEB	MAR	APR	MAY	JUN	JUL	AUG	SEP	OCT	NOV	DEC
Rouyn-Noranda	Rise 15th	8:02	7:23	6:29	5:26	4:36	4:14	4:31	5:10	5:53	6:36	7:24	8:01
	Set 15th	4:49	5:38	6:22	7:07	7:50	8:19	8:12	7:30	6:28	5:27	4:37	4:22
	Twl	±1:56	±1:50	±1:49	±2:04	±2:38	NONE	±3:07	±2:15	±1:55	±1:49	±1:54	±1:59
St. John's 47°35' N 52°40' W TZ **3.5** (2.5)	Rise 1st	7:49	7:27	6:42	5:40	4:44	4:07	4:07	4:38	5:19	5:59	6:44	7:28
	Set 1st	4:20	5:02	5:45	6:30	7:13	7:50	8:02	7:35	6:41	5:40	4:44	4:11
	Twl	±1:58	±1:50	±1:47	±1:54	±2:15	±3:05	NONE	±2:28	±1:59	±1:49	±1:49	±1:57
	Rise 15th	7:44	7:07	6:14	5:12	4:24	4:02	4:18	4:56	5:38	6:19	7:06	7:42
	Set 15th	4:36	5:24	6:06	6:50	7:31	8:00	7:54	7:13	6:13	5:13	4:25	4:10
	Twl	±1:55	±1:47	±1:49	±2:01	±2:34	NONE	±2:56	±2:12	±1:52	±1:47	±1:52	±1:58
Saskatoon 52°10' N 106°38' W TZ **6**	Rise 1st	9:16	8:47	7:53	6:41	5:36	4:52	4:50	5:28	6:18	7:08	8:02	8:53
	Set 1st	5:05	5:54	6:46	7:41	8:32	9:18	9:31	8:57	7:54	6:44	5:38	4:58
	Twl	±2:12	±2:02	±1:58	±2:07	±2:46	NONE	NONE	±3:18	±2:15	±2:00	±2:01	±2:10
	Rise 15th	9:08	8:22	7:21	6:10	5:12	4:45	5:04	5:50	6:41	7:32	8:27	9:09
	Set 15th	5:24	6:20	7:11	8:05	8:55	9:29	9:21	8:31	7:20	6:12	5:15	4:54
	Twl	±2:08	±1:59	±2:00	±2:20	±4:11	NONE	NONE	±2:38	±2:06	±1:59	±2:04	±2:12
Sudbury 46°30' N 81°00' W TZ **5** (4)	Rise 1st	8:08	7:48	7:04	6:04	5:10	4:35	4:35	5:05	5:44	5:22	7:06	7:47
	Set 1st	4:48	5:28	6:10	6:53	7:33	8:09	8:21	7:55	7:03	6:04	5:09	4:39
	Twl	±1:54	±1:49	±1:44	±1:50	±2:11	±2:50	±3:00	±2:21	±1:55	±1:46	±1:47	±1:53
	Rise 15th	8:04	7:28	6:37	5:37	4:50	4:30	4:46	5:22	6:02	6:41	7:26	8:01
	Set 15th	5:04	5:49	6:30	7:12	7:51	8:19	8:13	7:34	6:36	5:38	4:51	4:37
	Twl	±1:52	±1:46	±1:45	±1:57	±2:26	±3:05	±2:44	±2:07	±1:49	±1:45	±1:50	±1:55
Thunder Bay 48°20' N 89°15' W TZ **5** (4)	Rise 1st	8:48	8:26	7:39	6:35	5:38	5:00	5:00	5:32	6:14	6:56	7:43	8:27
	Set 1st	5:13	5:56	6:41	7:27	8:11	8:50	9:02	8:34	7:39	6:36	5:38	5:05
	Twl	±1:59	±1:52	±1:49	±1:56	±2:19	±3:20	NONE	±2:33	±2:01	±1:50	±1:51	±1:58
	Rise 15th	8:43	8:04	7:10	6:07	5:17	4:55	5:12	5:51	6:34	7:17	8:05	8:42
	Set 15th	5:30	6:19	7:02	7:48	8:30	9:00	8:54	8:11	7:10	6:08	5:18	5:03
	Twl	±1:56	±1:50	±1:50	±2:03	±2:41	NONE	±3:06	±2:15	±1:54	±1:49	±1:54	±1:59

Note: Some locations in Canada do not experience an end of twilight during the summer

➜ **Sunrises & Sunsets HAVE NOT been adjusted for Daylight-Saving Time.**

SunRISE & SET

Sunrises & Sunsets
Canada/Mexico

		JAN	FEB	MAR	APR	MAY	JUN	JUL	AUG	SEP	OCT	NOV	DEC
Toronto	Rise 1st	7:51	7:34	6:54	5:59	5:10	4:39	4:40	5:06	5:41	6:15	6:53	7:31
43°39' N *79°20' W*	Set 1st	4:51	5:28	6:06	6:44	7:20	7:52	8:03	7:40	6:53	5:59	5:08	4:42
	Twl	±1:49	±1:43	±1:39	±1:45	±1:59	±2:25	±2:31	±2:08	±1:48	±1:40	±1:43	±1:47
TZ **5** (4)	Rise 15th	7:48	7:16	6:30	5:35	4:52	4:35	4:50	5:22	5:57	6:31	7:11	7:44
	Set 15th	5:06	5:47	6:24	7:01	7:36	8:01	7:57	7:21	6:28	5:34	4:52	4:41
	Twl	±1:47	±1:41	±1:40	±1:49	±2:10	±2:32	±2:21	±1:57	±1:43	±1:40	±1:44	±1:49
Winnipeg	Rise 1st	8:27	8:02	7:12	6:06	5:05	4:25	4:24	4:58	5:44	6:29	7:18	8:05
49°54' N *97°09' W*	Set 1st	4:38	5:23	6:11	7:00	7:47	8:29	8:41	8:11	7:12	6:07	5:06	4:30
	Twl	±2:04	±1:57	±1:52	±2:00	±2:29	NONE	NONE	±2:46	±2:07	±1:54	±1:55	±2:02
TZ **6** (5)	Rise 15th	8:21	7:39	6:42	5:36	4:43	4:19	4:37	5:18	6:04	6:50	7:41	8:20
Note: Some locations in Canada do not experience an end of twilight during the summer	Set 15th	4:56	5:47	6:34	7:22	8:08	8:39	8:32	7:47	6:42	5:38	4:45	4:27
	Twl	±2:00	±1:54	±1:53	±2:10	±2:57	NONE	NONE	±2:22	±1:59	±1:52	±1:58	±2:04
# **Mexico** **Chihuahua**	Rise 1st	7:57	7:52	7:29	6:54	7:23	7:07	7:10	7:26	7:42	7:57	7:16	7:40
	Set 1st	6:19	6:44	7:04	7:22	8:40	8:58	9:06	8:55	8:26	7:50	6:19	6:07
28°40' N *106°03' W*	Twl	±1:27	±1:24	±1:23	±1:24	±1:29	±1:37	±1:39	±1:33	±1:25	±1:22	±1:24	±1:28
TZ **6** (5)	Rise 15th	7:58	7:43	7:14	7:39	7:13	7:06	7:16	7:33	7:49	8:05	7:27	7:49
	Set 15th	6:29	6:54	7:13	8:30	8:48	9:04	9:04	8:44	8:09	7:34	6:10	6:09
	Twl	±1:27	±1:23	±1:22	±1:26	±1:34	±1:39	±1:37	±1:28	±1:23	±1:23	±1:26	±1:29
Hermosillo	Rise 1st	7:18	7:13	6:49	6:14	6:42	6:25	6:28	6:45	7:02	7:17	6:37	7:01
29°10' N *111°00' W*	Set 1st	5:37	6:03	6:24	6:42	8:00	8:19	8:27	8:16	7:46	7:10	5:38	5:26
	Twl	±1:28	±1:25	±1:23	±1:24	±1:30	±1:38	±1:40	±1:33	±1:25	±1:22	±1:24	±1:28
TZ **7** (6)	Rise 15th	7:19	7:03	6:34	6:58	6:32	6:24	6:35	6:53	7:09	7:25	6:48	7:10
	Set 15th	5:48	6:14	6:32	7:50	8:09	8:25	8:25	8:04	7:29	6:54	5:29	5:28
	Twl	±1:27	±1:24	±1:23	±1:27	±1:34	±1:40	±1:37	±1:29	±1:24	±1:23	±1:27	±1:29
Monterrey	Rise 1st	7:29	7:26	7:05	6:33	7:05	6:51	6:54	7:09	7:22	7:34	6:50	7:11
25°40' N *100°30' W*	Set 1st	6:03	6:26	6:44	6:59	8:13	8:29	8:37	8:28	8:01	7:29	6:01	5:51
TZ **6** (5)	Twl	±1:25	±1:22	±1:20	±1:21	±1:27	±1:34	±1:34	±1:29	±1:23	±1:20	±1:21	±1:25

➡ **Sunrises & Sunsets HAVE NOT been adjusted for Daylight-Saving Time.**

Sunrises & Sunsets

Mexico

		JAN	FEB	MAR	APR	MAY	JUN	JUL	AUG	SEP	OCT	NOV	DEC
Monterrey	Rise 15th	7:30	7:17	6:51	7:19	6:57	6:51	7:00	7:15	7:28	7:41	7:00	7:21
	Set 15th	6:13	6:36	6:51	8:05	8:20	8:35	8:36	8:17	7:46	7:15	5:53	5:54
	Twl	±1:24	±1:20	±1:19	±1:24	±1:30	±1:34	±1:31	±1:26	±1:21	±1:20	±1:24	±1:25
Tamaulipas	Rise 1st	7:15	7:14	6:55	6:26	7:00	6:47	6:50	7:03	7:15	7:25	6:39	6:58
23°30' N	Set 1st	5:59	6:20	6:36	6:49	8:01	8:16	8:24	8:16	7:51	7:21	5:55	5:46
98°20' W	Twl	±1:24	±1:21	±1:19	±1:20	±1:25	±1:30	±1:31	±1:26	±1:21	±1:18	±1:20	±1:23
TZ **6 (5)**	Rise 15th	7:17	7:06	6:42	7:13	6:52	6:47	6:56	7:09	7:20	7:30	6:48	7:08
	Set 15th	6:08	6:29	6:43	7:55	8:08	8:21	8:23	8:06	7:37	7:07	5:48	5:50
	Twl	±1:23	±1:19	±1:19	±1:21	±1:27	±1:32	±1:30	±1:24	±1:19	±1:20	±1:22	±1:24

➙ **Sunrises & Sunsets HAVE NOT been adjusted for Daylight-Saving Time.**

Page 353. Very early morning launch of space shuttle Atlantis on May 19, 2000.

SunRISE & SET

Astronomical Glossary

A

Absolute Magnitude. The magnitude of a star if it were placed at a distance of 10 parsecs from Earth. The Sun's absolute magnitude is +4.8, and most stars range from −5 to +15. Absolute magnitude is used for comparing the actual brightness of stars.

Absolute Zero. The coldest possible temperature, at which all molecular motion stops. Absolute zero is 0K, −273° C or −459° F.

Airy Disk. Amateur telescopes cannot resolve stars into actual disks because the stars are too far away. So, the stars viewed through a telescope behave like points of light and have no dimension. However, if you look closely at stars through any telescope, you will notice that they are not points but rather small round disks, surrounded by a fainter ring that hugs closely to the disk (It is easier to see this at higher magnifications). Brighter stars show larger disks than fainter stars. This disk is called the Airy disk after George Airy (1801–1892). These disks have NOTHING to do with the actual diameter of the star. Instead, they are created by diffraction, a phenomena of the wave nature of light. Larger diameter telescopes produce smaller Airy disks.

Albedo. The amount of sunlight reflected from a Planet, moon or asteroid. Albedo is normally expressed as a decimal between 0 and 1 (or the equivalent percentage). A mirror would have an albedo of 1 (reflects 100% of sunlight); Venus has a high albedo of 0.65 (65%); the Earth, 0.37 (37%) and the Moon, 0.11 (11%).

Altazimuth Telescope Mount. A mount that moves in altitude and azimuth, allowing a telescope to move "up" and "down" vertically (altitude) and rotate horizontally to any compass point (azimuth). Everyone is familiar with this mount because it is the type used with binoculars at tourist attractions. This mount has become increasing popular because of its simplicity and low cost. Most professional telescopes today use computer controlled altazimuth mounts.

Altitude. For an altazimuth telescope mount, altitude refers to the movement of the telescope "up" and "down" vertically from the horizon to directly overhead. Altitude also refers to a measurement system, where the height of an object above the horizon is expressed in arc degrees. This measurement system ranges from 0° at the horizon to 90° at the zenith (of the observer).

Angstrom (Å). A unit of measurement that once was widely used to express the wavelength of light. The angstrom is being replaced by the nanometer (abbreviated nm). An angstrom is 10^{-10} meters; a nanometer is 10^{-9} meters, so 10 Å = 1 nm.

Annular Eclipse. An eclipse of the Sun by the Moon in which the whole Moon moves in front of the Sun but does not completely cover the Sun. Because the Moon's orbit is an ellipse, its distance to the Earth varies. Annular eclipses occur when the Moon is a little farther away than normal, making its arc diameter a little smaller than the Sun's. During a total eclipse of the Sun, the Moon's arc diameter is slightly larger than the Sun's.

Aphelion. The point in a Planet's, asteroid's or comet's orbit where it is farthest from the Sun. Since all celestial objects have elliptical orbits,

Astronomical Glossary

they have a closest and farthest point from the object they orbit.

Apochromatic. Optical term that refers to the highest quality telescope optics which are free of spherical, chromatic and other optical aberrations. The term is usually associated with refractor telescopes.

Apogee. The point in the orbit of the Moon or an artificial satellite where it is farthest from the Earth. Since all celestial objects have elliptical orbits, they have a closest and farthest point from the object they orbit.

Arc Degree (°). Unit of angular measurement used in astronomy. One arc degree is the same as one compass point degree. There are 360 arc degrees in a circle; each arc degree is divided into 60 arc minutes; and each arc minute is divided into 60 arc seconds. Arc seconds are further divided into tenths. The word "arc" is usually omitted when using this measurement system, but this omission can cause confusion when minutes (time) are used in the same dialog with arc minutes. The Sun and Moon are both about 1/2 of an arc degree (30 arc minutes) in angular diameter. Notation example: 6° 26' 3.2"

Arc Minute ('). 1/60 of an arc degree. The Moon is about 30 arc minutes in diameter.

Arc Second ("). 1/3600 of an arc degree or 1/60 of an arc minute.

Ascending Node. The point at which the orbit of a Solar System member, like one of the Planets, crosses the celestial equator or ecliptic from south to north (in declination). See also Descending Node.

Asterism. A recognizable or distinguished group of stars. Often a sub-group of a constellation. The Big Dipper is an asterism of the constellation Ursa Major.

Asteroid. A large, irregularly shaped "rock" that circles the Sun. Most asteroids orbit in a belt between Mars and Jupiter. The largest asteroid, Ceres, is 568 miles (914 km) in diameter and takes approximately 4.6 years to circle the Sun. Asteroids are also referred to as minor planets.

Asteroid Belt. Most asteroids orbit the Sun in a belt between Mars and Jupiter. These asteroids represent remnants left over from the formation of the Solar System.

Astrology. Astrology is not astronomy! Astronomy is a science; astrology is not. Astrology is a system of predictions based on Planetary and lunar positions. Although astronomy and astrology share some terminology and concepts, astrology's foundation is not based on the scientific gathering and analysis of information; hence it is an arbitrary system. Until modern times, astronomy and astrology were linked together. In the early 1600s, Johannes Kepler, who discovered the laws that govern the orbits of the Planets, used astrology to help earn a living. Kings, queens and nobles hired astrologers to predict their futures (obviously, making positive or favorable predictions helped an astrologer to stay in business). Astrological predictions offer a feeling of control and power in a chaotic world.

Astronomical Unit (AU). Unit of distance in astronomy. One astronomical unit is 92,955,800 miles (1.48 billion km), the average distance from the Earth to the Sun.

Astronomical Glossary

A
B

Greek Alphabet

α	alpha
β	beta
γ	gamma
δ	delta
ε	epsilon
ζ	zeta
η	eta
θ	theta
ι	iota
κ	kappa
λ	lambda
μ	mu
ν	nu
ξ	xi
ο	omicron
π	pi
ρ	rho
σ	sigma
τ	tau
υ	upsilon
φ	phi
χ	chi
ψ	psi
ω	omega

Aurora (plural: Aurorae). A beautiful display of illumination in the night sky caused by charged particles from the Sun spilling into the atmosphere. These displays are concentrated around the polar regions of the Earth. In the northern hemisphere, the aurorae are called Aurora Borealis (Northern Lights) and in the southern hemisphere, Aurora Australis. Their red and green colors can shimmer, move and pulsate in large diffuse patches, ribbons or folded curtains. Their shape and intensity can change in minutes.

Autumnal Equinox. Occurs on or near September 23. At this time, the Sun is crossing the celestial equator from north to south. This occasion is one of two during the year (the other is at the vernal equinox) when day and night are equal in length.

Averted Vision. An observing technique which helps one see faint objects. Instead of looking directly at a faint object, you look slightly away from it, using peripheral vision for viewing. In the dark, our peripheral vision is more sensitive to faint light than our direct vision.

Azimuth. For an altazimuth telescope mount, azimuth refers to the rotation of the telescope in a circle, around the horizon to any compass point. Azimuth is also part of a measurement system. Azimuth starts with 0° at true North and arcs eastwardly, through 360° of the compass.

Barlow Lens. A barlow lens increases the magnification of eyepieces, usually by a preset factor of 2 or 3. Barlows are popular because one barlow effectively doubles the range of magnification possible from a set of eyepieces. Barlow lenses fit into a telescope's eyepiece holder. Eyepieces are then inserted into the barrel of the barlow.

Barred-Spiral Galaxy. Similar to a spiral galaxy except that the center bulge has a straight arm, or "bar" passing through it. The curved arms then radiate off the ends of the bar. Our Milky Way Galaxy is a moderately barred-spiral galaxy.

Bayer Letters. The formal name of the lowercase Greek letters assigned to the brightest stars in each of the constellations. Also see Flamsteed Numbers.

Big Bang. The predominant theory describing the creation of the Universe. This theory states that all the matter in the Universe was once compressed together and then rapidly expanded or exploded to form the galaxies that exist today.

Binary Star. A pair of stars where one revolves around the other (actually, each star revolves around a mutual center of gravity). Binary stars have revolutions that can last just days or thousands of years.

Black Hole. An astronomical body with a density so great that the resulting gravity will not even let light escape from its surface. Black holes cannot be directly observed, but there are telltale signs that indicate their presence. A black hole can be created from a star with as little as three times the mass of our Sun. As massive stars age and burn out, their remaining matter collapses upon itself, creating black holes, the densest objects in the Universe. Some galaxies have giant black holes at their centers. A rudimentary idea of a black hole was formulated in the late 1700s.

Astronomical Glossary

Brown Dwarf. A "star" that never ignited because it did not have sufficient mass to produce nuclear fusion. It is essentially a ball of hydrogen gas. Brown dwarfs are difficult to locate because they do not give off visible light.

Catadioptric Telescope. Any telescope that uses a combination of lenses and mirrors to focus light. The SCT is a popular catadioptric.

CCD (Charged-Coupled Device). A term often used for the digital imaging technology employed in astronomy. This is the same technology as digital cameras.

Celestial Equator. A great circle that is the projection of the Earth's equator onto the sky. The celestial equator has declination 0° (corresponding to a latitude of 0°).

Celestial Horizon. The meeting of the sky and the horizon. At sea, the celestial horizon is unobstructed and perfectly round.

Celestial Meridian. A celestial meridian is a great circle that divides the sky into eastern and western halves. This circle passes through the observer's zenith and the North and South Celestial Poles. On Earth, a meridian is a longitude line.

Celestial Sphere. At one time, it was thought the Sun, Moon, Planets, comets and stars resided on the inside of a giant sphere called the Celestial Sphere. Today, it is a convenient term to indicate the visible Universe.

Chromatic Aberration. Optical term referring to the inability of a refracting lens to focus all colors of light at the same point. This aberration is particularly noticeable in lower-quality binoculars, refractor telescopes and eye-

Celestial Sphere illustration from 1708.

pieces as orange and blue halos around viewed objects.

Coma (Comet). The large, cloudy veil that forms around the nucleus of a comet when it gets close to the Sun. The coma is the brightest part of a comet.

Coma (Telescope). An optical aberration that occurs in short focal length reflectors, causing stars toward the edge of an eyepiece's field of view to appear elongated instead of as points of light.

Comet. Sometimes referred to as "dirty snowballs," because they are composed mostly of dust and ices. As comets approach the Sun, the ices vaporize, creating the bright, reflective, gaseous coma and tail. Most comets have highly elliptical orbits and take hundreds to thousands of years to revolve around the Sun.

Conjunction. The alignment of two or more Solar System members as viewed from Earth. Conjunction usually applies to the Sun, Moon and Planets. When two or more Planets, the Moon and a Planet (or Planets) or the Sun and a Planet (or Planets) appear very close to one another in the sky, they are said to be in conjunction. The

Astronomical Glossary

inferior Planets, Mercury and Venus, are at Inferior Conjunction when they are directly between the Earth and the Sun. They are at Superior Conjunction when they are on the opposite side of the Sun from the Earth. In both cases, these Planets will rise and set with the Sun. A Superior Planet (Mars through Pluto) is in conjunction when it is on the opposite side of the Sun from the Earth.

Constellation. A group of visible stars that has been assigned a name. The stars in a constellation usually form a pattern that aides in their recognition. The visible stars were first categorized into constellations thousands of years ago and are associated with lore. Today the constellations are not just named groups of stars, but also include the area of sky around the stars. Each constellation has a boundary just like each state in the United States. One of the most recognizable constellations is Orion because of its bright stars and striking pattern. There are a total of 88 constellations.

Corona. The "atmosphere" of the Sun above the photosphere (visible surface). It extends outward from the Sun for several million miles and is visible during a total solar eclipse as the irregular white halo surrounding the Moon.

Cosmic Rays. Cosmic rays are not rays but highly-charged particles from space, traveling at nearly the speed of light. Most of these particles are the nuclei of hydrogen atoms, but they can be from any of the elements in the periodic table. These particles are thought to have been ejected from supernovae explosions. Cosmic rays are not part of the electromagnetic spectrum.

Cosmology. The study of the Universe as a whole, on its grand scale.

Cosmogony. The study of the origin and evolution of the Universe.

Crater. A concave depression on a Planet, moon or asteroid created from the impact of a comet, asteroid or meteoroid.

Crater Rays. Bright streaks that radiate from some craters on the Moon. They are the result of the ejection of reflective material from craters during their formation (from cometary or meteoroid impacts).

Crescent. A phase of the Moon between New Moon and either First or Last Quarter.

Dawes' Limit. A number indicating the resolving power of a telescope, usually expressed in arc seconds. This number represents the angular size of the smallest detail that can be resolved for a particular telescope diameter (for double stars, it is the minimum angular separation of two stars that a telescope can "split"). These limits were first calculated by William Dawes (1799–1868). The resolving power for small telescopes is as follows: 4-inch — 1.1 arc seconds; 6-inch — 0.8 arc seconds; 8-inch — 0.6 arc seconds; 10-inch — 0.5 arc seconds; 12-inch — 0.4 arc seconds; 20-inch — 0.2 arc seconds. The turbulent nature of the atmosphere generally limits resolving power to about 0.5 arc seconds. See more about resolving power in the discussion of double stars on page 255.

Dawn. The time around sunrise. Dusk is the time around sunset.

Astronomical Glossary

Daylight-Saving Time. The advancing of clocks from Standard Time by one hour. Most of the world changes to Daylight-Saving Time. In the US, the clocks have been advanced from the first Sunday in April through the last Saturday in October, but this could change. The practice of advancing the clocks occurs for social, rather than scientific reasons.

Dark Energy. There is no scientific evidence for dark energy. It is a theoretical construct to help scientists account for current observations of the Universe. Dark energy is believed to be a negative force, almost like an "anti-gravity," that is driving the Universe to expand at an increasing rate or acceleration since the Big Bang. Dark Energy may be a concept that falls by the wayside as our understanding of the Universe improves.

Dark Matter. Scientists use Newton's law of gravity to make the necessary calculations for the navigation of spacecraft to our Planets. Scientists believe that Newton's law of gravity applies everywhere in the Universe and over any distance. If this is true, then there is a problem because all the celestial observations made by astronomers can account for only 10% of the matter required to gravitationally hold or bind galaxies together. Where is the other 90%, that is, the rest of the matter to produce the gravity that is required to keep galaxies from flying apart? This is a major mystery! Either our physics is incorrect or we don't fully understand the nature of the Universe. One solution to this problem has been to invent "dark matter," that is, matter we have been unable to see or account for. For example, there could be huge or many gas clouds that are invisible (like air is invisible) or difficult to detect. And there could also be numerous failed-stars that give off no light and are difficult to detect. However, even if we start finding some of this dark matter, it probably will account for just a fraction of the 90% astronomers are trying to find. A true mystery indeed.

Declination (also Dec or δ). Latitude-type coordinate used to indicate the position of an object in the sky. Declination is equivalent to and is expressed in the same manner as latitude. 0° declination is at the celestial equator (0° latitude is at the equator). The north celestial pole has declination +90°, the south celestial pole, −90°. Declination is used in conjunction with Right Ascension to determine coordinates of celestial objects.

Deep Sky Objects (DSOs). Refers to star clusters, nebulae and galaxies. Although the term connotes objects that are distant and faint, some deep sky objects are bright and span a large area of the sky. The Andromeda Galaxy, for example, spans more than six Moon diameters and can be seen with the naked eye. Through tradition, the stars, Planets and other members of our Solar System are not considered deep sky objects.

Descending Node. The point at which the orbit of a Solar System member, like one of the Planets or a comet, crosses the celestial equator or ecliptic from north to south (in declination). See also Ascending Node.

Astronomical Glossary

Dobsonian Telescope. Named after John Dobson, who in the 1970s popularized astronomy through larger, simpler and cheaper Newtonian telescopes. The key to this concept was the use of simple but effective altazimuth mounts.

Double Star. Double stars can be optical or binary. Optical doubles are two stars that appear visually very close to each other because they just happen to be in the same line of sight. On the other hand, binary doubles, also called binary stars, are a pair of stars that revolve around each other.

Dusk. The time around sunset.

Dwarf Star. Our Sun is a typical dwarf star. The term "dwarf" refers to luminosity rather than to size. More than 90% of stars are classified as "dwarfs," but they often represent the average-size stars.

Earthshine. Sunlight reflected off the Earth which slightly illuminates the dark side of the Moon facing Earth (that is, the side that is not being directly lit by sunlight). Earthshine is especially noticeable when the Moon is a crescent. During this time, the highlands and maria can be glimpsed on the dark side through a telescope.

Eccentricity. A number between 0 and 1 used to indicate the elongation of an ellipse. An eccentricity of 0 indicates a circle; and ellipses with eccentricities close to 1 would look similar in shape to a submarine.

Ecliptic. The apparent path that the Sun describes in the sky over the course of a year. The ecliptic is a great circle (cuts the sky into two halves) and crosses 13 constellations — the constellations of the zodiac. The Sun appears to revolve around the Earth once a day, but this movement does not "create" the ecliptic. The ecliptic is described from the Earth revolving around the Sun. Since the background stars remain stationary, it appears from the Earth as if the Sun slowly moves in a circle against the background stars over the course of a year.

Ellipse. An oval or elongated circle. All celestial orbits (of Planets, moons, comets, binary stars) are ellipses and not circles. An elliptical orbit may be very close to a circle, as is the case of Venus' orbit, or highly elongated as with comets.

Elongation. The arc angle distance between the Sun and a Solar System member (Planet, Moon, comet or asteroid) as viewed from Earth.

Emission Nebula. A nebula that produces its own light from the stimulation of its gas by ultraviolet radiation from a nearby star or stars.

Epicycles and Deferents. An epicycle is a small circle that rotates on a point of a larger circle, called a deferent, that circles the Earth. Movements of the epicycles and deferents were used by the Egyptian astronomer Ptolemy (circa 85–165 AD) and others to help explain the retrograde motion of the Superior Planets about Earth, which was considered to be at the center of the Universe. This system went unchallenged for centuries partially because it could accurately predict the motions of the Planets.

Equatorial Mount. A type of mount that facilitates observing and photographing celestial objects because an observer has to make only one movement to keep an object centered in the eyepiece. Equatorial mounts

Astronomical Glossary

have two perpendicular axes. The polar axis points to the north celestial pole; the other declination axis is positioned 90° to the polar axis. Until the mid-1970s, the majority of telescopes at professional observatories had equatorial mounts. Today, most professional telescopes have computer-controlled altazimuth mounts because they cost less than equatorial mounts. A German equatorial mount is a particular type of equatorial mount that is recognizable by having weights on its declination axis.

Equinox. See Vernal Equinox or Autumnal Equinox.

f/number. See Focal Ratio.

Field of View. The expanse of sky that can be seen through binoculars or a telescope. Expressed in degrees (arc degrees), field of view can be true or apparent. True field of view is the actual amount of sky that can be seen through a telescope or binoculars. For example, if you look through a telescope and you see the whole Full Moon, nothing more and nothing less, then the true field of view for that eyepiece is 1/2° or 30 arc minutes (30'). Apparent field of view is a design attribute of an eyepiece. The greater an eyepiece's apparent field of view (usually ranges from 50° to 83°), the larger is the true field of view. A difference in apparent field of view is like the difference between looking out a large and small window.

First Quarter. Phase of the Moon, halfway between New and Full, when the Moon is "half" lighted on the right or eastern side.

Fission. The splitting apart of atoms which was the process employed in early nuclear weapons. This is not the mechanism that fuels stars.

Flamsteed Numbers. Numbers assigned to the stars, by constellation, to aid in identification. Flamsteed numbers are an expansion of the system that identifies the brightest stars with Greek letters (Bayer letters).

Focal Length. The distance from the primary mirror or objective lens to the point where light comes to a focus. Usually expressed in millimeters.

Focal Ratio (f/ratio). The ratio of a lens or mirror's focal length to its diameter. A focal ratio is calculated by dividing the diameter of the primary or objective *into* its focal length (the units of measurement must be the same for the focal length and primary/objective diameter).

Full Moon. Phase of the Moon when the lighted side presents a full, circular disk in the sky. The Full Moon rises as the Sun sets.

Fusion. The process that fuels the stars and our Sun. Fusion occurs when four hydrogen atoms fuse to form one helium atom. The resulting helium atom is 1% less in mass than the four hydrogen atoms. The energy from the Sun comes from this 1% difference in mass. Fusion is triggered by the tremendous pressure from the sheer mass of stars.

Galactic Cluster. Relatively young open clusters found in the spiral arms of our Galaxy. The spiral arms have the highest concentrations of hydrogen gas, where stars are born.

Galaxy. A basic grouping in the Universe. Galaxies represent a collection of billions to hundreds of billions of stars that are gravitationally bound. They are generally circular, like a disk or spherical in shape. All galaxies are outside of our Milky Way Galaxy.

Astronomical Glossary

G
H
I

Gas Giants. The Planets Jupiter, Saturn, Uranus and Neptune.

Gegenschein. A German word that means "counterglow." It is a very faint patch of light in the night sky, visible opposite the Sun and on the ecliptic that is more often seen around midnight. This glow is created from sunlight reflecting off dust particles that reside in the same plane that the Planets orbit. See Zodiacal Light, which is a related-type glow.

Giant Star. A large and bright star representing a "bloated" condition that occurs toward the end of the life of an average-size star like our Sun.

Gibbous. The phase of the Moon between First and Last Quarter (but not counting Full Moon). During this time, the Moon is considered to be respectively a waxing and waning gibbous Moon.

Globular Cluster. This deep sky object is a tight group of up to a million stars resembling a ball (like a cotton ball). Globular clusters are not galaxies, but are parts of galaxies. The globular cluster M13 in Hercules is just visible to the naked eye at a dark location.

GMT. See Universal Time.

Great Circle. Any circle in the sky that divides the sky in half (creating two equal hemispheres). Examples are the celestial equator and the ecliptic.

Green Flash. A flash of green light that sometimes appears at the place and moment the Sun dips below the horizon. Green flashes are more often seen at sea.

Greenwich Mean Time. See Universal Time.

Harvest Moon. The Full Moon closest to the autumnal equinox, around September 23.

Hertzsprung-Russell Diagram. A famous diagram in astronomy that shows the relationship between the luminosity and surface temperature of stars.

Hubble Space Telescope (HST). Launched into orbit 375 miles (600 km) above Earth in 1990, this 94-inch (2.4 meters) diameter telescope has revolutionized astronomy by providing the most detailed images of the Universe.

Huygens Eyepiece. The first true eyepiece, invented by Christian Huygens in the 1600s, uses two lens elements.

IC (Index Catalogue of Nebulae and Star Clusters). An additional listing of more than 5,000 deep sky objects to the NGC catalogue compiled by J. L. E. Dreyer in 1908 and still in use. The majority of IC objects are faint galaxies. Also see NGC.

Inferior Conjunction. See Conjunction.

Inferior Planets. Mercury and Venus — the two Planets that orbit closer to the Sun than Earth.

Inner Planets. The four Planets — Mercury, Venus, Earth and Mars — that orbit inside the asteroid belt.

Iridescent clouds.

Astronomical Glossary

Ion. An atom or molecule that has gained a positive or negative charge by acquiring or losing outer electrons.

Iridescent Clouds. A rainbow of colors that can sometimes be seen spread over thin clouds that have similar size droplets of water. More often, the colors are seen in clouds that are closer to the Sun. Wearing polarized sunglasses helps to see the iridescent colors easier.

Jupiter. The 5th Planet from the Sun. This Gas Giant is famous for its Great Red Spot, cloud bands and four bright moons. It even has a faint ring around it. Comet Shoemaker-Levy 9 collided with Jupiter in July 1994. Astronomers believe that Jupiter may act like a gravitational magnet and has probably incurred the largest proportion of comet and meteoroid impacts in our Solar System, thus giving Earth a chance to harbor life.

Kellner Eyepiece. A "medium-line" eyepiece with three or more lens elements. Kellner eyepieces are "superior" to Ramsden eyepieces but do not "perform" as well as Orthoscopic or Plössl eyepieces.

Kelvin (K). A temperature system based on absolute zero (the lowest temperature possible) and the Celsius scale. 0K is absolute zero; 273K is 0° C and 373K is 100° C. Note that the little circle used to denote degrees is not used with the K.

Last Quarter. Phase of the Moon, between Full and New, when the Moon is half lighted on the left or western side. Also referred to as Third Quarter.

Libration. A slight up-and-down and side-to-side movement of the Moon that enables observers on Earth to see more than just half of its surface — in fact, close to 59%. The Moon's elliptical orbit combined with its small axial tilt allows for glimpses around its edges.

Light Year (ly). Unit of distance in astronomy. One light year is the distance light travels in one year. Since light travels at the rate of 186,282 miles per second, it will travel 5,880,000,000,000 miles (almost 6 trillion miles) in one year. It takes light 1.3 seconds to travel the distance from the Earth to the Moon and 8.3 minutes to travel from the Sun to the Earth. Our Solar System is about 11 light hours in diameter and our Galaxy is about 80,000 light years in diameter.

Local Group. A group of about 30 galaxies that includes our Galaxy and the Andromeda Galaxy. Galaxies are clumped together in groups throughout the Universe.

Lunar Eclipse. The blockage of the sunlight illuminating the Moon by Earth's shadow. Lunar eclipses can occur only at Full Moon and do not occur every month because the Moon's orbit is inclined to Earth's orbit. This usually places the Moon above or below Earth's shadow.

Maksutov Reflector. A catadioptric or "compound" telescope that has a deeply concave front correcting lens. Maksutov reflectors provide better image quality over a larger field of view than Schmidt-Cassegrain Telescopes.

Mare (plural: Maria). Original name given by Galileo to the smooth, dark plains on the Moon because they resemble bodies of water. Mare is the Latin word for sea. The maria were created by lava flow.

I
J
K
L
M

Astronomical Glossary

M

Mars. The 4th Planet from the Sun. Mars appears reddish but is actually pale brown. Mars became well known for its "canals," the result of erroneous observations made in the early 1900s. The canals do not exist. Mars is the most hospitable Planet in our Solar System (after Earth) and its north polar cap contains huge amounts of frozen water. Mars may have harbored primitive life in the past, and will hopefully be visited by humans this century.

Mercury. The closest Planet to the Sun. Mercury resembles the Moon because it is small, pitted with craters and has no atmosphere.

Meridian. See Celestial Meridian.

Messier Objects. A collection of 112 deep sky objects originally recorded and described during the mid-1700s by Charles Messier of France. These objects include the brightest star clusters, nebulae and galaxies. Messier was the leading observational astronomer of his time. He observed and reported on the whole gamut of astronomical phenomena, including the weather. He had a passion for comets and discovered 20 during his lifetime. He lived and worked just a 7-minute walk from Notre Dame in Paris.

Moon halo.

Meteor. The light trail in the sky created when a meteoroid enters Earth's atmosphere. Often called a shooting star.

Meteorite. A rock from space that has fallen to the ground.

Meteoroid. The term used to describe a space rock before it enters the Earth's atmosphere to become a white streak known as a meteor. Most meteoroids that produce meteors are about the size of a grain of sand and burn up completely in the Earth's atmosphere.

Meteor Shower. A display of a greater than average number of meteors that appear to originate from a particular spot in the sky. Twelve major meteor showers occur annually. These showers are the result of the Earth passing through semi-permanent swarms of cometary debris that orbit the Sun.

Micrometeorite. A meteoroid as small as or smaller than a grain of sand.

Milky Way. A hazy, cloudy (milky) band in the night sky. This band is a permanent part of the sky and has an average width of five arc degrees (10 Moon diameters). The Milky Way is impossible to see in larger cities because of light and air pollution, however, it is very prominent in country skies. It appears milky because it is composed of countless stars — the bulk of the stars in our Galaxy. With a telescope or binoculars, one can see that there are many more stars in the region of the Milky Way than in other areas of the sky. The "Milky Way" is also the name given to our Galaxy.

Minor Planet. Another term for an asteroid.

Astronomical Glossary

Moon Halo. A halo visible around the Moon created by six-sided, pencil-shaped ice crystals higher up in the atmosphere. See Sun Halo.

Multiple Star. Three or more stars that are gravitationally bound and revolve around one another.

Multiple Universes. Astronomers and theorist have been thrashing over the idea of the Big Bang, which includes reviewing and analyzing many formulae in physics. Some insights in this research suggest that there might be other universes, ones outside our own. Although this idea is entertaining, there is no means, at this time, to verify or test whether this is true.

Nadir. The point directly below an observer. We each have our own nadir.

Nebula (plural: Nebulae). Gaseous cloud, comprised mostly of hydrogen, that resides in galaxies. Most nebulae are irregular in shape; however, some are spherical shells of hydrogen left by the collapse of a giant star. In spiral galaxies, the highest concentration of hydrogen gas is in the arms, where most new stars are born.

Neptune. The 8th Planet is a Gas Giant and was discovered in 1871. It is slightly smaller than Uranus and has a very faint ring system.

Neutron Star. An extremely dense star created from the supernova explosion of a massive star. The compression from the explosion merges electrons and protons into neutrons. The mass of a neutron star ranges from 1.4 to 3 times that of our Sun, but it only has a diameter of about 12 miles (19 km). Since neutron stars give off very little light, they are often studied as pulsars with radio telescopes. Pulsar is a de-

scriptive term for a neutron star that is highly magnetized and spins rapidly, anywhere from 4 to 200 times a second.

NGC (New General Catalogue of Nebulae and Star Clusters). A listing of nearly 8,000 deep sky objects compiled by J. L. E. Dreyer in 1888 and still used today. The majority of NGC objects are galaxies and open clusters. Overall, they are not as faint as Dreyer's additional list of 5,000 IC objects (Index Catalogue of Nebulae and Star Clusters). See IC.

New Moon. The Moon is considered New when it is between the Earth and Sun. It cannot be seen at this time because it is near the Sun.

Newtonian Telescope. The simplest and most widely used reflector telescope. First built by Isaac Newton in 1668, this telescope uses a parabolic mirror to focus light.

Northern Lights. See Aurora.

Nova. A nova explosion is cyclical, caused by the repeated infusion of hydrogen gas from a giant star to a white dwarf (binary pair).

Occultation. The eclipsing of one celestial body by another. The Moon frequently occults stars and the Planets. Less frequent are occultations of a star by the Planets or an asteroid.

Open Cluster. A group of up to several thousand stars that were born together and reside in close proximity to one another. Several open clusters are visible to the naked eye. The Pleiades in Taurus is the best known, however, most open clusters can be seen only with a telescope.

Astronomical Glossary

Opposition. The alignment of one or more Superior Planets (Mars through Pluto) with the Earth and Sun. These Planets are in opposition when they are directly "behind" the Earth, away from the Sun. The Superior Planets are closest to the Earth at opposition and they rise in the east as the Sun is setting in the west.

Orthoscopic Eyepiece. An excellent four-element lens eyepiece that was very popular during the 60s and 70s. The Plössl lens design has superseded the orthoscopic eyepiece in popularity because it has a wider field of view.

Outer Planets. Jupiter, Saturn, Uranus, Neptune and Pluto: the Planets that orbit outside the asteroid belt.

Parabolic. The adjective of the noun parabola, which is a mathematical shape that describes a curve found frequently in nature. This shape has the unique property of allowing incoming light to focus at the same point — something that a simple circle shape cannot do. The primary mirrors of Newtonian reflectors are parabolic.

Parsec. Unit of distance in astronomy. One parsec is about 3.2 light years. The parsec is derived by using the astronomical unit and trigonometry. It is the distance that one astronomical unit would have to be from the Earth in order for it to appear 1 arc second in length (1/3600 of 1 compass degree).

Penumbra (Eclipse). The shadow adjacent to the dark umbra shadow. If you are in the penumbra shadow during a solar eclipse, you will see the Sun partially blocked by the Moon.

Penumbra (Sunspot). The lighter part of a sunspot that immediately surrounds the dark inner umbra.

Perigee. The closest point that the Moon or an artificial satellite comes to the Earth. Since all orbiting bodies have elliptical orbits, they have a closest and farthest point from the object they orbit.

Perihelion. The point in a Planet's, asteroid's or comet's orbit where it is closest to the Sun. Since all Solar System members have elliptical orbits, they have a closest and farthest point from the Sun.

Photosphere. The visible surface of the Sun. The photosphere is 125 miles deep (200 km), reaches a temperature of 10,000° F (5,500° C) and is comprised of granules, or cells, about 650 miles (1,050 km) in diameter. Sunspots are on the photosphere.

Planetary Nebula. A huge spherical shell, a ring or opposed lobes of hydrogen gas left by the collapse of a red giant or supergiant star. The gas is stimulated to emit its own light by ultraviolet radiation from the collapsed star. Planetary nebulae can measure a light year or more in diameter (or greatest length) and can be seen with small telescopes.

Planisphere. A circular star chart that is used to find the constellations. The word planisphere refers to a sphere of stars plotted on a flat plane. Planispheres are handy charts for stargazers because unlike star charts in books, they can be adjusted to show the stars visible for a specific hour and day of the year.

Plössl Eyepiece. A popular optical design for eyepieces. It utilizes four lens elements and provides a generous field of view. See illustration on page 87.

Astronomical Glossary

Pluto. The 9th Planet in our Solar System. Discovered in 1930 by Clyde Tombaugh in Flagstaff, Arizona, after an extensive photographic search of the sky. Pluto's orbit is greatly inclined compared to the other Planets. Its largest moon, Charon, is more than half Pluto's diameter.

Population I and II Stars. Population I stars, which include our Sun, are relatively young stars and contain a much higher abundance of metals than the older Population II stars. Population I stars are often found in the arms of spiral galaxies. Globular clusters are composed mainly of the older Population II stars.

Precession. The Earth spins on its axis like a top. At the same time, the Earth's axis is slowly wobbling around a "giant" circle, similar to a top wobbling as it slows down. This wobble is known as precession and is caused by the gravitational pull from the Moon and Sun. The precession wobble describes a 47° arc diameter circle in the sky and it takes approximately 25,800 years for the Earth's axis to move and complete this circle. Today, the Earth's axis points toward Polaris, the North Star. In about 12,000 years, the axis will be pointing to the star Vega, in the constellation Lyra. Some ancient civilizations, including the Egyptians, knew about precession.

Prominence. Protrusion of ionized gas from the surface of the Sun. Large prominences can easily extend 10 to 30 Earth diameters from the photosphere and sometimes loop back to the surface, creating beautiful arches.

Proper Motion. The movement of the stars in relationship to one another as viewed from our Solar System. Any

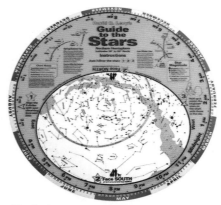

Planisphere.

movement is measured against stars that are even farther away. Generally, the stars that are closest to our Sun have the largest proper motions and show movement by changing their position in respect to the stars around them. Proper motion is usually measured in thousands of years.

Pulsar. See Neutron Star.

Pyrex. Annealed pyrex is a preferred glass for reflector telescope mirrors. Pyrex is significantly more stable with temperature variations than plate glass.

Quadrature. A separation in the sky of 90° between Solar System members. A Superior Planet (Mars through Pluto) would be at quadrature with the Sun if the Planet were at the zenith as the Sun was rising or setting.

Quasar. Extremely bright galaxy that outputs enormous amounts of energy over the entire electromagnetic spectrum. Quasars are the farthest and thus among the oldest objects in the Universe. The energy from quasar galaxies is produced from the interaction of enormous amounts of matter being pulled into giant black holes at the galaxies' centers.

Astronomical Glossary

R

Primary and secondary rainbows.

Radio Telescope. An instrument used to study celestial objects by mapping their radio waves instead of light rays. Radio astronomy uses very large dish antennae.

Rainbow. Rainbows are created by the reflection and refraction of sunlight through water droplets in the atmosphere, usually created during rainstorms. The primary rainbow is often accompanied by a secondary fainter rainbow.

Ramsden Eyepiece. An inexpensive eyepiece that uses two lens elements. Ramsden eyepieces often are included with inexpensive telescopes. They are not generally used today.

Redshift. A lengthening or stretching of the wavelength of light in the spectrum of a celestial body that is moving away from Earth. The redshift can be used to determine the speed of receding objects.

Reflecting Telescope. Any telescope that uses a concave mirror as the primary means for focusing light.

Refractor Telescope. Any telescope that uses a glass objective lens as the primary means for focusing light. Camera lenses and Galileo's telescope are refracting instruments. Refracting telescopes are more expensive per aperture inch than other telescopes. For the price of a quality 4-inch refractor, you could purchase a 16 to 18-inch Dobsonian reflector.

Regolith. The "soil" on the surface of the Moon created by the bombardment of micrometeorites. Most of the meteors that we see in our night sky are caused by micrometeorites, but they burn up in the atmosphere.

Resolving Power. See Dawes' Limit.

Retrograde. An apparent backward movement in the sky (as viewed from Earth) of the Superior Planets (Mars through Pluto). As the Superior Planets move in their orbits around the Sun, from Earth they appear to move slowly eastward against the background of stars. However, for several months each year, these Planets reverse their course and move westward, then resume their eastward course. This apparent backward/westward movement is called retrograde motion. This effect is created by a faster orbiting Earth "passing" the slower orbiting Superior Planets.

Richest-Field Telescope (RFT). A telescope with a low focal ratio, generally ranging from f/4 to f/6. You can see more sky in the eyepiece of a RFT than with higher focal ratio telescopes.

Right Ascension (also RA or α). West-to-east coordinate used in conjunction with Declination to determine the position of an object in the sky. Right Ascension is equivalent to longitude but is expressed differently. It is derived by dividing the celestial sphere into 24 hours. Each hour is further di-

Astronomical Glossary

vided into 60 minutes and each minute into 60 seconds. Zero hours (0h) starts at the vernal equinox. Examples of R.A. are 12h 23.7m and 1h 14m 23s.

Rille. Fairly straight, long "lines" on the Moon's maria produced from faults on these plains.

Saturn. The 6th Planet is magnificent in the sky with its beautiful ring system. Until the 1980s, it was thought these rings were unique to Saturn. The other Gas Giants (Jupiter, Uranus and Neptune) also have ring systems, but none are as spectacular as Saturn's.

Schmidt-Cassegrain Telescope (SCT). This catadioptric telescope has two mirrors and a front correcting lens. Its folded optical path makes it one of the most compact telescopes. The 8-inch SCT is a very popular amateur telescope.

Seeing. An observing term indicating the atmospheric viewing condition of the night sky. Good, fair, poor and turbulent are adjectives often used with seeing.

Setting Circles. Circular, graduated scales sometimes attached to the right ascension and declination axes of equatorial mounts that aid in locating celestial objects by using their RA and Dec coordinates.

Shooting Star. See meteor.

Sidereal. The true orbital or rotational period of a Planet, moon, asteroid or comet. This is the time it takes to complete one revolution or rotation. Earth's sidereal rotational period (23 hours, 56 minutes, 4 seconds) is obtained by measuring successive passages of a star in a fixed telescope. This is not used for clock time because if it were, in six month's time, noon would occur at midnight (4 minutes x 180 days = 12 hour change).

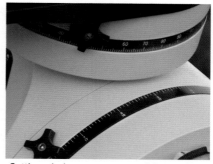
Setting circles on an equatorial mount.

Solar Eclipse. Occurs when the Moon moves in front of the Sun, which can happen only at New Moon. There are three types of solar eclipses: total, partial and annular. A total eclipse occurs when the Sun is completely blocked by the Moon. An annular eclipse occurs when the Moon passes completely in front of the Sun, but does not totally cover the Sun. Partial eclipses occur when the Moon covers only a portion of the Sun.

Solar Flare. A spontaneous eruption on the surface of the Sun that releases enormous amounts of energy and energetic particles into the Solar System. These eruptions cause the aurorae as well as radio and communication disruptions.

Solar System. A system composed of a star and revolving planets, asteroids and comets. We normally use the term to refer to our Solar System, however, astronomers have found numerous nearby stars with their own orbiting planets.

Solar Wind. A "wind" in the Solar System caused by the release of charged protons and electrons from the Sun. The solar wind is partially responsible for pushing a comet's tail away from the Sun.

Astronomical Glossary

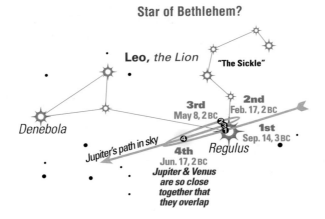

Star of Bethlehem?

Leo, *the Lion*   "The Sickle"

Denebola

Jupiter's path in sky

3rd May 8, 2 BC   **2nd** Feb. 17, 2 BC

1st Sep. 14, 3 BC

Regulus

4th Jun. 17, 2 BC

Jupiter & Venus are so close together that they overlap

Solstice. The time of year when the Sun is at its highest or lowest point in the sky. Also see Summer Solstice and Winter Solstice.

Spectrum. The light from the Sun, Planets, stars, nebulae and galaxies can be directed through a prism (or diffraction grating) to obtain a spectrogram (photographic or digital image of a spectrum). Spectrograms look like long, horizontal bands marked with numerous dark parallel lines. The arrangement of these lines is used to identify the chemical makeup as well as the velocity of celestial objects.

Spherical Aberration. The inability of an optical system to focus all light rays at the same point. For example, the light rays from the outer edge of an objective mirror or lens may focus short or long compared to the light rays that pass near the center of the objective.

Sporadic Meteor. A meteor not associated with a shower. Between three and seven sporadic meteors can be observed every hour.

Standard Time. Local time, the time on our clocks. The continental United States has four standard time zones.

Star Cluster. An open cluster, galactic cluster or a globular cluster.

Star of Bethlehem. What was the star of Bethlehem? No one knows for certain but some scholars think that the Magi witnessed three conjunctions of Jupiter with Regulus, and a finale where Jupiter and Venus blended into one star, all within a span of 9 months. To many cultures, Regulus was the "regal" star while Jupiter was the king of the Planets. What could be more propitious than these two royal bodies coming together? This event is an example of retrograde motion bringing about several conjunctions. The orange line in the illustration above shows Jupiter's retrograde motion above Regulus (creating a crown) and ends in a rare conjunction where two Planets overlap (not physically, but from a perspective view). This merging of the Planets created a very bright apparition that truly represented a heavenly punctuation. Researchers have found no evidence of this 9-month event ever happening again. The Magi certainly realized that something rare and special occurred, even if it was only an astronomical event.

Astronomical Glossary

Sublimate. To change directly from a solid to a gas or from a gas to a solid without becoming liquid. The volatiles in a comet sublimate to create the coma and tail.

Summer Solstice. The day on which the Sun reaches its highest point in the sky (at noon), approximately June 21. The day with the most amount of sunlight (in the northern hemisphere).

Sun halo.

Sun Halo. A large halo around the Sun produced from the refraction of light through higher altitude, thin clouds that contain six-sided, pencil-shaped ice crystals. See Moon Halo.

Sunspots. Dark spots on the surface of the Sun. Large sunspots are visible to the naked eye and have been recorded by ancient civilizations. Sunspots rotate with the Sun. They continuously form, grow, decrease in size, and dissolve away. Often larger than the Earth, sunspots are cooler than the surrounding brighter photosphere (about 6,300° F or 3,500° C compared to 10,000° F or 5,500° C) and have intense magnetic fields.

Supergiant Star. A star with a diameter up to 1,000 times that of our Sun. Because of their size, supergiants are very luminous; but they have low densities. Betelgeuse in Orion is a supergiant star.

Superior Conjunction. See Conjunction.

Superior Planets. Mars, Jupiter, Saturn, Neptune, Uranus and Pluto.

Supernova. A stellar explosion of such magnitude that the light emitted can outshine the star's galaxy. A supernova is about 1,000 times brighter than a nova, and can remain brilliant for several weeks. Supernovae occur infrequently and are observed more often in galaxies other than our own.

Synodic Period. A relative period of revolution as viewed from Earth. For example, the time a Superior Planet takes to go from opposition to opposition, the time from one inferior conjunction with Venus to the next, or, the time from Full Moon to Full Moon. All of these examples represent revolution periods that are not true periods (the actual completion of one revolution around the Sun or Earth).

Syzergy. The alignment of three or more celestial objects, especially Solar System members. New Moon and Full Moon are examples of three bodies lining up — the Sun, Earth and Moon.

Terra (plural is Terrae). The brighter or lighter-colored areas of the Moon, which are also called the highlands. These areas have the highest concentration of craters, created from impacts that mostly occurred during the first 2.5 billion years of the Solar System's birth. The terrae are covered with regolith, a fine grain "soil" that may be as deep as 49 feet (15 meters).

Terrestrial Planets. The Planets Mercury, Venus, Earth and Mars that have rock-type surfaces.

Terminator. The "border" on the Moon between the lighted side and the dark side. The terminator is visible to

Astronomical Glossary

observers on Earth when the Moon is in a phase other than Full and New. Craters near the terminator appear sharp and contrasty because of their longer shadows.

Third Quarter. See Last Quarter.

Transparency. A measure, given in magnitude, of the faintest star that can be seen with the naked eye at a particular time and location. The transparency in large cities is generally "poor" because various types of pollution prevent seeing fainter stars. Transparency is usually best in the country and on high mountains. Transparency, like seeing, can change in a "short" period of time depending on weather or other factors. See Seeing.

Twilight. The transition time between day and night either before sunrise or after sunset. There are three officially defined twilights — civil, nautical and astronomical. Each is based on an arc angle distance that the Sun is below the horizon. The sky is at its darkest at astronomical twilight.

Umbra (Eclipse). The inner, darkest part of a shadow. Total solar or lunar eclipses involve two types of shadows, the umbra and penumbra. Observers in the umbra shadow will experience a total eclipse. Those in the adjacent penumbra shadow will see a partial eclipse. Observers outside of both shadows will not see even a hint of an eclipse. Partial solar and lunar eclipses involve only penumbra shadows.

Umbra (Sunspot). The inner and darkest part of a sunspot. The umbra is surrounded by the lighter penumbra.

Universal Time (UT). The occurrence of astronomical events is expressed in Universal Time in order to avoid confusion due to time zones and Daylight-Saving Time. Universal Time was adopted by an international conference in 1884 and is the local time at the Greenwich Observatory near London, England. Expressed using the 24-hour clock, Universal Time must be converted to Local Standard Time to adjust for time zone differences. The WWV radio station in Fort Collins, Colorado, as well as CHU in Ottawa, Ontario, Canada broadcast Universal Time 24 hours a day. These broadcasts, by radio signal, are known as Coordinated Universal Time (UTC). Universal Time is often referred to as Greenwich Mean Time (GMT).

Uranus. The 7th Planet from the Sun was discovered officially by William Herschel in 1781, however, it may have been known to some ancient cultures because it is just visible to the naked eye. This Gas Giant is the third largest Planet in our Solar System and has a faint ring system.

Variable Star. A star whose brightness changes over a period of time. Stars change in brightness for various reasons. Some stars, like Algol in Perseus, change in brightness because they are eclipsed by a dimmer companion star. Other stars, called Cepheid variables, vary in brightness because their diameters periodically expand and contact up to 10%.

Venus. The 2nd Planet from the Sun is the brightest Planet in the sky, reaching magnitude −4.6. Venus once was referred to as Earth's sister Planet because its diameter is about the same as Earth's. However, this distinction is rarely used anymore because Venus' environment is totally hostile to life. Completely covered with sulfuric acid

Astronomical Glossary

clouds, Venus has an atmospheric pressure 90 times Earth's with surface temperatures reaching 900° F (480° C).

Vernal Equinox. One of two points in the sky where the ecliptic (the apparent path of the Sun over the course of a year) crosses the celestial equator. The other is the autumnal equinox. The vernal equinox is located in the constellation of Pisces and represents the beginning of Spring, as the Sun crosses the celestial equator from south to north. The vernal equinox is also the starting point for all celestial coordinates (R.A. 0h, Declination 0°). The Sun is at the vernal equinox on approximately June 21. Day and night are equal in length on this day.

Vulcan. A Planet once thought to orbit inside of Mercury's orbit. Vulcan does not exist.

Waning. Shrinking, decreasing. The Moon wanes as it decreases in size from Full to New. Opposite of waxing.

Waxing. Increasing, growing. The Moon is waxing as it increases in size from a Crescent to Full. Opposite of waning.

White Dwarf. The final stage in the life of an average star, before it becomes a cold, dark object. White dwarfs have high densities because they are about the size of the Earth with the mass of our Sun. They also have hot surfaces that are two to four times hotter than our Sun. Sirius, the brightest star in the sky, has a white dwarf binary companion.

Winter Solstice. The day on which the Sun reaches its lowest point in the sky (at noon), which occurs approximately December 22. For the northern hemisphere, this is the day with the least amount of sunlight.

Zenith. The highest point in the sky, directly overhead. Everyone has their own zenith (unless you are carrying someone on your shoulders, then you share a zenith).

Zodiac. Twelve constellations traditionally make up the zodiac, however, there are actually 13 constellations that make up the zodiac (the 13th is Ophiuchus between Scorpius and Sagittarius). These constellations lie along a great circle in the sky called the ecliptic, the apparent path the Sun travels in the sky over the course of a year. The ecliptic is created from the Earth's revolution around the Sun.

Zodiacal Light. A soft glow of "cone-shaped" light in the sky that appears in line with the western ecliptic after the Sun has set or the eastern ecliptic before sunrise. The widest part of the "cone" is toward the horizon. It is produced by sunlight scattering off dust particles that reside and are concentrated along the ecliptic plane, that is, the plane where the Planets orbit. Its glow is fainter than the Milky Way Band and cannot be seen when the Moon is out. The zodiacal light is much brighter than the gegenschein (also in this glossary).

V
W
Z

...ur modern society provides us with a good scientific understanding of the world but ancient civilizations did not have this luxury, so they made up stories to explain everyday natural events like thunder and lightning, the movement of the Sun and Moon, the wind and waves, and even the shapes of mountains. Often these stories involved mighty characters or gods who wielded the power to move heaven and Earth. Over time, these stories became traditions, beliefs and even religions. This occurred in every corner of the world — no civilization or group of people were exempt.

But the "stories" that influenced our culture the most came from the Greeks and were adopted by the Romans.

The Greek stories are plentiful and rich in content but they differ from the stories that we tell and write today. Our modern-day stories unfold in a way that is familiar because they reflect our experiences and perceptions. And so did the Greek's but they saw life differently! To them, life was capricious and heavily laced with non sequitur twists and turns. As such, their mythological stories often take us on a wild roller-coaster ride that jumps rails.

The mythological stories vary and overlap. Here, I relate some of the more popular versions as they relate to the heavens.

Mythology corresponding to Chart A on page 61

Ursa Major and **Ursa Minor**, respectively the **"Big Bear"** and **"Little Bear,"** are better known as the Big and Little Dippers. In Greek mythology they represent a mother, Callisto and her son, Arcas sent to the sky by Jupiter. Jupiter came upon the beautiful Callisto, daughter of King Lycaon of Arcadia when he was on Earth, inspecting carnage caused by Phaethon, son of Helios, who had arrogantly tried to ride the Sun Chariot across the sky. Jupiter took favor upon Callisto, and against her will, fathered her a son, Arcas. Jupiter's wife, Juno discovered her husband's escapade and turned Callisto into an ugly bear. Later, when Arcas had grown up and was hunting, he encountered a bear running towards him. Not knowing that it was his mother, he aimed an arrow for the kill but Jupiter took sympathy and intervened, turning Arcas into a bear and hurling both into the sky as restitution for all the agony he caused.

Cepheus and **Cassiopeia** were the king and queen of Ethiopia and parents of a daughter, **Andromeda**. The gods became angry at Cassiopeia because of her boastings that she and her daughter were more beautiful than the Nereids mermaids, whose protector was Poseidon. To appease the gods for Cassiopeia's disrespect, Cepheus had to sacrifice his daughter to the Sea Monster, **Cetus**. About this same time **Perseus**, the son of Jupiter, had cut off Medusa's head as a wedding gift, and was heading back from a journey. He noticed Andromeda chained to a sea cliff, and instantly fell in love.

Mythology

Noticing her parents watching in agony, he agreed to rescue her for marriage and then chopped Cetus' head off with the sickle he had used on Medusa. At his wedding, a prior suitor showed up which prompted the royal parents to renege on their promise to Perseus.

A fight ensued, and Perseus was almost overpowered but was saved by using Medusa's head, for all who looked upon her face turned to stone. Afterwards, the royal couple was banished to the heavens by Poseidon for their misdeeds.

Draco the Dragon was one of the many monsters fighting along with the great Titans against the Olympians, commanded by Jupiter. Near the climax of a battle, the dragon opposed the goddess of Wisdom, Minerva, who in turned flung it into the heavens where it froze twisted, after landing so close to the frigid North Celestial Pole.

Camelopardalis, the Giraffe, **Lacerta**, the Lizard and the **Lynx** are faint constellations that were added in the 1600's.

Mythology corresponding to Chart B on page 63

Eridanus is a meandering connection of stars that were recognized by various cultures as a river. In Egypt, it represented the Nile. In Greek mythology, its water was used by Hercules to help clean the stables of King Augeas, as one of his twelve labors. Phaethon fell into this river after being thrown from the Sun Chariot. Although Eridanus is not near the Milky Way, it is sometimes associated with it.

Cetus was an ugly, evil Sea Monster that lived deep in the ocean and personified everything bad. It almost devoured Andromeda, but Perseus chopped its head off before it reached her. It is sometimes referred to as a Whale.

In illustrations, **Auriga** the charioteer or wagoneer, is often shown holding a goat, represented by the star Capella, and two kids. One of the charioteer's responsibilities was supervising the royal livestock. One story has it that the milk from the goat Amaltheia was fed to Jupiter when he was a child. Another has Jupiter placing the chariot in the sky as an appeasement for causing the physical disability of his offspring Hephaestus, whose son inherited the disability, but invented the chariot to move about more easily.

The **Pleiades** or Seven Sisters are the daughters of Atlas and Pleione. They were changed into doves and sent into the heavens as stars to avoid the amorous clutches of Orion. Thus, the Seven Sisters always rise before

Mythology

Orion, forever escaping him. A Native American legend also has Seven Sisters who longed to wander among the stars, lost their way home and huddled together so as not to get separated. The seventh star is difficult to see and in both stories it is said that crying blurs its brightness.

The **Hyades** are piglets and the half-sisters of the Pleiades, all having Atlas as their father. Together, they make up the 14 Atlantides which reside in Taurus.

There are two stories related to **Taurus**, the Bull. Jupiter's wife, Juno, turned the beautiful Io, the daughter of the river god Inachos, into a white heifer to stop Jupiter's affair with her. In another story, Jupiter fell in love with the beautiful Europa, daughter of Agenor, King of Sideon. To lure her away, he changed himself into a mighty white bull and stood among her father's cattle. She went to see the white bull and was captivated by its friendliness. After getting on its back for a ride, Jupiter rode off with her to Crete. Afterward she bore a son, Minos, who became King of Crete.

Fornax, the Furnace and **Caelum**, the Engraver's Tool have no lore, since they were added in the 1600's.

The **Phoenix** is a great bird that lives for 500 years and can regenerate itself from its own ashes. At the end of its life, it builds a nest and lays until the noon sunlight strikes it, setting it aflame. From the ashes comes forth a worm that transforms into a new Phoenix.

Columba the Dove was set aflight by Jason to see how it would fare between the dangerous rocks of a channel. It returned safely, providing Jason with a good omen to sail his ship Argo through the same waters. The god of wisdom, Minerva, placed the bird in the sky as a reward for its helpful role.

Mythology corresponding to Chart C on page 65

Gemini the Twins, represented by the stars Castor and Pollux, were warlike heroes who protected seafarers from pirates. Pollux was immortal but Castor was not and was eventually killed in a quarrel. Pollux then asked Jupiter for death so he could be with his twin, but immortals cannot be killed. However, Jupiter allowed him to live alternately one day with the gods and the other in Hades with his brother. Thus, the stars Castor and Pollux take turns in rising and setting.

Orion, the Hunter was the handsomest man

place where Helios rises from the ocean. He did, and then returned for revenge, but he could not find Oenopion anywhere. During his pursuit, he met up with

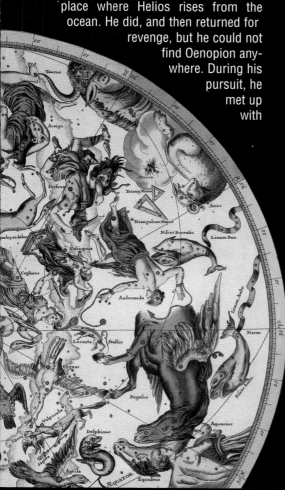

Lepus the Hare is quiet at Orion's feet, waiting to spring if discovered. **Canis Major** and **Canis Minor** are respectively Orion's loyal Greater and Lesser Dogs.

Monoceros the Unicorn was the ultimate prize for any hunter, even just to catch a glimpse of it. Its horn had magical powers that could protect from evil.

The three stars, Sirius, Procyon and Betelgeuse are commonly known as the **Winter Triangle**. The "Dog Days of Summer" refers to the fact that the bright dog star Sirius rises and sets with the Sun during the summer.

Mythology corresponding to Chart D on page 67

Around 150 AD, **Leo** the Lion extended eastward to **Cancer** and westward to **Coma Berenices**. Its whiskers were the Beehive and its tail ended up in the cluster of stars at the top of Coma Berenices. Regulus, the brightest star in Leo, has been identified with the birth of Christ. Its

Mythology

name implies King, Mighty, Great, Center or Hero, depending on the culture.

There is no classical mythology for **Leo Minor**, because this constellation was created in the 1600s. **Cancer** the Crab was sent to prevent Hercules from killing the Hydra. However, Hercules trampled the crab and succeeded in killing the Hydra anyway. The **Hydra** had nine heads and if one was chopped off, two grew back in its place. Hercules had to burn each stub to prevent the heads from growing back. **Corvus** was a bird placed in the heavens on Hydra's back by Apollo for being slow in bringing him water and lying about his tardiness. **Crater** represents the container of water that is always out of reach of Corvus. **Puppis** refers to the stern (poop) of Jason's ship Argo, and **Vela**, its sail.

Mythology corresponding to Chart E on page 69

Canes Venatici are the Hunting Dogs of **Bootes**, the Bear Driver who is sometimes seen as a Herdsman or Ploughman. One story has it that Ceres, the goddess of Agriculture, asked Jupiter to place Bootes amongst the stars in gratitude for his invention, the plough. Another story is that Bootes was a grape grower taught to make wine by Bacchus, the god of Wine. Upon doing so, he celebrated and got his friends so drunk that they fell asleep. The next morning, his friends killed him because they thought he was trying to poison them. His hunting dogs were so shaken by his death that they died with him.

An interesting story about **Virgo** the Maiden is that she was Proserpina, the daughter of Ceres. Pluto, the god of the Underworld noticed her beauty one day when she was playing in her mother's fields. He swiftly abducted her to the Underworld. Ceres was enraged at his action and decided to abandon all the crops. Jupiter intervened when he noticed the Earth becoming barren, so he struck a compromise. Pluto would have Proserpina for half a year and Ceres for the other half. When Virgo is in the night sky, crops grow, but when she has sunk below the horizon to the Underworld, the growing season ends.

Centaurs were offspring of the gods, half-man and half-horse creatures that walked on four legs. Some say that **Centaurus** represents Chiron, the wisest and gentlest of his kind, whom Jupiter placed in the heavens to reward him for educating Hercules, Jason, Achilles and others. **Lupus** the Wolf was a generic wild animal to the Greeks but was also seen as the centaur's offering to the gods or a wine skin for libation. Take your pick!

Mythology corresponding to Chart F on page 71

There is probably more lore about **Hercules** the Strongman than any other mythological figure. It is ironic however, that his stars are not as prominent as his stature. Hercules should have the stars of Orion. Hercules' mother was Alcmene and his father Jupiter, but, Alcmene was married to the Thebesian military leader Amphytrion. Once, when he was off to battle, Jupiter came to Alcmene in the form of her husband, feigning a short leave. Hercules, like many offspring of Jupiter, had to endure the wrath of Jupiter's wife Juno for most of his life.

Mythology

One day, Hercules met two women, Pleasure and Virtue, who foretold that he could have either of their lives, but that the life of Virtue which Hercules picked would be difficult yet have a glorious end. This leads to the famous twelve labors of Hercules which were tasks directed by King Eurystheus. The labors often involved fighting ferocious beasts with themes loosely based on the twelve zodiacal constellations. Hercules was placed into the heavens by Jupiter after his wife Deianeira gave him a caustic poison because she wrongly believed that he was interested in another women.

Corona Borealis, the Northern Crown, was the golden crown that always sat atop the head of Bacchus, the god of Wine. He threw it to the heavens to prove to the beautiful mortal Ariadne that he was a god. She then married him and later was made immortal.

Ophiuchus the Snake Bearer, a healer, holds **Serpens**, the Snake. Ophiuchus is identified with Aesculapius, the son of Apollo. One day, Aesculapius strangled a snake. Immediately afterwards, a live snake slithered in and gave the dead snake an herb that brought it back to life. Aesculapius then took some of the herb and used it to raise the dead. This angered Pluto because he was losing clientele, so he complained to Jupiter who sent **Aquila** the Eagle to kill Aesculapius with a thunderbolt. Jupiter placed Aesculapius in the heavens so as not to raise suspicion about his death and disappearance. Serpens accompanied him. Today, Serpens is the only constellation that has discontinuous boundaries because part of the snake lies across Ophiuchus.

Libra, the Scales, represents the weighing of the length of day and night and signifies the location of the Autumnal Equinox, which was located in this constellation during ancient times. When the Sun is in this position, day and night are equal. This also happens at the Vernal Equinox.

Puppis, the Stern, represents that of the great ship Argo that Jason and his 50 Argonauts used to search for the golden fleece. **Carina** is the Keel and **Vela** the Sail.

Norma, the Carpenter's Square, was a tool needed to build ships and was a constellation added in the 1600s.

Mythology corresponding to Chart G on page 73

Cygnus the Swan is widely recognized as the beautiful Northern Cross amidst the Milky Way. Cycnus was friends with Phaethon, son of Helios, who unsuccessfully rode the Sun Chariot across the sky. After Phaethon was thrown into the river Eridanus, Cycnus

Mythology

diligently dove in to retrieve all his bones so he could ensure his friend a proper afterlife in the Underworld. For this consideration, Jupiter transformed Cycnus into Cygnus, a swan and placed him in the Milky Way river.

Lyra, the Lyre, was invented by Mercury as he sat on a shore, playing around with a tortoise shell. Apollo took a liking to this marvelous instrument and passed it to his son Orpheus. Orpheus mastered the lyre and when he played, its music could stop arrows and knives midair if thrown at him. The lyre was placed in the heavens by Jupiter after Orpheus was killed by jealous women who became enamored of him through his enchanted music.

Aquila the Eagle was Jupiter's bird who carried out various tasks for the supreme god. Hercules killed Aquila with **Sagitta**, the Arrow, because Jupiter had ordered the bird to daily eat the liver of Prometheus, one of the Titans, while he was chained to a mountain. His liver grew back each day.

Delphinus the Dolphin was placed in the sky by Neptune in return for helping him find and win over the woman he loved, Amphitrite, daughter of Oceanus.

Scutum the Shield was a constellation added in the 1600s.

Sagittarius the Archer is usually represented by a centaur, a warlike hunter distinctly different from Centaurus, representing Chiron the educator.

I have a fond memory of **Scorpius**, the Scorpion, because it was the first constellation that my daughter learned to recognize. In the sky, the scorpion's tail lies over a dark part of the Milky Way, signifying a crevice leading to the Underworld from which it came. One version of Orion's story has him boasting about killing all the animals on Earth. For this reason, Mother Earth, Gaia, sent a giant scorpion to kill him, and it bit him in the heel. The healer Ophiuchus, who stands above Scorpius in the sky, brought Orion back to life, and keeps the scorpion at bay under his feet.

Corona Australis, the Southern Crown, was placed into the sky by Bacchus, the god of Wine, in honor of his mother Semele who was accidentally destroyed by the trickery of Juno because of her affair with Jupiter.

Mythology corresponding to Chart H on page 75

Aquarius the Water Carrier is depicted as holding a container of water that is pouring into the mouth of the Southern Fish, **Piscis Austrinus**, which is sometimes seen as the parent of Pisces. Aquarius and Ganymede were considered cup-bearers and waiters for the gods. Ganymede was eventually made a god and after that, Aquarius and Ganymede were referred to as the same person. Ancient mythology sees Aquar-

Mythology

ius as the one who poured the water for the great flood, killing all but two people, Deucalion, a man and Pyrrha, a woman who repopulated the world.

Capricornus the Seagoat represents the half-transformed body of Pan. One day, the titanic, ill-willed demon Typhon took the gods by surprise. Many of them quickly changed form to get out of its way. Pan, who often took the form of a goat playing pipes, hurriedly jumped into the water to become a fish, but because of the ensuing panic (the word panic is derived from Pan), only his back half changed into a tail. When Pan came out of the water, he saw that Typhon had incapacitated Jupiter by ripping him to shreds. Upon seeing Jupiter's helplessness, Pan blew on his pipes with such an awful shrill sound that it scared Typhon away, but also caught Mercury's attention. Both helped put Jupiter back together again. Typhon was then struck hard by one of Jupiter's largest thunderbolts. Jupiter put Pan in the stars in gratitude for his service.

Microscopium, the Microscope, **Grus**, the Crane and **Sculptor** were constellations added in the 1600s and 1700s.

Mythology corresponding to Chart I on page 77

Pegasus, the winged horse, was born from the drippings of Medusa's severed head. He was tamed by Bellerophon with a golden bridle given to him by Athena. While riding Pegasus, he was able to kill the Chimaera, a creature with a lion's head, goat's body and the tail of a serpent, by shooting it with arrows from above. Bellerophon became a conceited king and had Pegasus fly him to Olympus, to live with the gods. This angered Jupiter who sent a gadfly to bite Pega-

sus, making him rear, throwing Bellerophon to Earth where he wandered destitute and aimlessly. Pegasus became the deliverer of Jupiter's thunderbolts.

Triangulum the Triangle is believed to have represented the mathematical accomplishments of ancient Greece.

Aries is the Ram with the golden fleece. King Athamas had two children by Nephele, the goddess of the Nebulous Cloud. After Nephele returned to Olympus (gods usually didn't stay with mortals for long), Athamas took another wife, Ino, who disliked his children. She blamed a crop failure on them and convinced Athamas that the gods were angry at his children and that they had to be sacrificed for appeasement. The King was taken aback, but Ino had even convinced the local priests that this was necessary. Of course, the goddess Nephele saw all this from Olympus and planned a rescue for her children, Phrixos and Helle. A ram with a curly golden fleece would

Mythology

appear at the moment of sacrifice. They were to jump on and hold tight, for it was to fly them to safety. Nephele specified that the only thing they could not do while on the ram was to look down. Unfortunately, Helle did, and fell to the ocean. The place where she landed is now called Hellespont.

Pisces represents the Fishes, transformations of Venus, the goddess of Love and Beauty, and Cupid, the god of Love. One day, Venus and Cupid were startled by Typhon, the monster-dragon who could live in fire but not water. To escape, they changed themselves into fishes and dove into the sea. To stay together, they tied themselves to a long line. The constellation represents two fishes connected by a v-shaped line.

This section of the sky is inundated with water-related constellations. Eridanus, Cetus, Pisces, Aquarius and Capricornus are all next to each other. It is ironic that the constellations on or near the Milky Way are not water-related.

Mythology corresponding to Chart J on page 79

There is no classical Greek and Roman mythology for the stars around the south celestial pole because the empires of these civilizations resided mostly in the mid-latitudes of the northern hemisphere, hence they never got to see these stars.

Obviously, the people of South America and southern Africa had lore associated with the stars in this area, but the patterns that prevailed were those drawn by early European explorers.

The Large and Small Magellanic Clouds, which are companion galaxies to our Milky Way Galaxy, were named in honor of Magellan for his voyage around the world that began in 1519. In 1596, Dutch explorer Pieter Dirckszoon Keyser constructed a dozen constellations, mostly named after animals and using brighter stars. Keyser's only inanimate constellation was Triangulum Australe. During the 1600s, Frenchman Augustin Royer created Crux, · the "Southern Cross," by breaking off part of the constellation Centaurus. Then in the 1750s, Frenchman Nicolas Louis de Lacaille, while on a respite at the Cape of Good Hope, constructed fourteen new constellations mostly based on scientific instruments and mainly using faint stars. Lacaille's patterns were the last to be recognized and many consider his to be clutter. His constellations were kept in recognition of contributions he made to astronomical cataloguing.

To the Greeks and Romans, the stars were lights from the fires of the god's palaces shining through many holes in the fabric of the sky. Meteors were embers the gods threw down for amusement.

Historical Timeline

13.7 billion years ago Big Bang. Universe comes into existence.

4.6 billion years ago Our Solar System forms.
4.57 billion years ago Our Moon forms.

3.5 to 4 billion years ago Heavy asteroid bombardment of the Solar System ends. Simple life on Earth appears.

245 to 570 million years ago Palaeozoic Era. Life proliferates.
65 to 245 million years ago Mesozoic Era. Age of the dinosaurs.

3 to 4 million years ago Hominids flourish in East and South Africa.
100,000 to 1.5 million years ago Homo erectus emerges.
200,000 years ago Modern humans emerge (Homo sapiens sapiens).
100,000 years ago Modern humans spread outside Africa.
30,000 years ago Neanderthals become extinct.

10,000 BC Modern humans found throughout the world. The "Paleolithic Age" or Stone Age transitions into systematic agriculture. This also marks the end of the last Ice Age.

4240 BC The Egyptians institute the first 365-day calendar. It includes twelve 30-day months and five festival days.

3000 BC The Babylonians predict eclipses.

2600 BC Great pyramids of Egypt built at Giza.

2296 BC Chinese observers make the first known record of a comet sighting.

800 BC Rise of the Arabs who will make significant contributions to astronomy.

763 BC Babylonians make the earliest known record of a solar eclipse.

500 BC The Pythagoreans teach that Earth is a sphere and not a disk. The golden age of the Greeks starts and continues through 323 BC.

380 BC Democritus, a Greek philosopher, recognizes that the Milky Way consists of numerous stars, that the Moon is similar to Earth, and that matter is composed of atoms.

352 BC Chinese observers report a supernova, the earliest such record.

270 BC Aristarchus of Samos (Greek island near Turkey) challenges Aristotle's teachings by asserting that the Sun is the center of the Solar System and that the Planets revolve around the Sun.

240 BC Chinese astronomers record a comet that is the first known record of Halley's Comet.

Historical Timeline

170 BC	The Greek Seleucus is the last known astronomer to champion the heliocentric theory of the Solar System until Copernicus in 1543.
165 BC	Chinese astronomers record sunspots.

140 AD	Ptolemy of Egypt (Claudius Ptolemaeus, 100–175 AD) writes *Megale Syntaxis tes Astronomias* (Great Astronomical Composition), which becomes the most important astronomy text of the Middle Ages. It so impresses the Arabs that they call it *Almagest* (The Greatest). The work describes a model of Planetary motion in which the Earth is the center of the Universe, and the Sun and Moon orbit in perfect circles.
476 AD	Fall of the Roman empire that began around 500 BC.
635 AD	The Chinese record that a comet's tail always points away from the Sun.
1054	The Chinese, Japanese and Arabs observe the supernova that forms the Crab nebula in the constellation Taurus, on July 4. It is visible for 22 months.
1250	Alfonso X of Castile (Spain) orders the compilation of tables, which become known as the *Alfonsine Tables,* listing the positions and movement of the Planets. Fifty astronomers work on this project.
1300	Eyeglasses become common.
1504	Christopher Columbus of Spain uses Regiomontanus' *Ephemerides Astronomicae* to predict a total lunar eclipse and frighten a group of Native Americans.
1543	Nicolas Copernicus (1473–1543) of Poland publishes *De Revolutionibus Orbium Coelestium* (On the Revolutions of Celestial Bodies). It offers a heliocentric model. Copernicus delays publishing the work almost until his death for fear of reprisals from the church.
1572	Tycho Brahe (1546–1601) of Denmark observes a supernova in the constellation Cassiopeia in 1572 and publishes *De Nova Stella* (On the New Star), giving an exact description of his observation. Tycho was a consummate observer who recorded the positions of the Planets and stars which Kepler later used to formulate the fundamental laws of orbits.
1599	Tycho Brahe moves to the court of Holy Roman Emperor Rudolph II in Prague.
1600	Johannes Kepler (1571–1630) of Germany begins assisting Tycho Brahe at his Prague observatory.
1604	Johannes Kepler observes a supernova in the constellation Ophiuchus — the last supernova observed in our galaxy.

Historical Timeline

1609   Galileo Galilei (1564–1642) of Italy builds one of the earliest refractor telescopes and observes the Moon, four of Jupiter's moons, Saturn, individual stars of the Milky Way and the phases of Venus. He reports on his observations and findings in *Sidereus Nuncius*. Kepler's book, *Astronomia Nova* (New Astronomy) contains his views that the Planets revolve around the Sun in elliptical orbits and that these orbits sweep out equal areas in equal time intervals.

1656   Christian Huygens (1629–1695), a Dutch scientist, discovers that Saturn's odd "handles" are actually rings. He also discovers Saturn's largest satellite, Titan, and observes dark patches in the Orion Nebula as well as surface features on Mars.

1668   Isaac Newton (1643–1727) of England makes the first reflecting telescope. His theory of gravity and invention of calculus revolutionalize science.

1675   Greenwich Observatory is founded by King Charles II of England. He appoints John Flamsteed (1646–1719) as the first Astronomer Royal.

1682   Edmond Halley (1656–1742) of England observes "The Great Comet." He predicts in 1705 that it will return in 1758, and it is then named after him.

1781   Charles Messier (1730–1817) of France becomes the first astronomer to publish a catalogue of deep sky objects with more than 100 entries. William Herschel (1738–1822) of England discovers Uranus on March 13, although he first believes it to be a comet.

1794   Ernst Chladni, a German-born Hungarian, shows that meteors are extraterrestrial.

1798   Pierre Simon de Laplace (1749–1827) of France predicts the existence of black holes.

1801   Giuseppe Piazzi (1746–1826) of Italy discovers the first asteroid, Ceres.

1821   The Catholic church lifts its ban on teaching the Copernican system.

1822   The Catholic church removes Galileo's *Dialogue Concerning the Two Chief World Systems* from the *Index of Prohibited Books* 190 years after its publication.

1839   The Harvard College Observatory is founded, the first official observatory in the United States. A 15-inch (38 cm) refractor is installed in 1847. It is one of the two largest refractors in the world at the time.

1846   Johann Galle (1812–1910) of Germany discovers Neptune using the predictions of its position by Urbain Le Verrier (1811–1877) of France.

Historical Timeline

1851	Baron von Humboldt's *Kosmos* gives currency to Heinrich Samuel Schwabe's 1843 discovery of the 11-year sunspot cycle.
1863	William Huggins of England uses the spectra of stars to show that the same elements that exist in stars also exist on Earth.
1864	John Herschel (1792–1871), son of William Herschel, publishes a catalogue of nebulae and star clusters that contains more than 5,000 entries, building upon William Herschel, his father's earlier work.
1868	Pietro Secchi of Italy completes the first spectroscopic survey of the stars, cataloguing the spectrograms of about 4,000 stars.
1873	Richard Proctor suggests that the craters on the Moon were formed by the impacts of meteorites instead of by volcanoes as was previously assumed.
1877	Giovanni Schiaparelli (1835–1910) of Italy thinks he discovers canals or channels on Mars. This observation is considered a possibility for years, but eventually fails to be confirmed.
1882	David Gill photographs Halley's comet and notices the multitude of stars surrounding the comet — the idea of stellar cataloguing by photography is born.
1884	An international meeting in Washington, DC, sets the Prime Meridian through Greenwich, England.
1887	The Lick 36-inch (91 cm) refracting telescope is completed on Mount Hamilton near San Francisco, California.
1888	Johan L. E. Dreyer (1852–1926), a Danish astronomer working in Ireland, publishes *A New General Catalogue of Nebulae and Clusters of Stars* containing 7,840 nebulae and star clusters.
1891	Maximilian Wolf makes the first discovery of an asteroid (Brucia) from photographs.
1894	Percival Lowell (1855–1916) founds his observatory at Flagstaff, Arizona, and starts searching for a hypothetical ninth Planet. He also maps what he believes to be canals on Mars.
1897	George Hale (1868–1938) sets up the Yerkes Observatory in Williams Bay, Wisconsin. The Yerkes telescope at 40 inches (1 meter) is still the largest refracting telescope ever built.
1900	James Keeler photographs a large number of nebulae and discovers that some have a spiral structure (The nebulae with spiral structure are galaxies).
1908	Hale installs a 60-inch (1.5 meters) reflecting telescope at Mount Wilson Observatory, near Pasadena, California.
1912	Studies of short-period variable stars in the Small Magellanic Cloud by Henrietta Leavitt (1868–1921) lead to the period-luminosity law of Cepheid variables — a key that is used to unlock the distances to the stars.

Historical Timeline

1913   Henry Russel announces his theory of stellar evolution which was independently theorized by Hertzsprung in 1905. This concept becomes the famous Hertzsprung-Russell diagram depicting the relationship and evolution of stars.

1914   Arthur Eddington suggests in *Stellar Movements and the Structure of the Universe* that spiral nebulae are galaxies.

1917   George Hale installs a 100-inch (2.5 meter) reflecting telescope at Mount Wilson Observatory in California. It will be the world's largest telescope until 1948. Karl Schwarzschild develops the equations that predict the existence of black holes from Einstein's General Theory of Relativity.

1919   The International Astronomical Union (IAU) is founded which has the authority to name celestial bodies and their features.

1924   Edwin Hubble (1889–1953) demonstrates that galaxies are true independent systems rather than parts of our Milky Way system.

1927   Georges Lemaître (1894–1966), a Belgian priest and astrophysicist, proposes the first version of the Big Bang theory, that the Universe was created by the explosion of a concentration of matter and energy which he called the "cosmic egg" or "primeval atom."

1929   Edwin Hubble establishes that the more distant a galaxy is, the faster it is receding from Earth (Hubble's law), confirming that the Universe is expanding.

1930   Clyde Tombaugh (1906–1997) discovers Pluto from Flagstaff, Arizona.

1931   Experiments by Karl Jansky (1905–1950) with an improvised aerial lead to the founding of radio astronomy.

1938   German physicists Hans Bethe and Carl von Weizsäcker independently propose that the cause of the energy produced by stars is the nuclear fusion of hydrogen into helium. J. Robert Oppenheimer (1904–1967) and George Volkoff predict the existence of rapidly rotating neutron stars which are discovered in 1967 by Jocelyn Bell and become known as pulsars.

1939   J. Robert Oppenheimer calculates that if the mass of a star is more than 3.2 times the mass of the Sun, a collapse of the star would create what would come to be known as a black hole.

1942   Grote Reber makes the first radio maps of the Universe, and locates individual radio sources.

1946   A V-2 rocket carries a spectrograph to record a spectrogram of the Sun to a height of 34 miles (55 km).

1947   Lyman Spitzer, Jr., speculates that astronomers might put telescopes of various kinds in orbit around Earth on artificial satellites.

Historical Timeline

1948   The 200-inch (5 meter) Hale reflecting telescope at Palomar, California is completed.

1949   Fred Whipple (1906–2004) suggests that comets are "dirty snowballs" consisting of ice or ammonia ice and rock dust. A rocket testing ground is established at Cape Canaveral, Florida.

1955   The US Vanguard project for launching artificial satellites is announced.

1957   The first artificial satellite, *Sputnik I*, is launched by the Soviet Union on October 4.

1958   American physicist Eugene Parker demonstrates that there is a "solar wind" of particles thrown out by the Sun. Wernher von Braun's (1912–1977) team launches the first American satellite to reach a successful orbit around Earth.

1961   On April 12, soviet cosmonaut Yuri Gagarin (1934–1968) becomes the first human being to orbit Earth during his 108-minute mission in *Vostok I*. Alan Shepard, Jr. (1923–1998), becomes the first US astronaut in space as his *Mercury 3* capsule *Freedom 7* completes a 15-minute suborbital flight on May 5.

1962   The US space probe *Mariner 2* becomes the first object made by humans to voyage to another Planet when it reaches the vicinity of Venus. John Glenn, Jr. (1921–), is the first American to orbit Earth in his *Mercury 6* space capsule *Friendship 7* on February 20.

1963   Valentina Tereshkova-Nikolayeva (1937–) of the Soviet Union becomes the first woman in space, making 48 orbits in 78 hours on June 16.

1965   *Mariner IV* reaches the vicinity of Mars on July 15, passing within 7,500 miles (12,000 km) of the Planet.

1966   *Luna 9* (Soviet Union) becomes the first spacecraft to soft land on the Moon.

1969   American astronaut Neil Armstrong (1930–) becomes the first human to stand on the Moon on July 20.

1970   *Venera 7* (Soviet Union) becomes the first spacecraft to soft land on a Planet, Venus.

1972   The first Earth-resources satellite, *Landsat I*, is launched.

1973   The first *Skylab* is launched on May 25 by a Saturn rocket. A 3-man crew conducts medical and other experiments for 28 days.

1975   The first pictures from the surface of Venus are received from the Russian probes *Venera 9* and *Venera 10*.

1976   US space probes *Viking 1* and *2* land on Mars and begin sending back direct pictures and other information from the surface of the

Historical Timeline

	Planet. Space probes *Voyager 1* and *2* are launched on a journey to Jupiter and other outer Planets.
1978	James Christy and Robert Harrington discover Charon, Pluto's moon.
1981	The first Space Shuttle, *Columbia,* is launched on April 12 with John Young and Robert Crippen as crew.
1983	The *Challenger* space shuttle flight launched on June 18 carries the first 5-person crew and the first American woman in space, Sally Ride. The remote manipulator structure is used to deploy and retrieve a satellite.
1986	The space shuttle *Challenger* explodes 73 seconds after launch on January 28, killing six astronauts and teacher S. Christa McAuliffe.
1987	Bruce Campbell, Gordon Walker and Stephenson Yang announce the discovery of planet-size bodies orbiting Gamma Cephei and Epsilon Eridani.
1989	The space probe *Galileo* is launched toward Jupiter and enters orbit in 1995. The COBE satellite is launched to measure the background microwave radiation from the Big Bang.
1990	*Hubble Space Telescope* (HST) is launched into orbit around Earth.
1994	Comet Shoemaker-Levy 9, discovered by Gene and Carolyn Shoemaker along with David Levy in March of 1993, slams into Jupiter.
1995	Comet Hale-Bopp is discovered by Alan Hale and Thomas Bopp.
1997	*Pathfinder* becomes the first roving vehicle on another Planet, Mars.
1998	*Lunar Prospector* becomes the first spacecraft project conceived and directed by a scientist, Alan Binder. Among other accomplishments, this highly successful mission detects a signature indicating that frozen water may exist at the Moon's poles.
1998/99	Construction on the *International Space Station* begins.
2003	The space shuttle *Columbia* explodes on reentry into Earth's atmosphere killing all seven astronauts aboard. On October 15, the Chinese successfully launch their first astronaut into space, Yang Liwei.
2004	The Mars rovers *Spirit* and *Opportunity* discover evidence for the prior existence of water on Mars' surface. The original 90-day missions are extended to over a year. The *Cassini* spacecraft with the attached *Huygens* probe enters orbit around Saturn.
2005	The *Huygens* probe becomes the first spacecraft to land on the moon of another Planet, Saturn's Titan. Comet Tempel 1 impacted by a high-velocity "slug" launched from a spacecraft to gain more information about the interior make up. The discovery of a tenth "Planet," Zena is announced, although it had been found in 2003.
2006	*New Horizons* spacecraft launched for a flyby of Pluto in 2015.

Historical Timeline

New Entries

Resources

Telescope Reviews

Cloudy Night Telescope Reviews
www.cloudynights.com

Todd Gross' Weather and Astronomy Site
www.weatherman.com

The Telescope Review Web Site by Ed Ting
www.scopereviews.com

Affordable Astronomy Equipment Reviews
members.tripod.com/irwincur/index.html

Major Telescope Manufacturers

Celestron
www.celestron.com

Meade Instruments Corporation
www.meade.com

Tele Vue
Quality refractors and eyepieces
www.televue.com

Major Planetariums

Adler Planetarium, Chicago, IL
www.adlerplanetarium.org

Albert Einstein Planetarium,
Smithsonian, Washington, DC
www.nasm.edu/nasm/planetarium/einstein.html

Hansen Planetarium, Salt Lake City
www.hansenplanetarium.net

Hayden Planetarium, New York, NY
www.amnh.org/rose

Griffith Observatory Planetarium,
Los Angeles, CA
www.griffithobs.org/Planetarium.html

Atmospheric Phenomenon

Atmospheric Optics
www.sundog.clara.co.uk/atoptics/phenom.htm

Outdoor Telescope Events

Check the popular monthly astronomy magazines for listings of amateur astronomy events. One of the largest that I recommend for beginners and families is the

RTMC Astronomy Annual Expo
held near Big Bear City, CA
at the end of May
www.rtmc-inc.org

Popular Monthly Astronomy Magazines

Astronomy
www.astronomy.com

Sky & Telescope
www.skyandtelescope.com

SkyNews (Canadian)
www.skynewsmagazine.com

Star Charts

Guide to the Stars by David Levy
Published by Ken Press
www.whatsouttonight.com

Sky Atlas 2000.0
by Wil Tirion and Roger Sinnott
Published by Sky Publishing
www.skyandtelescope.com

General Astronomy Internet Sites

www.astronomy.com

www.skyandtelescope.com

www.space.com

www.nasa.gov

www.science.nasa.gov

Resources

National Organizations

The Astronomical League
A federation of astronomical societies and clubs. Awards. Newsletter.
www.astronomicalleague.com

Astronomical Society of the Pacific
General membership. Newsletters. Educator support. Books and science materials.
www.astrosociety.org

The Planetary Society
Supports planetary exploration. Newsletter.
www.planetary.org

Eclipse Tours
Check ads in the popular monthly astronomy magazines for eclipse tours.

Major Observatories
These observatories have visitor's centers that are open during the day. A few have evening observing programs which require reservations. Call ahead for hours/tours, etc.

Kitt Peak near Tucson, AZ
www.noao.edu/kpno

McDonald near Fort Davis, TX
vc.as.utexas.edu

Mount Palamor near Pasadena, CA
www.astro.caltech.edu/palomar

Grifford in Los Angeles, CA
www.griffithobs.org

Mauna Kea on Hawaii
www.ifa.hawaii.edu/mko

Lowell in Flagstaff, AZ
www.lowell.edu

Space Weather Reports
Science news and information about the Sun-Earth environment.
www.spaceweather.com

Buying, Selling and Trading Telescope Equipment
A premier site for telescope equipment. Skip ebay.
www.astromart.com

Astronomy Bed & Breakfast

The Sky Watcher's Inn
Benson, Arizona
Featuring a 20-inch telescope, many others and a wonderful breakfast.
www.communiverse.com/skywatcher
tel/fax (520) 615-3886

Astronomy Radio Show

Let's Talk Stars
Hosted by famous comet discoverer David Levy.
www.letstalkstars.com

A Favorite Astronomy "Adventure" Book

Starlight Nights: The Adventures of a Star-Gazer by Leslie C. Peltier
Read about the passions of a famous comet discover. Published by Sky Publishing.
www.skyandtelescope.com

Resources

Astronomical Almanacs

Both *Sky & Telescope* and *Astronomy* magazines publish yearly almanacs that are available from newsstands at the end of each year. Two other wonderful, but more advanced almanacs are:

Observer's Handbook
Royal Astronomical Society of Canada

Astronomical Calendar
by Guy Ottewell
Published by Universal Workshop

AAVSO

The American Association of Variable Star Observers is open to amateur participation in measuring the brightness of variable stars.
www.aavso.org

Astronomy Textbook

One of the most comprehensive textbooks on astronomy that is well-written, expensive, but worth it.

Foundations of Astronomy
6th Edition or later
by Michael Seeds
Published by Brooks/Cole

Planetarium Software

Mac or Windows. Complete planetarium programs to display sky anywhere on Earth. Find out where the planets are, and lots more.

Starry Night Pro by Space Com

International Dark-Sky Association

An organization that promotes keeping our skies dark so everyone can enjoy the night sky.
www.darksky.org

Telescopes & Accessories

Check your yellow pages for local dealers. In smaller communities, camera stores often carry telescopes. Or, purchase one of the popular monthly astronomy magazines for dealer ads.

Satellite Tracking Website

Check this website to find out when the International Space Station and other satellites can be seen overhead.
www.heavens-above.com

Educational Resources

For books, slides, posters or science items, get catalogs from the following:

Astronomical Society of the Pacific
www.astrosociety.org

Sky & Telescope
www.skyandtelescope.com

Charles Messier, History & Objects

The Next Step:
Finding & Viewing Messier's Objects
by Ken Graun
www.kenpress.com

Photo Credits

Index

Index

Index

Index for Mythology

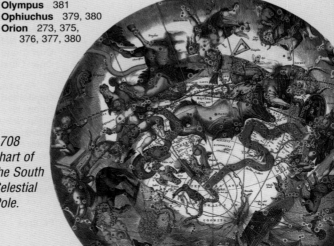

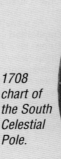

1708 chart of the South Celestial Pole.

Index

Index

Greek Alphabet

α alpha
β beta
γ gamma
δ delta
ε epsilon
ζ zeta
η eta
θ theta
ι iota
κ kappa
λ lambda
μ mu
ν nu
ξ xi
ο omicron
π pi
ρ rho
σ sigma
τ tau
υ upsilon
φ phi
χ chi
ψ psi
ω omega